One hundred years of Reading weather

By

Roger Brugge and Stephen Burt

Department of Meteorology
University of Reading

A Climatological Observers Link publication

www.colweather.org.uk

Current weather data and updates to this publication can be found at
www.met.reading.ac.uk/observatory

First published 2015

Edition 1.0, June 2015

Published by the CLIMATOLOGICAL OBSERVERS LINK, 16 Wootton Way, Maidenhead, Berkshire SL6 4QU

Copies of this publication may be obtained from the address above, or from

University of Reading, Department of Meteorology, Reading, RG6 6BB

ISBN 978-0-9569485-1-9

Set in Calibri and Georgia

The CLIMATOLOGICAL OBSERVERS LINK (COL) is the largest organisation of weather observers in the UK and Ireland. COL was formed in 1970 to facilitate the exchange of weather observation data and information between enthusiasts. A monthly weather bulletin summarising members' observations and the weather across the British Isles has been produced since May 1970. New members are always welcome, particularly from those making their own weather observations. More details on COL and how to join can be found at **www.colweather.org.uk**

Printed and bound by RIVERPRINT LTD, Riverside Park, Farnham, Surrey GU9 7UG   www.riverprint.co.uk

Contents

Acknowledgements

The **motivation for writing this book** arose from the many requests we have received, and continue to receive, from the press, public and members of the University of Reading (notably those in the Department of Meteorology at our weekly 'Weather and Climate Discussion' seminars) for information, news or statistics on Reading's weather.

This book would not have been possible without the help of many people. Firstly, we would like to thank Rowena Brugge and Emily Brugge, who both did a lot of transcribing of many of the early hand-written measurements into electronic format during their summer university vacations. Thanks are also due to Mike Stroud (the current observer) and Ken Spiers (his predecessor) for numerous conversations during which various aspects of the weather station in Reading over the years were sorted out.

We are grateful to staff at the Met Office in Exeter, in particular to Mark Beswick and Joan Self, for help in locating missing records from Reading in the Met Office Library and Archive, and to Nicholas Klingaman in the Department of Meteorology for providing gridded 20th century reanalysis data of pressure from the National Centers for Environmental Prediction (NCEP) database, against which we were able to verify many early pressure observations from the university.

We are also grateful to Rosy Wilson and Andrew Lomas for maintaining our current automatic weather station and for providing easy access to these observations.

Ann Smith, from Reading Central Library, provided valuable assistance in tracking down many of the archive photographs used in this book, and her colleague Craig Selley kindly allowed us to use several of his own photographs. Nigel Frankland, Head of Estates, University of Reading, helped to pin down the position of the original weather station at the London Road site.

We would also like to thank numerous colleagues within the Department of Meteorology for their support and assistance in preparing this book as part of the fiftieth anniversary commemorations of the Department.

Finally, and most importantly, we thank all the weather observers and deputy observers of the University for making the meteorological observations, day in day out, come rain or shine. Without their dedication and experience, Reading's weather records could not have been maintained for over a century.

We hope you will enjoy reading and using this book as much as we have enjoyed delving into the archives – both paper and electronic - used to prepare it. Here's to the next hundred years of Reading's weather!

Roger Brugge *PhD, DIC, FRMetS*   **Stephen Burt** *MSc, DipM, DipDM, FRMetS*

Department of Meteorology
University of Reading
May 2015

Preface

At the turn of the 1900s the University Extension College at Reading was developing rapidly, ultimately to receive its charter as a University in 1926. The Reading of that era was strongly influenced by Oxford, but there are indications (such as the first university-level appointment of a woman professor in 1908) that its location also gave it a pioneering freedom from the then-established university world. A particularly distinctive activity that emerged was the study of agriculture, which may provide one reason why regular meteorological observations also became an early priority. Through these observations, as the many analyses in this book make clear, even the founding decades of university level education at Reading helped to firmly establish a legacy in meteorology. Ultimately of course, the entire academic Department of Meteorology, now celebrating its 50th anniversary, was founded.

How these observations were viewed originally probably contrasts strongly with how they are regarded today. The mid-Victorian acquisition of national rainfall records was originally motivated by a desire to classify the natural world, in part, because of its applications to civilising infrastructure. These were, by any measure, enduringly commendable ideals, and led to a broadening of meteorological observations as the enabling technology. To our contemporary environmental science however, the quantitative archive which resulted is truly unique and irreplaceable. Consequently the importance of these early observations has vastly increased, in a way no doubt unrecognisable to the dedicated individuals who began our rainfall measurements in 1901.

The observation site on the Whiteknights campus would also be unrecognisable to those early pioneers in the breadth of measurements it now supports. It operates as a teaching laboratory, research site, automatic weather station, node in the climatological network and balloon launching station. Beyond traditional meteorological observations – which are underpinned by an observer, technicians, volunteer observers and student helpers – there are regular and occasional measurements concerned with lidar, ceilometers, lightning, space weather and atmospheric electricity. This increasingly wide range of activity centred on atmospheric science led to the Whiteknights site being renamed as the Reading University Atmospheric Observatory in 2006.

In summary, this volume captures the essence of the sustained study of the natural environment, and a reminder that the fastidious discipline of experimental work in applied physical science can yield outcomes far beyond those originally conceived. But there is an even wider value to society, in that no Reading birthday or anniversary card need ever again be without a rigorous and meticulously researched notable local weather fact.

Professor Giles Harrison *MA, PhD, ScD, FRMetS*
Head of Department

Department of Meteorology, University of Reading
May 2015

Current weather conditions ... and updates to this book

The website of the Department of Meteorology at the University of Reading shows current weather data, updated every 10 minutes, from the automatic weather monitoring equipment located within the Atmospheric Observatory on the Whiteknights campus. Observations are presented in both tabular and graphical formats, and cover all major weather elements. You can also add your e-mail address to an automated mailing list which will send you details of the previous 24 hours weather shortly after the 0900 GMT observation every morning. For more information, please go to

www.met.reading.ac.uk/observatory

This site also includes much more detail on the nature and exposure of the current meteorological sensors than can be accommodated in a volume of this size – follow the links to find out more.

Inevitably, any physical publication of this nature is by definition out-of-date as soon as it goes to the printers. With this in mind, the site above includes links which will **regularly update the contents of this book** as future significant weather events occur.

The information in this book is given in good faith. No liability can be accepted for any loss, damage or injury occasioned as a result of using this book or any of the information contained within, howsoever caused.

1   The climate of Reading

Reading is a large town in central southern England, in the county of Berkshire, located about 65 km west-south-west of central London (see Figure 1.1). There has been a settlement on this important confluence of the River Thames and the River Kennet since at least the early Saxon era, and Reading has been an regional centre of commerce and transport since medieval times. Today Reading is an important commercial centre, hosting the headquarters of several British companies and the UK or European offices of foreign multinationals, as well as being a major retail centre and home to the University of Reading. The town has excellent rail and road transport connections via the Great Western mainline railway and the M4 motorway respectively.

The population of the Borough of Reading was 155,698 at the 2011 census: Reading formed the largest component of the Reading/Wokingham Urban Area which had a 2011 population of 318,014. Reading is the most populous town in the United Kingdom not to have city status. The town is twinned with Düsseldorf (Germany), Clonmel (Ireland), Meaux (France), San Francisco Libre (Nicaragua), and Speightstown (Barbados).

Figure 1.1 *Reading's location in central southern England (Courtesy and © Google Maps)*

Reading itself is built on a series of gravel terraces above the Thames and Kennet flood plains; the town has relatively slight but noticeable relief. The highest ground is found in the suburbs of Caversham, to the north-west of the town centre, and in Tilehurst, to the west – the highest points of Tilehurst lying around 105 m above MSL. The lowest parts of the town, along the Kennet and Thames watercourses, are a little above 40 m above MSL, and the town centre lies within the river valleys. The town itself is mostly composed of moderate to high-density suburban fabric, bounded to the south and west by the M4 motorway and rural 'green belt', and to the north by the hills of south Oxfordshire. To the east, the floodplain of the River Loddon separates the urban areas of eastern Reading (Earley, Lower Earley and Woodley) from the western edges of Wokingham.

Located within the zone of temperate westerlies, the south-east has a more continental climate than other parts of England, with warmer summers and colder winters (for its latitude). The south coast of England also has the highest annual duration of sunshine, although amounts diminish inland with greater cloud cover. Rainfall is lower than in western and northern districts, although upland areas in the south-east can still receive in excess of 1000 mm precipitation per annum. Thunder is more frequent, and snowfall less frequent, than further north and west. Reading is considerably drier than the moderate upland areas to its north, west and south; the highest point in south-east England, Walbury Hill (297 m above mean sea level) lies in west Berkshire, 36 km south-west of Reading town centre. The surrounding hills and the town's location within the middle reaches of the Thames Valley provides some shelter from the prevailing south-westerly winds, although cold easterly or north-easterly airstreams crossing the shallow North Sea in winter or spring can easily penetrate across lowland eastern England.

As described in the following chapter, the first meteorological observations made at what is now the University of Reading commenced at a town centre site in London Road, at 45 m above MSL, in 1901. The expansion of the university in the 1960s led to a move to the Whiteknights campus some 2 km south-east, and meteorological observations were transferred here from 1 January 1968. Site details for the two locations are given below, and more details of the observation sites in the following chapter.

Table 1.1 Meteorological observation sites of the University of Reading

Site name	Period of record	Latitude and Longitude	Altitude above MSL
London Road	1901-1904 (rainfall only)	51.45°N, 0.97°W	45 m
	1908-1967	NGR SU (41) 723 728 [*]	
Whiteknights	1968-70	51.437°N, 0.944°W *approximately*	70 m
	1971 to date	51.441°N, 0.938°W NGR SU (41) 739 719	66 m

Over the standard 30 year average period 1981-2010, the **mean temperature** at the University of Reading Whiteknights site was 10.6 °C (mean daily maximum 14.5 °C, mean daily minimum 6.7 °C). The coldest month of the year is January (mean temperature 4.8 °C) and the warmest July (mean temperature 17.6 °C). Since climatological records commenced in 1908, the lowest observed air temperature has been -14.5 °C (in January 1982) and the highest 36.4 °C (in August 2003).

The **annual average rainfall** is 634 mm, falling on 154 days per year. The driest period of the year is late winter to early spring (February average 41 mm) and the wettest autumn (October average 72 mm), but with wide variations from year to year. The wettest day, calendar month and calendar year on the record since 1901 have produced 76 mm, 180 mm and 961 mm, respectively. Snow can be expected to fall on 11 days in a typical year, with the ground snow-covered on six mornings. The greatest observed snow depth since records of this element began in 1950 has been 31 cm (in January 1963). Thunderstorms occur on around nine days per annum, most frequently during the summer half-year.

The mean annual cloud cover at 0900 GMT is 72%, and the average **annual sunshine duration** 1522 hours, about 34% of the possible duration of daylight at this latitude. Contrary perhaps to perceived wisdom, sunshine is recorded on twice as many days per year (just over 300) as measurable rainfall (154).

---

[*] Throughout the 1950s and 1960s the National Grid Reference of the London Road site was given in Met Office publications as SU (41) 738 748. This is incorrect, as that grid reference places the site in Caversham Marina.

2 The makers of the observations

Meteorological observations have been made almost continuously at the University of Reading (known until 1926 as University College) since 1901. Although records for some of the earlier years have been lost, an almost complete daily record of many elements can be assembled from January 1908 to date. Summaries of the records were published in the *Monthly Weather Report* of the Meteorological Office from March 1917 until the cessation of that publication in 1993; earlier observations of rainfall had appeared (with some breaks) in *British Rainfall* from 1903. The station has occupied two major sites - from 1901 to 1967 on the London Road campus and then on the Whiteknights campus since 1968 (see Figure 2.1 for locations).

Some of the historical notes which follow are based upon unpublished notes written by Dr R D Thompson (RDT; *Meteorological Observations at the University of Reading, 1901-1986*) and George Goodhind (*Reading University Meteorological Station*). In addition, use has been made of unpublished notes (*Details of meteorological measurements at Reading*) written by Ken Spiers (KS).

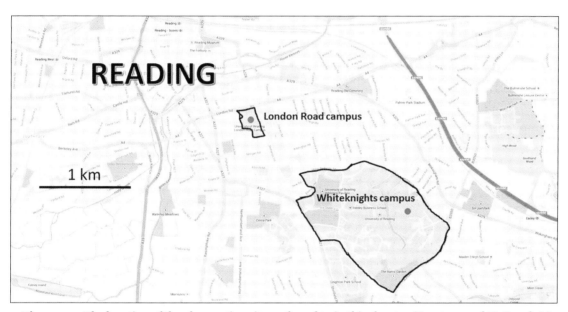

Figure 2.1 *The location of the observation sites referred to in this chapter (Courtesy and © Google Maps)*

1901-1920

In 1901, Reading University College (as it was then known) began observations of daily rainfall amounts, the raingauge being a five-inch pattern (127 mm diameter – which remains the standard gauge type, still in use today) with its rim 3 ft 6 in (107 cm) above ground level, and believed to be on the Library Lawn at the London Road site. (The London Road campus in central Reading was gifted in 1904 by the local Palmer family, of the famous biscuit manufacturer Huntley & Palmers.) Summaries were included in *British Rainfall* under the station name of 'Reading, London Road' in 1901 and 1902, and during 1903 as 'Reading (University College)'.

Records are believed to have continued from 1904 to 1907, but have not so far been traced (see 'Gap filling in the monthly records' on page 10). RDT notes that the station was steadily developed over the next four years, and from January 1908 we have manuscript tabulations of once-daily (0900 GMT) readings of barometric pressure, dry bulb, wet bulb, maximum and minimum air temperatures, earth temperatures at 1 foot (30 cm) and 2 feet (60 cm), cloud type and amount, wind force and direction, 'present weather' and general observations of the weather of the day. These observations were continued until 1960. A grass minimum thermometer was added in 1920, the 2 feet (60 cm) depth earth thermometer was changed to 4 feet (120 cm) in 1924 and a Campbell-Stokes sunshine recorder was installed in April 1956 (on the parapet of the Agricultural Botany building).

A Meteorological Office form dated 15 June 1917 noted that the University College was a third order station. The station description includes a Kew-pattern mercury barometer made by J.H. Steward of London, dry and wet bulb and maximum and minimum thermometers (all four made by Negretti and Zambra) and Casella earth thermometers at depths of 1 foot (30 cm) and 2 feet (60 cm). The air thermometers were housed in a standard Stevenson-type thermometer screen with the base of the screen being 100 cm above the level of the underlying turf. Rainfall was measured using a Casella Snowdon five-inch (127 mm diameter) raingauge with the rim now at the standard 30 cm above the ground. The site plan (Figure 2.2) consisted of an elevated grass plot (some 30-60 cm higher than the surrounding paths) near the Geographical Department of the College and on the outskirts of the Horticultural Gardens.

The first site inspection of the weather station by the Meteorological Office (M.O.) took place in 1919. Mention is made in the inspection report of a mercury barometer read in inches, while the exposure of the raingauge was 'bad by M.O. standards' as the nearby building elevation was about 45 degrees. (This meant that the nearby buildings were only about half the distance away from the instruments that they should have been, leading to possible shading/warming effects upon the records.)

The inspector also noted 'Two large evaporation gauges about 1 metre in diameter are arranged so that readings may be taken indoors in Dr Dickson's room. I did not see more than the tanks themselves.' The observer also noted that 'the number of days of fog is found at the Meteorological Office to be

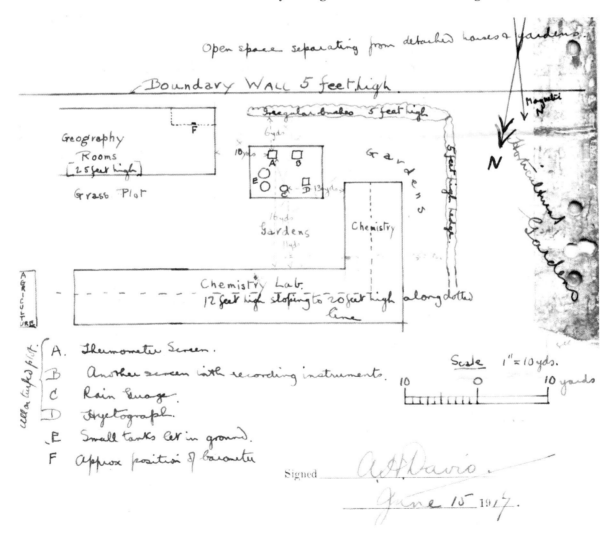

Figure 2.2 *The University College site details at London Road, 15 June 1917. The site is believed to be close to the position shown as Site 1 on Figure 2.6 (note that North is at the bottom of this plan, and at the top of Figure 2.6)*

rather high. Local experience agrees. The Leighton Park people say they often walk down into fog.'* The earth thermometers were found to 'be on a much better site than the other instruments' with the present site being 'especially unrepresentative for the evaporation gauges'. Overall the site exposure was considered to be 'poor' due to the rather sheltered aspect.

1921-1940

A second site inspection was carried out on 21 July 1924 with the site exposure being classified as 'unsatisfactory'. The screen was in need of painting and readings from the grass minimum thermometer were considered to be suspect. The report noted that the station (along with the site at Shinfield) were maintained by the Physics Department of the College. The station was originally maintained by the 'Geographical Dept' but, owing to wartime conditions (shortage of staff) the meteorological work was transferred to the Physics Department and in 1924 efforts were being made to have the work transferred back. The inspector noted that 'in the meantime the Physics Dept seem inclined to regard the maintenance of the meteorological station as not being their "pigeon"'. Nevertheless, the actual taking of the observations was done to a high standard as the observer was keen and interested in the work.

The 1924 inspection noted that the site and exposure of the thermometer screens and raingauge remained the same as indicated in the communication from the College in June 1917 (Figure 2.2), except for two changes. A new building had been built to the west which in 1924 subtended an angle of 6 degrees at the top of the screen, while bushes which in 1917 were said to be about 1.5 m in height were now 3-5 m tall. As a result the overall exposure was 'very enclosed'. A more suitable site would have been 'in the centre of the large lawn on the north side of the Chemical Laboratory' according to the inspector. On 20 July 1926 the thermometer screens, etc., were moved to a new position according to a note in the register – presumably somewhere near 'Site 2' marked on Figure 2.6. Also in 1926 a Royal Charter was awarded, marking the formal inauguration of the University of Reading.

1941-1967

An inspection in July 1947 again classified the site as unsatisfactory and the site was moved once more to reduce shading effects. But by May 1952 further building had taken place to the south and west and the site was, again, very enclosed. By then an anemometer (a cup generator MK1a) had been installed on the roof of the Agricultural Botany building. Figures 2.3-2.5 show the general condition of the site at this time. A note in the weather section of the *1954 Reading Natural History Society Bulletin* says 'The site of the University Station was changed at the beginning of the year (January 1953), and comparisons made so indicate that maximum temperatures at the new site are about the same as at the old but that minimum temperatures tend to be lower by an average of about 0.5 degF [0.25 – 0.3 degC].' Sunshine records from a Campbell-Stokes recorder commenced in April 1956[†].

On 29 November 1960 a large thermometer screen was erected to hold a thermo-hygrograph. Also in 1960, a 2 foot (60 cm) earth thermometer, black-bulb- and silvered-bulb-in-vacuo maximum thermometers, a cup counter anemometer (on 3 November 1960), a tilting syphon rainfall recorder and a Besson comb nephoscope were installed. Visibility observations at 0900 GMT also began in 1960. Pollution monitoring was started in 1961 and was still being carried out in 1986. On 7 June 1961, 5 cm, 10 cm and 20 cm earth thermometers and a bare soil minimum thermometer were installed.

---

[*] There was another climatological station, run by the Meteorological Office, at Leighton Park – less than 1 km to the south-west of the current site at Whiteknights – between 1904 and 1919; confusingly, records from both sites during this period are shown and catalogued simply as 'Reading' in the Met Office archives.

[†] Sunshine records quoted in this book are from a Campbell-Stokes recorder throughout. The current Observatory equipment also includes an electronic sunshine sensor, the output logged every second.

Figure 2.3 View of inside of Stevenson (thermometer) screen, 9 May 1952. Rather unusually the dry- and wet-bulb thermometers are located on the right-hand side of the screen, rather than in the centre

Figure 2.4 A view of the site from the east, 9 May 1952 – note the (non-standard) close proximity of some trees

Figure 2.5 The London Road site on 9 May 1952 viewed from the west. The official screen is the smaller (nearer) one, the larger one being used by students: the official raingauge is the one closest to the manhole covers

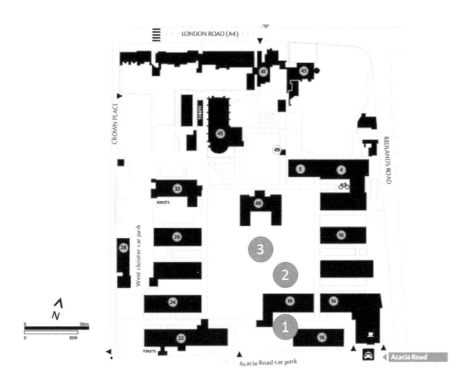

Figure 2.6 *The approximate location of the meteorological observation sites at London Road. Site 1 is the original site, 1908 or earlier to July 1926. This area is now paved, but on the site map of 1917 is shown as grassed. Site 2 is the 'large lawn on the north side of the Chemical Laboratory' site, where observations were maintained 1926-47. Site 3 is the approximate position of the 'Library Lawn' site from 1947-67 – there appear to have been minor moves within this general area during this period. (Base map courtesy University of Reading)*

The various positions at the London Road campus where observations were made are suggested on Figure 2.6. There are some uncertainties about the exact locations, but these are probably accurate to within 10 metres or thereabouts.

1968-1990

The University had gradually outgrown its London Road site, and in 1947 purchased what was to become the main Whiteknights campus, the former country estate of the Marquis of Blandford. The weather station was subsequently relocated there, with records beginning on Whiteknights campus on 1 January 1968. Whiteknights is a more rural (parkland) site and some 20 m higher – and more open – than the London Road site.

Following the move to Whiteknights an in-line Munro wind recorder (mounted on a 15 m tower), a ground level raingauge (described as having a plastic 'egg box' grill surround), British Standard evaporation tank and a Kipp & Zonen pyranometer with chart recorder were added. The sunshine recorder was probably on the roof of the new Chemistry Department building by the end of 1968.

Furthermore, with the development of the Whiteknights campus, the station was moved again in late 1969, this time about 600 m north-east from its original position between the boiler house and Wilderness Wood to its current site, where observations commenced on 1 January 1970. It took a little longer for the wind tower to be relocated: according to KS by the middle of 1970 wind measurements were being made on a 'Munro tower' located on the 'right angled junction of path from Bridges Hall tennis court' (by the late 1990s the tower was located on the north-west corner of the Observatory enclosure). Also in 1970, a concrete minimum thermometer was installed and an electronic digital integrator was linked to the pyranometer. When Arthur Moon retired in 1977, the black-bulb-in-vacuo and nephoscope readings were discontinued.

Metrication arrived in the early 1970s. Rainfall measurements, formerly in inches, were made in millimetres with effect from 1 January 1971. Twelve months later, all the existing Fahrenheit scale thermometers were replaced by Celsius models, while the depth of the earth thermometers were changed to 50 cm and 100 cm from 60 cm (2 feet) and 120 cm (4 feet). The 30 cm (1 foot) records remained unchanged. Throughout, observations have always been made at 0900 GMT. During 1961-1963 additional readings were made at 1200 hours and 1700 hours clock time during an air pollution study.

The weather station remained part of the Department of Geography until 1987, when it was formally taken over by the Department of Meteorology (KS): by 1988 the site and range of research instruments had been expanded (Figure 2.7). During 1992, the Food Science building (now the Science and Technology Centre) had been erected close to the southern border of the enclosure, giving some shelter to wind observations. This building also casts shade over most of the observatory site until about 0930 GMT in mid-winter.

Figure 2.7 *The Whiteknights site, 22 June 1988. During 1992, the Food Science building was erected beyond the fence visible in the top right of the photograph on the southern side of the site. Photograph copyright © Stephen Burt*

Figure 2.8 *The Whiteknights site on 18 April 2015, viewed from a similar position as Figure 2.7. The large screen in left foreground contains the 'manual' thermometers, while the smaller screen right of centre is part of the Met Office AWS system installed during 2012. Photograph copyright © Stephen Burt*

1991-2014
In 1997, when the Department of Meteorology relocated to its current building, the sunshine recorder was removed from its position close to the centre of the instrument enclosure and installed on the fourth-storey roof of the Meteorology building – prior to this there had been at least one theft of the 'glass ball' of the instrument. In August 2012, the Met Office installed a new automatic weather station (AWS) on the site, whose readings are interrogated over a telephone line hourly by the Met Office network operations control centre: this equipment took on the official station number of the previous manual equipment.

Figure 2.8 shows the layout of the Reading Atmospheric Observatory (as the whole site became known in 2006) as at April 2015. Although manual observations continue to be made 365 days per year, they were not submitted to the Met Office for climatological purposes after August 2012.

THE OBSERVERS

Observations have been made by many observers over the years, usually under the direction of one of the principal observers listed in Table 2.1.

Table 2.1 Principal meteorological observers of the University of Reading weather station, 1901 to date

Period	Principal observer	Period	Principal observer
1901-1902	C.H. Jones	1915-1916	E.R. Tufnail
1903	C. Foster	1916-1918	*Observer unknown*
1904-1907	*Observer unknown*	1918-1960	James S. Burgess
1908	S. Cook	1960-1977	Arthur E. Moon
	Dr H.N. Dickson		
1909	W. Low	1977-1985	George W. Goodhind
1910-1911	Dr H.N. Dickson	1985-2009	Ken Spiers
1912	W. Wellbelove	2009 to date	Mike R. Stroud
1913-1915	G.B. Jones		

James Burgess (observer for 42 years, 1918-60) received a special Met Office award in 1955 for long service by a co-operating station observer. Arthur Moon (observer for 17 years, 1960-77) was presented with a barograph by the Met Office in 1977 in recognition of a long period of co-operation as he also observed for Hastings Corporation and the Royal Air Force. Ken Spiers retired in 2009 after 'doing the obs' for 24 years.

Since 1918, the observations have been the responsibility of just five principal observers. Today most of the observations are made by the current principal observer, Mike Stroud, one of the technicians

Figure 2.9 *Thirty years of meteorological observing at the University of Reading. Mike Stroud (right), the principal meteorological observer at the University of Reading Atmospheric Observatory since 2009, photographed together with Ken Spiers (left), the principal observer 1985-2009. Photograph taken on 21 April 2015: © Stephen Burt*

within the Department of Meteorology. Mike is assisted by a small team of mostly volunteer 'deputy observers' who stand in for occasional weekday and weekend duties; since Mike took over in October 2009 these have included Anthony Illingworth, Chris Scott, Claire Ryder, Curtis Wood, George Rogers, Keri Nicoll, Keith Shine, John Lally, Nicola Chalmers, Pete Inness, Giles Harrison, Rosy Wilson and Ross Reynolds, in addition to both of the authors.

HOW DO THE LONDON ROAD AND WHITEKNIGHTS OBSERVATIONS COMPARE?

Moving the university weather station from the town centre site at London Road to the more suburban, parkland site at Whiteknights meant a change to the underlying climatology of the site. To quantify this difference, a third nearby site whose record overlapped both sites was used, namely the standard climatological station at Shinfield, located about 3.5 km south of Whiteknights and about 4.5 km south of the London Road site, at a similar altitude (61 m AMSL). Records were made here between 1917 and 1980.

By comparing, month-by-month, the monthly mean maximum and minimum temperatures and the monthly rainfall totals for 1961-1967 at London Road and Shinfield, the difference between measurements at the two sites was determined. A similar comparison was carried out between Shinfield and Whiteknights observations for 1968-1974 to benchmark the Whiteknights site characteristics. Given that the Shinfield site was unchanged during the 14 year period 1961-1974, the two comparisons revealed (Table 2.2) that the London Road site was about 0.5 degC warmer than Whiteknights. Closer inspection reveals that there are probably two main factors accounting for the difference. The first is simply the difference in altitude – the London Road site (at 45 m above MSL) is lower than Whiteknights (66 m above MSL). Assuming a standard atmospheric lapse rate (reduction of temperature with height) of around 0.6 degC per 100 m, this accounts for about 0.15 degC difference. The second element is urban density – the London Road site is in a more densely built-up area of Reading. This is more difficult to quantify, but the evidence in Table 2.2 suggests this accounts for 0.3-0.4 degC additional warmth in winter increasing to 0.8 degC at midsummer. This latter factor is closely related to solar radiation amount, as the seasonal variation more closely follows solar radiation receipts (minimum December, maximum June) than the annual temperature cycle (minimum early to mid-February, maximum late July).

The comparisons also show that there was less than 1 mm difference in the average annual rainfall between London Road and Whiteknights. In respect of sunshine, London Road and Whiteknights had similar monthly sunshine totals during November to March, while in mid-summer the monthly differences suggested that Whiteknights was about 10-15 hours sunnier each month. It is probable that these differences arose from imperfections in the exposure of the sunshine recorder, rather than a genuinely sunnier atmosphere at Whiteknights.

GAP-FILLING IN THE MONTHLY RECORDS

Monthly rainfall totals are missing for the years 1904-1907 at London Road. Fortunately, a nearby site at Forbury Gardens in central Reading, some 700 metres north of London Road, reported daily rainfall measurements during this period, and these were retained in the Met Office archives. (Daily rainfall measurements were made in Forbury Gardens from 1887 until at least 1965.) Long-period average annual rainfall values at the two sites differ by less than 2 per cent (equivalent to about 10 mm in a year). Consequently, the actual daily and monthly rainfall totals at Forbury Gardens were used as estimates for London Road during 1904-1907.

Daily observations of air temperature are missing for some months after 1911, particularly for the periods July to October 1912, April 1914, July 1916 to February 1917, October 1917, and April 1924. Fortunately, monthly values can be estimated using equivalent observations from several neighbouring weather stations in east Berkshire. The mean temperature difference between the London Road site and each of these other stations was determined for the months around any missing period (and for the calendar month in the previous and following years), and then used to estimate the missing London Road monthly values over that period.

In a similar way, monthly sunshine amounts were estimated for the three months when the London Road sunshine total was missing, namely June 1956, June 1957 and April 1958.

Table 2.2 London Road minus Whiteknights temperature differences - illustrating the relative warmth of the London Road site compared to that of Whiteknights. See text for derivations.

	Mean maximum temperature difference (degC)	*Mean minimum temperature difference (degC)*	*Mean temperature difference (degC)*
January	0.3	0.7	0.5
February	0.3	0.5	0.4
March	0.4	0.5	0.4
April	0.5	0.6	0.5
May	0.5	0.6	0.5
June	0.7	0.8	0.7
July	0.6	0.7	0.6
August	0.4	0.6	0.5
September	0.3	0.6	0.5
October	0.2	0.5	0.3
November	0.3	0.6	0.4
December	0.2	0.5	0.4
Year	**0.4**	**0.6**	**0.5**

3 **The annual cycle**

The plots on these pages show (*top*) the average temperature (daily mean maximum, mean and daily mean minimum, ℃), (*middle*) average precipitation (mm) and (*bottom*) average sunshine duration (hours) for every day of the year over the standard averaging period 1981-2010. Whilst there is considerable variation from year-to-year, these serve to illustrate the general progression of the main weather elements throughout the annual cycle. These plots are referred to in more detail in the monthly chapters which follow.

Temperature

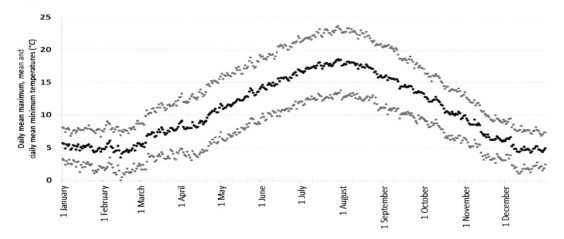

Precipitation

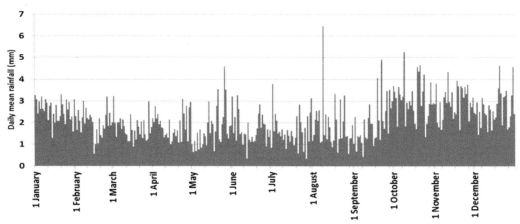

Sunshine

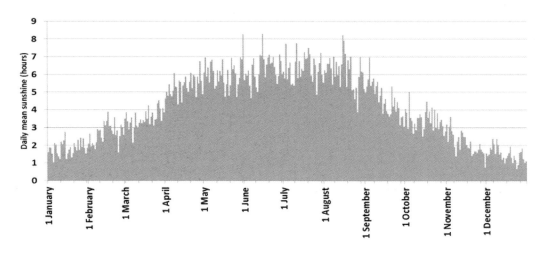

4 January

January is, by a short head, on average the coldest month of the year in Reading. In the 100 years to 2014, January was the coldest month of the year on 31 occasions, February and December in 32 years, while December and January tied one year. (November was the coldest three times, and March just once.) The mean temperature in January over the standard 30 year period 1981-2010 was 4.8 °C (average daily minimum temperature 1.9 °C, average daily maximum temperature 7.7 °C). There is little systematic variation during the month, although on average the end of the month tends to be slightly colder than the beginning, as can be seen on the 'annual cycle' plots In Chapter 3.

The monthly mean precipitation for January (averaged over 1981-2010) is just over 60 mm. Rain falls on 16 days in an average January; although rainfall can be persistent, daily totals in excess of 25 mm are rare. Some precipitation can be expected to fall as snow in most years, and snow is likely to cover the ground on one or two mornings in an average January. Thunderstorms are infrequent but not unknown in January, occurring about three times per decade, but rarely last for more than a few minutes at this time of year.

Sunshine duration in January creeps up a little from December's low point, averaging 56 hours during the month – 1 hour and 50 minutes of bright sunshine daily, although this is slightly misleading as on average 11 January days will remain sunless.

TEMPERATURE
Between 1908 and 2015, air temperatures in January ranged 30 degrees Celsius, from 15.5 °C on 9 January 2015 to -14.5 °C on 14 January 1982 — the latter the lowest air temperature on record in Reading.

The air temperature has reached or exceeded 14 °C on only nine occasions in January since 1908, the most recent being 15.5 °C on 9 January 2015 when, unusually, the highest temperature was reached after dark (see Figure 4.1); the previous January highest was 14.7 °C on 9 January 1998 (see Table 4.1).

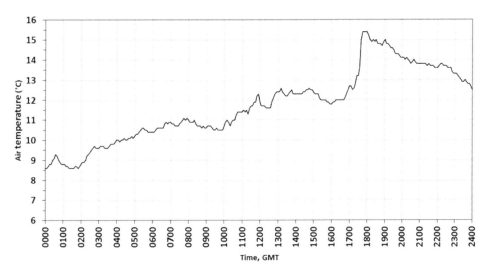

Figure 4.1 *Air temperatures recorded at the University of Reading on 9 January 2015: the highest January temperature on record (15.5 °C) was reached just before 1800 GMT, two hours after sunset. This plot is from 5 minute AWS data*

In sharp contrast, Reading saw its lowest maximum temperature on its long record during an outbreak of bitterly cold air from Europe in January 1987. On 12 January 1987 the maximum temperature reached only -6.8 °C, more than a degree below that on the second-coldest day (see Table 4.1). Diesel froze in lorries on the M4 motorway, and firemen struggled to put out a fire at a disused cinema in Reading because water used by ten appliances froze as it was applied to the flames. Two days in January 1963 (23rd and 24th, with maximum temperatures of -4.5 °C and -5.6 °C respectively) were almost as cold. January is the month most likely to have an 'ice day', one in which the air temperature fails to reach 0 °C: these occurred on 91 January days between 1908 and 2015, an average of a little less than once per year. The longest spells of consecutive 'ice days' since 1908 have been the eight days commencing 17 January 1963 (maximum temperatures ranging from -0.6 °C to -5.6 °C) and five days commencing 26 January 1947 (maximum temperatures ranging from -0.3 °C to -1.8 °C). Three other spells of four consecutive 'ice days' have occurred in January since 1908 (in 1945, 1982 and 1987).

Table 4.1. Highest and lowest maximum and minimum temperatures in January, 1908-2015. Records are from the (slightly milder) London Road site 1908-67, and from Whiteknights 1968-2015: no corrections for site differences have been applied.

Rank	Mildest days	Coldest days	Mildest nights	Coldest nights
1	15.5 °C, 9 Jan 2015	-6.8 °C, 12 Jan 1987	11.7 °C, 20 Jan 2008	-14.5 °C, 14 Jan 1982
2	14.7 °C, 9 Jan 1998	-5.6 °C, 24 Jan 1963	11.2 °C, 5 Jan 1957	-13.4 °C, 15 Jan 1982
3	14.4 °C, 19 Jan 1930	-4.5 °C, 16 Jan 1985	11.1 °C, 4 Jan 1948	-12.5 °C, 23 Jan 1963
4	14.3 °C, 29 Jan 2002	-4.5 °C, 23 Jan 1963	11.1 °C, 1 Jan 2012	-12.1 °C, 24 Jan 1963
5	14.3 °C, 27 Jan 2003	-3.9 °C, 13 Jan 1987	11.0 °C, 6 Jan 1983	-11.7 °C, 25 Jan 1963

Air temperatures of -10 °C or lower are infrequent in Reading, but have occurred on 13 January mornings since 1908, the lowest January temperature (and the lowest for any month) being -14.5 °C on 14 January 1982. The 'grass minimum' temperature, above snow on this occasion, was -20.1 °C that morning – also the lowest yet recorded at the university. This occurrence was preceded by air minima of -11.6 °C on the 13th and followed by -13.4 °C on the 15th – during a spell of ten consecutive nights with air frost (Figure 4.4). In January 1963 minimum temperatures included -12.5 °C, -12.1 °C, -11.7 °C and -11.3 °C on consecutive mornings from 23-26 January – arguably the coldest spell in the record for any month (during the 36 mornings from 23 December 1962, only one failed to record an air frost).

Air frosts (minimum temperature over the 24 hours ending at 0900 GMT of -0.1 °C or below) can be expected on around nine mornings in an average January, and ground frosts on 20 days. January 1963 recorded 27 air frosts, and January 1940 26, while ground frost occurred on all but one morning in the Januarys of 1940 and 1985. No air frost was recorded in the Januarys of 1938 or 2008, and only a single air frost in January 2005; January 1938 saw six ground frosts.

Minimum temperatures above 10 °C over a 24 hour period in January are equally likely at any time of the month – they depend upon the source of the prevailing air mass and not, generally, on sunny or mild conditions the previous day. On the morning of 20 January 2008 the temperature did not drop below 11.7 °C, while on 5 January 1957 a minimum temperature of 11.2 °C was recorded (both during dull spells of weather).

The largest daily temperature ranges – the difference between the daily minimum and maximum temperatures – occurred on 1 January 1932 and 15 January 1982 (both 17.9 degC) and 13 January 1968 (17.7 degC). The 1982 event was the third of four consecutive days with large daily ranges resulting from very cold mornings – on 15 January the minimum temperature was -13.4 °C. Small diurnal ranges – sometimes only 1 degC in 24 hours – are not uncommon in January.

Monthly temperature ranges in January have varied between 11.8 degC, in 1915, and 26.7 degC, in 1982.

Figure 4.2 *The River Thames at Reading, seen from Caversham Bridge in January 1940. The river is frozen, and people are venturing onto the ice from both banks. Christchurch Meadows are to the left, De Montfort Island (or Fry's Island), is in the centre, and on Thames Side, three barges are moored by the wharf, and the power station appears in the background. (Reading Central Library, image 1395 320)*

Figure 4.3 *Sledging on Christchurch Meadows, Reading, during January 1963. (Courtesy* Reading Chronicle *collection, Reading Central Library)*

Figure 4.4 *A wintry scene just outside Wokingham during the severe cold spell in January 1982: this photograph was taken on 10 January. Photograph © Stephen Burt*

Warm and cold months

January 2007 and January 2008 were the mildest Januarys yet recorded in Reading, although those of 1916, 1921 and 1975 were only slightly less mild (Table 4.2). The Januarys of 1963 and 1940 were the coldest (Figure 4.3 and 4.2). The Thames froze over at Caversham for part of January 1940 (Figure 4.2). Some families in Reading had to endure a fortnight without water as pipes froze and burst: schools closed due to a shortage of fuel, and an Alsatian dog and a swan were found frozen in Whiteknights Lake. In January 1963 (Figure 4.3), the Thames at Reading was only kept open for navigation by the use of heavy barges acting as icebreakers. This was the coldest month yet recorded in Reading, with snow on the ground every morning throughout the month.

Table 4.2. January mean temperatures at the University of Reading, 1908-2015. In January the London Road site (1908-67) is about 0.5 degC warmer than the Whiteknights site (1968 onwards) due to its location closer to the town centre. The observed mean temperatures at the London Road site (shown in brackets) have been adjusted by this amount to facilitate comparison between the two records.

January mean temperature 4.8 °C (average 1981-2010)

Mildest months			Coldest months		
Mean temperature, °C	*Departure from 1981-2010 normal degC*	*Year*	*Mean temperature, °C*	*Departure from 1981-2010 normal degC*	*Year*
7.6	+2.8	2007	-2.5 (-2.0)	-7.3	1963
7.2	+2.4	2008	-1.4 (-0.9)	-6.2	1940
7.1	+2.3	1975	0.0	-4.8	1979
6.9 (7.4)	+2.1	1921	0.4 (0.9)	-4.4	1945
6.8 (7.3)	+2.0	1916	0.7	-3.7	1985

PRECIPITATION

Precipitation in this context includes rain, drizzle, snow, sleet, hail and occasionally fog or dew. January is – on average – slightly less wet than October, November or December, with an average monthly precipitation of just over 60 mm during the 1981-2010 period. Monthly precipitation totals for January over the period since 1901 have varied from less than 10 mm in 1987 (14% of normal) to over 150 mm in 2014 (251% of normal) (Table 4.3).

Three Januarys since 1901 have received in excess of 125 mm rainfall, with 2014 being the wettest on record (at 251% of normal) by some margin (Table 4.3). The very wet winter of 2013/14 saw 165 mm of rain fall in the 28 days ending 8 January 2014; in the 22 day period 15 December 2013 to 5 January 2014 152 mm of rain fell. The heavy and persistent rains led to widespread flooding along Reading's waterways and floodplains – in places from 24 December; Sonning Bridge was closed on two occasions and the Loddon Bridge Park and Ride was closed for much of January.

Table 4.3. January precipitation at the University of Reading, 1901-2015 (London Road 1901-1967, Whiteknights 1968-2015).

January mean precipitation 60.5 mm (average 1981-2010)

Wettest months			Driest months			Wettest days	
Total fall, mm	*Per cent of normal*	*Year*	*Total fall, mm*	*Per cent of normal*	*Year*	*Daily fall, mm*	*Date*
151.4	251	2014	8.7	14	1987	29.0	15 Jan 1918
128.7	213	1995	13.3	22	1997	27.7	7 Jan 1908
126.4	209	1939	13.8	23	1992	26.2	25 Jan 1939
115.3	191	1936	14.0	23	1950	24.1	28 Jan 1958
114.3	189	1988	14.3	24	1976	22.9	26 Jan 1940

In January 1936 flooding occurred on the Thames in Reading after a thaw of snow and heavy rain earlier in the month (5th-9th): a rower drowned when his boat was swamped during a practice for the

Reading University maiden eights. In January 1939 42 mm fell in 48 hours on the 24th-25th; much of this fell as wet snow after 3 a.m. on the 25th and 7000 subscribers lost their telephone connections in Reading. Many public clocks were reported to have stopped working after becoming clogged with snow. January 1995 was at that time the wettest January recorded, with 129 mm of rainfall – only 15 mm fell in the first half of the month, but 114 mm in the second half.

Only one January, 1987, has received less than 10 mm of precipitation, and of this only 1 mm fell in the final 18 days of the month. Notably dry spells for mid-winter set in in January in 1932 and 1993: only 9.4 mm fell in the 65 days commencing 17 January 1932, and 10.5 mm in the 62 days commencing 27 January 1993.

Heavy falls of rain are uncommon in January: only three January days have exceeded 25 mm of precipitation (in the 24 hour period commencing at 0900 GMT). The wettest January day on record was 15 January 1918, when 29.0 mm fell: 54 mm fell in four days from the 15th. On 7 January 1908, 27.7 mm fell – this turned out to be three-quarters of the month's total, turning a dry month into a near-average one. The fall of 22.9 mm on 26 January 1940 was mostly snow, the day's maximum temperature being only 3.3 °C.

Snowfall and lying snow

Snow or sleet falls on about three days in an average January, but as with any winter month there are large year-to-year variations. The snowiest Januarys since 1908 were in 1963 (15 days with snowfall - followed by a snowy February), 2010 (12 days – again with a snowy February following) and 1985 (11 days with snowfall). At the opposite extreme, between 1968 and 2015 there were nine Januarys without snowfall (all but one of these occurring since 1988).

Snowfall does not always lead to snow cover on the ground: in more than half of the years in the available record (56 years) there was no January snow cover at the morning observation. On 17 January 1918 – 'half a foot' (i.e. 15 cm) of snow reportedly fell in five hours in Reading and the surrounding area, causing chaos on the tramlines. On 16 January 1926, deep snow affected the Reading area (although no record of snow depths was kept at that time), with some local villages cut off. The observer noted 'Snow continued all day'. The deepest recorded snow depth in any month occurred on 3 January 1963, namely 31 cm. Every morning in January 1963 had lying snow - one of the snowiest winters across the UK in the past 120 years (for more on the winter of 1962/63, see the 'Seasons' chapter). January 1979 had 14 mornings with lying snow, and January 1942, 12. Aside from January 1963, the next-deepest snowfall occurred in January 2010, when 27 cm was noted on the morning of 6 January (Figures 4.5 and 23.2).

Figure 4.5 *'The lunchtime rush' - Broad Street in Reading on 6 January 2010. The snow depth at the university that morning was 27 cm, the second-deepest snowfall on the university's records since 1950. Photograph Copyright © Craig Selley*

Thunderstorms

Thunder is uncommon but not unknown in January, occurring about three times a decade. In January 1974, thunder was heard on three days, and two in both 1995 and 1998. 'Thundersnow' – the simultaneous occurrence of thunder with snowfall – is rarer still: thundersnow was noted on 28 January 2004 and 29 January 2015 (and 6 April 2008). On 20 January 1995 a heavy thunderstorm with large hail affected the south of Reading during the early hours of the morning (Figure 23.5).

SUNSHINE

January is normally slightly sunnier than December, the monthly average being 56 hours of bright sunshine, although on average 11 days will remain sunless. Monthly sunshine totals since 1957 are shown in Table 4.4.

Table 4.4 January sunshine duration at the University of Reading, 1957-2015 (London Road 1957-1967, Whiteknights 1968-2015).

January mean sunshine duration 56.5 hours, 1.82 hours per day (average 1981-2010)

Possible daylength: 262 hours. Mean sunshine duration as percentage of possible: 21.6

Sunniest months			Dullest months			Sunniest days	
Duration, hours	*Per cent of possible*	*Year*	*Duration, hours*	*Per cent of possible*	*Year*	*Duration, hours*	*Date*
91.2	34.9	1984	19.2	7.3	1996	8.1	30 Jan 1987
88.2	33.7	2003	29.7	11.4	2013	8.0	25 Jan 1986
79.1	30.2	1959	30.8	11.8	1993	8.0	31 Jan 1987
76.3	29.1	2000	34.9	13.3	1973	7.9	29 Jan 1974,
75.0	28.7	1976	37.0	14.1	1970		28 Jan 1994
							and 29 Jan
							2004

With just 19 hours of sunshine (a daily average of just 37 minutes, only 7 per cent of that possible), January 1996 was, by some margin, the dullest January on the record, and the third dullest month yet recorded – only the December months of 1956 and 2010 were duller. Nineteen days remained sunless, but in one of those oddities that punctuate weather statistics, almost one-third (6.0 h) of the month's total sunshine occurred on the last day of the month! The mean cloud cover at 0900 GMT that month was 95% - the second-highest of any month since complete daily records of that element commenced in 1960.

Long sunless spells are not uncommon in January. Since 1958 there have been 12 sunless spells lasting seven consecutive days or more during the month. The longest run of sunless days occurred in 1987, with 14 consecutive days commencing 14 January 1987 (with a contrasting 23.5 hours in the final four days of the month) and 10 days from 14 January 1979 and 16 January 2013. January 2013 was the only month in the record with the unenviable record of two sunless spells each lasting seven days or more, with an earlier seven day sunless spell commencing on 2 January. In all, 22 out of the 31 days in January 2013 remained sunless, the highest for any January to date: January 2007 saw only five sunless days.

The sunniest Januarys were those of 1984 and 2003, with an average approaching 3 hours sunshine per day, more than one-third of the possible duration: both months logged just six sunless days. January 1984 had more sunshine than either February or March of that year. Remarkably, January 1984's total is also not far short of the totals in the dullest summer months – for example June 1990 (109 hours) and August 1968 (117 hours) - despite the much greater length of daylight hours during the summer.

At this time of year, 7 hours of sunshine counts as a 'sunny day'. Owing to the slow increase in daylight hours during January, only at the very end of the month is 8 hours sunshine in a day possible. This value has occurred only in two years since 1968 – 1986 and 1987: 8.1 hours on 30 January 1987 (the sunniest January day on record) was followed by 8.0 hours the following day.

GALES

Gales (mean wind speed exceeding 34 knots or 39 mph for at least 10 minutes) are uncommon in Reading. Since continuous records of wind speed and direction commenced in 1961, the highest wind speeds recorded at the university in any month were the gusts of 76 knots (87 mph) on 2 January 1976 and 77 knots (88 mph) on 25 January 1990.

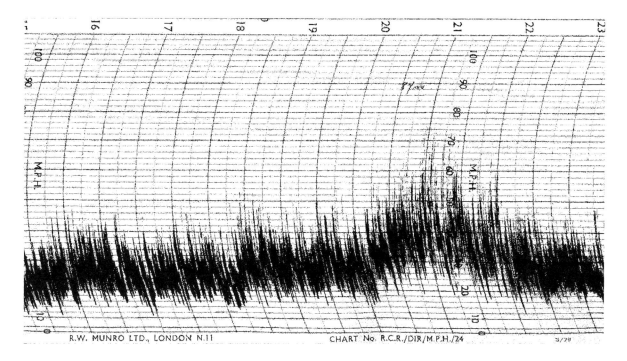

Figure 4.6 *The university's wind record for the severe gale of 2 January 1976, which resulted in the second-highest wind gust on Reading's records – 76 knots or 87 mph at 2115 GMT. The wind scale is in mph, and the time scale is shown along the top of the chart.*

The 2 January 1976 storm was a severe gale during the evening which was at its worst for about 2 hours. The wind recorder chart from that evening (Figure 4.6) shows that the wind was gusting in excess of 40 knots (45 mph) by 1800 GMT, increasing further after 2015 GMT. Around 2100 GMT the 10 minute mean wind speed reached 46 knots (53 mph): the highest gust came just before 2115 GMT, marked on the chart as '87 mph'. The gale had diminished somewhat by 2200 GMT, but gusts in excess of 60 mph (52 knots) were recorded as late as 2320 GMT. Considerable tree and structural damage resulted from this gale in the Reading area.

The 25 January 1990 storm caused considerable damage with many trees felled – in some respects the storm was worse than that of the 'Great Storm' of 16 October 1987. Over 200 casualties were treated at the Royal Berkshire Hospital in Reading for cuts and broken limbs due to flying debris. In Shinfield Road, near the university, one man narrowly escaped death when a tree fell in front of his car. Pupils were evacuated from Christ the King primary school in Reading when the roof blew off.

TEMPERATURE, PRECIPITATION AND SUNSHINE IN GRAPHS – JANUARY

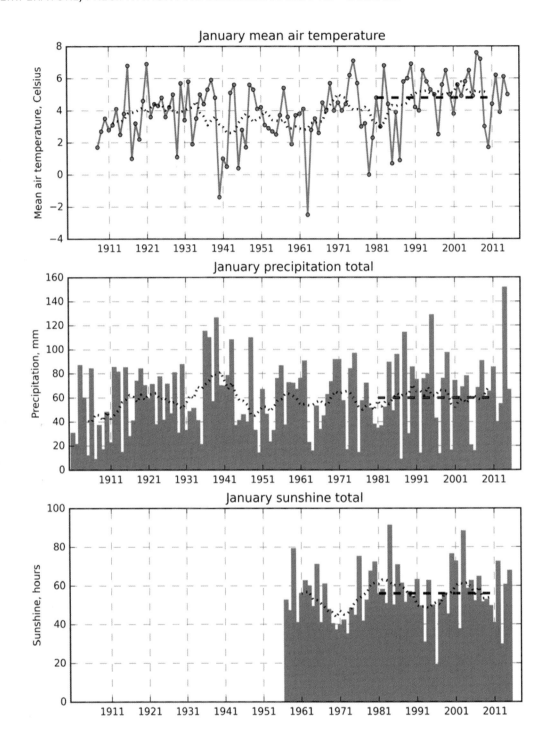

Figure 4.7 *Monthly values of (from top) mean temperature (°C), total precipitation (mm) and sunshine duration (hours) for January at Reading over the available period of record (plots include London Road rainfall records where available 1901-04, with estimates from other Reading stations to 1907 as necessary)*

The mean temperatures as recorded at London Road 1908-67 have been reduced by 0.5 degC to ensure approximate homogeneity with the records from the Whiteknights site, 1968 onwards. No site adjustments have been made for precipitation or sunshine. The 1981-2010 averages are indicated by the thick dashed line, while the 10 year running mean centred on the year shown is indicated by a dashed grey line

5 February

February is the driest month of the year in Reading, the mean monthly precipitation over the most recent 30 year averaging period (1981-2010) being just under 41 mm, one-third less than January. (Part of the reason for the low total is that the month has fewer days than other months: in fact the mean precipitation per day is fractionally lower in March.) Precipitation can be expected on about 12 days in an average February, and three or four of these can be expected to be of snow or sleet. The frequency of snowfall, and snow cover, is highest in February, and highest of all in the second week of the month.

The lowest mean temperatures of the year in Reading are reached during early to mid-February. Although there is of course considerable year-to-year variation, on average, 14 February was the coldest day of the year over the 1981-2010 averaging period, with a mean temperature of 3.5 °C and a mean minimum temperature of exactly 0.0 °C. Thereafter, increasing daylength and greater power of the Sun are reflected in a slow rise in temperatures, as shown in the annual plots (Chapter 3).

It is in February that increasing daylength and lighter evenings begin to become obvious after the gloomy mid-winter months: February is, by daily mean duration of sunshine, on average some 50% sunnier than January. The monthly mean duration of bright sunshine is 76 hours, with about 8 days remaining sunless on average.

TEMPERATURE

Temperatures in February in Reading have ranged from a summer-like 17.4 °C to a bitterly cold -12.9 °C during the period 1908-2015. The warmest and coldest days and nights in February over this period are shown in Table 5.1.

Table 5.1 Highest and lowest maximum and minimum temperatures in February, 1908-2015. Records are from the (slightly milder) London Road site 1908-67, and from Whiteknights 1968-2015: no corrections for site differences have been applied.

Rank	Mildest days	Coldest days	Mildest nights	Coldest nights
1	17.4 °C, 28 Feb 1959	-3.8 °C, 1 Feb 1956 and 7 Feb 1991	11.5 °C, 4 Feb 2004	-12.9°C, 15 Feb 1929
2	17.0 °C, 23 Feb 1990	-2.7 °C, 2 Feb 1956 and 9 Feb 1991	11.5 °C, 5 Feb 2004	-12.2 °C, 25 Feb 1947
3	16.8 °C, 13 Feb 1998	-2.5 °C, 4 Feb 1912 and 17 Feb 1947	11.4 °C, 2 Feb 2002	-11.6 °C, 10 Feb 1986
4	16.7 °C, 29 Feb 1948	-2.4 °C, 8 Feb 1991	10.9 °C, 8 Feb 1946	-11.5 °C, 14 Feb 1929
5	16.7 °C, 14 Feb 1961	-2.3 °C, 12 Feb 1947	10.8 °C, 24 Feb 1922	-11.0 °C, 24 Feb 1947

The end of February 1959 saw a remarkable four-day warm spell that gave temperatures above 16 °C each day from 27 February to 2 March, culminating in the warmest February day yet recorded of 17.4 °C on 28th. February 1998 was another very mild month, particularly so by day from the 8th to 25th: during this period temperatures reached at least 10 °C every day, and 15 °C on three occasions.

As well as summer-like warmth, February days can rival the coldest days of winter: daily maximum temperatures remained below 0 °C on 56 occasions during 1908-2015. On 1 February 1956 and again on 7 February 1991, the highest temperature was just -3.8 °C. Both days were part of very cold spells that persisted over several days: in 1956 a maximum temperature of -2.7 °C was recorded on 2 February, and in this cold spell the temperature dropped below -7 °C on five consecutive nights in an outbreak of easterly winds. The longest consecutive spells of 'ice days' on the record are six days commencing 11 February 1929, and five days commencing 9 February 1985. February 1929 was the coldest February since 1895, and in this six day cold spell the temperature did not rise above -1.4 °C.

In February 1991, the temperature did not rise above -2.4 °C in the three days commencing 7 February, during a spell of easterly winds with snow falling each day and a snow depth of 8 cm on the 8th.

Air minimum temperatures below -10 °C do occur occasionally in February, having been recorded in six February months in the 108 year record. February 1929 features once more with the lowest February air temperature in the entire record, namely -12.9 °C logged on the 15th of that month. This cold spell saw 14 consecutive nights with air frost, while three consecutive mornings (14th-16th) saw the temperature fall below -10 °C. The Thames froze from bank to bank through Reading, and many casualties resulted from skating activities on local streams, rivers and lakes (Figures 5.1, 5.2): others died from hypothermia and from falls on icy ground. The infamous snowy winter of 1947 reached its coldest in Reading on 25 February when the temperature fell to -12.2 °C at the London Road site: air frost was recorded on 26 nights that February, while temperatures below -10 °C continued into early March.

Figure 5.1 Ice-skating on Whiteknights Lake, Reading, 13 February 1929, during 'The Great Frost'. The three-arched bridge is in the background. (Reading Central Library, image 1394 315)

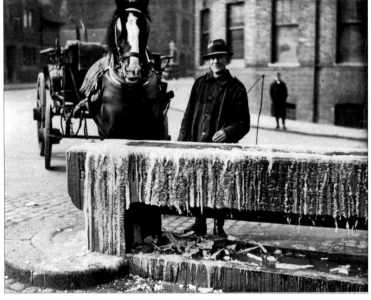

Figure 5.2 A man and a horse at the trough at the junction of Forbury Road and Valpy Street, Reading, in February 1929. The 'Great Frost' has frozen the water in the trough, and the outside of it is covered with icicles. (Reading Central Library, image 1395 313)

The longest spell of consecutive air frosts on Reading's records also occurred in 1947 – 33 days, ending 9 March. More recently, the site at Whiteknights recorded -11.6 °C on 10 February 1986 and -10.1 °C on 11 February 2012 (Figure 5.3). February 1986 was the coldest since 1947, and 1895 before that: three consecutive very cold nights resulted after a heavy fall of snow, while there were 28 consecutive days with air frost ending 4 March that year. However, only minor snowfall accompanied the very cold weather in February 2012.

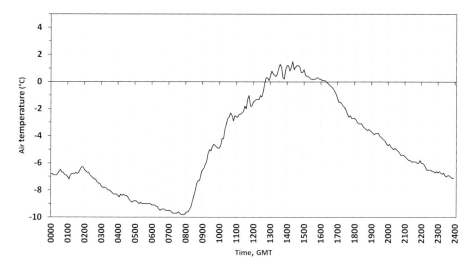

Figure 5.3
Air temperatures recorded at the University of Reading on 11 February 2012: the screen minimum temperature that morning was -10.1 °C, which at the time of writing was the most recent instance of a temperature below -10 °C. This plot is from 5 minute AWS data.

Given the right conditions – a cloudy, mild southerly airflow - February can also produce relatively mild nights. The mildest on record were 4 and 5 February 2004, both of which fell no lower than 11.5 °C: particularly noteworthy in that the temperature remained above 10 °C for three consecutive nights and didn't fall below 8 °C during the first six days of the month. Almost as mild, and the highest on record to that date, was the minimum temperature of 11.4 °C on 2 February 2002. However, these are the coldest 'mildest nights' of any month in the year.

The largest range in temperature on any February day was 18.7 degC on 18 February 1940: freezing fog in the morning was followed by snow in the afternoon, turning to rain in the evening as the temperature rose. As in January, daily ranges of just 2-3 degC are quite common in February.

Warm and cold months
February 1990 was by some margin the mildest February on Reading's records, being 3.3 degC warmer than average, with no air frosts recorded during the month – this was also the case in the Februarys of 1961, 1966 and more recently 2014. In contrast, the *mean* temperature was below freezing in both February 1947 and 1986, the coldest Februarys locally since 1895 (which nearby observations suggest was about 1 degC colder than in 1947). In February 1947 only two mornings remained frost-free, and in February 1942 just three: while February 1979 saw ground frost recorded every morning, a so-far unique distinction. Also particularly worthy of note is the low maximum temperature reading of just 3.9 °C for the entire month of February 1986: a temperature of at least 5 °C has been reached on at least one day during the month in every other calendar month during the period 1908-2014.

Monthly temperature ranges in February have varied between 11.2 degC in 1951 and 11.5 degC in 2014, to 26.5 degC in 2012 – the latter not far short of the February range on the entire record, namely 30.3 degC.

Table 5.2 February temperatures at the University of Reading, 1908-2015. In February the London Road site (1908-67) is about 0.4 degC warmer than the Whiteknights site (1968 onwards) due to its location closer to the town centre. The observed mean temperatures at the London Road site (shown in brackets) have been adjusted by this amount to facilitate comparison between the two records.

February mean temperature 4.8 °C (average 1981-2010)

Mildest months			Coldest months		
Mean temperature, °C	*Departure from 1981-2010 normal degC*	*Year*	*Mean temperature, °C*	*Departure from 1981-2010 normal degC*	*Year*
8.1	+3.3	1990	-1.6 (-1.2)	-6.4	1947
7.4	+2.6	2002	-1.0	-5.8	1986
7.4 (7.8)	+2.6	1961	-0.6 (-0.2)	-5.4	1956
7.4 (7.8)	+2.6	1945	-0.3 (0.1)	-5.1	1963
7.3	+2.5	1995, 1998	-0.2 (0.2)	-5.0	1929

PRECIPITATION

February is the driest calendar month of the year in Reading, with the mean monthly precipitation over the period 1981-2010 being just under 41 mm, one-third less than January. Precipitation is more likely to fall as snow in this month than in any other calendar month, the frequency of snow or sleet being the highest of the year in early to mid-February.

Table 5.3 February precipitation at the University of Reading, 1901-2015 (London Road 1901-1967, Whiteknights 1968-2015).

February mean precipitation 40.9 mm (average 1981-2010)

Wettest months			Driest months			Wettest days	
Total fall, mm	*Per cent of normal*	*Year*	*Total fall, mm*	*Per cent of normal*	*Year*	*Daily fall, mm*	*Date*
117.2	287	2014	2.5	6	1934	29.7	4 Feb 1901
115.6	283	1951	3.2	8	1993	29.2	25 Feb 1933
108.5	265	1990	3.7	9	1932	28.4	24 Feb 1933
107.7	263	1937	4.2	10	1998	26.8	9 Feb 2009
100.0	244	1916	4.5	11	1965	24.9	6 Feb 2014

Very wet months are rare at this time of year, and only five Februarys have attained 100 mm precipitation since 1901 (21 Octobers reached this threshold during the same period). February 2014 was the wettest of all, with 117 mm, part of the exceptionally wet winter of 2013/14. Flooding occurred frequently along parts of local rivers during the month (Figures 5.4 and 23.8): Sonning Bridge was closed for part of the month as a result, while flooding due to rising groundwater levels was also a problem in some areas.

Falls in excess of 25 mm of precipitation in a day are almost unknown in February, having occurred only four times since 1901. The most recent of these was on 9 February 2009, when 26.8 mm fell. Remarkably, two of the others were on consecutive days - 24 and 25 February 1933, with 28.4 mm and 29.2 mm, respectively. As a measure of rarity, this is one of only two occasions with consecutive days of 25 mm or more of precipitation on the entire record (the other was 19-20 July 2007). The meteorological registers for these days note 'heavy snow 9.30 a.m. onwards' and 'sleet and rain continuing all day' with 'rain continuing all day' on the 26th (which saw a further 13.7 mm fall). In all, 71 mm fell in just three days, close to double the average precipitation for February.

Figure 5.4 The Kennet in flood through The Oracle shopping centre in Reading, on 1 February 2014. See also Figure 23.8. Photographs © Stephen Burt

At the other end of the scale, February 1932 recorded just 2.5 mm – the wettest day (24th) receiving only 1.0 mm of precipitation. The longest spring drought on record, one of 34 consecutive days without rainfall, commenced on 20 February 1953. Only the 37 day dry spells commencing in August 1959 and July 1976 have been of longer duration. The most notable spring drought of the 20th century commenced in February 1938: in the 65 days commencing 27 February, just 12.9 mm precipitation was recorded.

Snowfall and lying snow

Despite being a short month, February is on average the snowiest month of the year in Reading: snow or sleet can be expected on three or four days, and to remain on the ground on two mornings, but as with the other winter months there are large variations from year to year. Between 1968 and 2015 nine Februarys recorded no snowfall (most recently 2011 and 2014), while the snowiest Februarys since 1908 were in 1963 (16 days with snowfall), 1955 (14 days) and 1947 and 1969 (both 13 days).

In terms of snow cover, February 1963 recorded 17 mornings with snow on the ground, closely followed by 15 in February 1986 – not surprisingly, both months feature in the 'Top ten coldest months' (Chapter 22, Table 22.4B): February 1963 came at the end of the unusually cold and snowy winter of 1962/63 when snow lay continuously on the ground for long periods. The greatest snow depths yet observed during February were 18 cm on 6 February 1986, and 13 cm on 26 February 1958 and 2-3 February 1963.

SUNSHINE

It is normally by the middle of February that the strength and duration of sunshine has increased noticeably over December and January, and February is, by daily mean duration of sunshine, on average some 50% sunnier than January, the largest percentage rise between any two months of the year. On average, eight of the 28 or 29 days in February will remain sunless, but the other days between them amount to around 76 hours of bright sunshine.

Table 5.4 February sunshine duration at the University of Reading, 1957-2015 (London Road 1957-1967, Whiteknights 1968-2015).

February mean sunshine duration 76.0 hours, 2.71 hours per day (average 1981-2010)

Possible daylength: 279 hours*. Mean sunshine duration as percentage of possible: 27.2

Sunniest months			Dullest months			Sunniest days	
Duration, hours	Per cent of possible	Year	Duration, hours	Per cent of possible	Year	Duration, hours	Date
126.7	45.3	2008	32.7	11.7	1965	9.5	20 Feb 1970
115.9	41.5	1988	32.7	11.7	1966	9.5	27 Feb 1973
115.4	41.3	1970	35.0	12.5	1972	9.5	26 Feb 1977
107.4	38.4	1998	38.6	13.8	2011	9.4	27 Feb 1959
100.1	35.8	2003	41.7	14.9	1976	9.3	26 Feb 1995

* This is for a 28 day February; for leap years, the figure is 290 hours

Despite the increasing daylength, sunshine totals do vary a lot in February. February 2008 recorded almost 127 hours of bright sunshine (with only six sunless days), considerably more than some summer months – the dismal 109 hours sunshine recorded in June 1990 and 111 hours in July 1965 have both been surpassed in three Februarys since 1968. In contrast, February 1980 saw the highest average cloud cover at 0900 GMT – 96 per cent – since continuous records commenced in 1960: only three of that month's 29 mornings saw even the slightest break in the overcast conditions.

As the days lengthen, so the possible duration of sunshine increases, and towards the end of the month more than 9 hours is possible on clear days. Three February days have managed 9.5 hours – a creditable total for a June day.

Long spells of anticyclonic weather can lead to persistent dry but cloudy conditions at this time of year, and the Februarys of 1965 and 1966 jointly hold the unenviable record of the dullest February, both with exactly the same total (32.7 hours, only 12% of possible daylight). February 2011, with 39 hours sunshine, was the fourth of four dull months, with 62 sunless days in total – more than half of the 120 days in this period. The longest spells of sunless days in February since 1968 have been the 10 days commencing 3 February 1993 and nine days commencing 6 February 1959: both were very dry months. In February 1979, only one day (14th) saw sunshine in a run of 14 days.

GALES

The second and third major storms in the space of a month affected Reading on 7 and 26 February 1990 (following on from the severe gale on 25 January of that year). On 7 February, one hotel resident in Reading escaped death when a chimney crashed through the roof into her bathroom: the wind gusted to 70 knots (81 mph) at the university, while the gale was accompanied by flooding along the Thames. Less than three weeks later, on 26 February, a bus was blown into the path of a lorry in Reading, and an even higher gust of 71 knots (82 mph) was recorded. These remain the two highest gusts on record for February; in all, February 1990 saw gusts of 50 knots (57 mph) or more on eight days.

TEMPERATURE, PRECIPITATION AND SUNSHINE IN GRAPHS – FEBRUARY

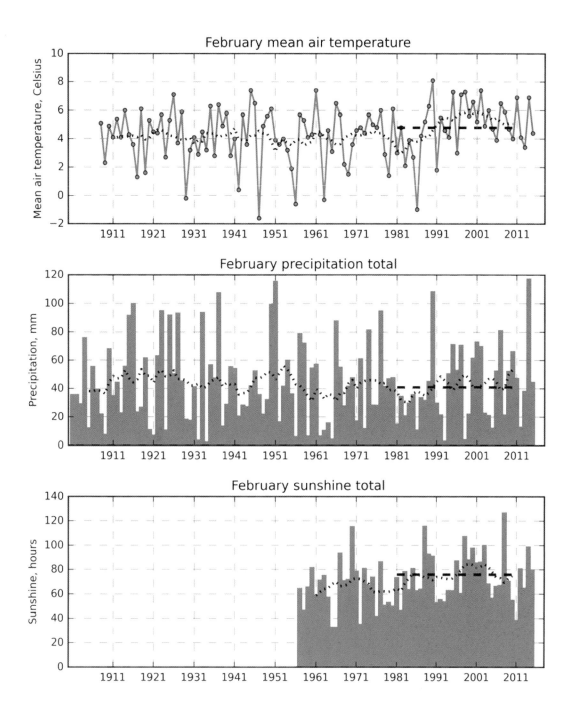

Figure 5.5 *Monthly values of (from top) mean temperature (°C), total precipitation (mm) and sunshine duration (hours) for February at Reading over the available period of record (plots include London Road rainfall records where available 1901-04, with estimates from other Reading stations to 1907 as necessary)*

The mean temperatures as recorded at London Road 1908-67 have been reduced by 0.5 degC to ensure approximate homogeneity with the records from the Whiteknights site, 1968 onwards. No site adjustments have been made for precipitation or sunshine. The 1981-2010 averages are indicated by the thick dashed line, while the 10 year running mean centred on the year shown is indicated by a dashed grey line

6 March

In most years, March marks the transition from winter to spring, and the weather can be very changeable – the old saying 'March comes in like a lion and goes out like a lamb' has more than an element of truth. March weather is sometimes an unrelenting continuation of winter with frost and snow, sometimes glorious early spring sunshine and early warmth – occasionally both within a week! Average daytime temperatures increase quite quickly from below 9 °C at the beginning of the month to 12 °C at the end of the month: the rise in average night minimum temperatures is less rapid, and sharp frosts are not unknown even at the very end of the month.

The monthly mean rainfall for March is slightly higher than February, although the difference is almost entirely due to March having the greater number of days. Despite being one of the driest months of the year, the most widespread and devastating floods of the twentieth century along the Thames and Kennet rivers in Reading occurred in March. Snow can be expected on one or two days in an average March, and thunder about one year in two, more often after mid-month. The duration of bright sunshine in March averages 109 hours, or about 3½ hours per day, although the sunniest Marches come close to the normal sunshine for a summer month. A daily total of 12 hours of sunshine is just possible by the end of the month, although typically five or six days will remain sunless.

TEMPERATURE

March marks the transition from winter to spring, and the weather can occasionally be very cold and wintry, or very warm and sunny. The average temperature for the month is 7.1 °C, but 20 °C has been reached at least once in March around once per decade over the last century: the earliest date in the year on which 20 °C has been reached in Reading since 1908 was 9 March (when, in 1948, 21.8 °C was recorded). The highest March temperatures tend to occur towards the end of the month – the highest of all in 1965, when 22.1 °C was reached on 28th followed by 22.8 °C the following day. In March 1918, the culmination of a five-day spell of high daytime temperatures was marked by 22.3 °C on 24th. More recently, 21 °C was reached in March 1968 and March 2012. The latter year saw a remarkable nine-day warm spell with temperatures reaching 17 °C every day, and three days surpassing 20 °C.

Despite increasing warmth by day, the mildest March nights are only slightly warmer than those in January or February, and a night minimum of 10 °C or more can only be expected in about one March in three. There is but a single occurrence on the record of a March minimum of 12 °C or more – on 30 March 1998, when the minimum was 12.4 °C. Interestingly, since 1908 only the two warmest March nights (in 1990 and 1998) were milder than any in the February record.

Daytime temperatures in March can occasionally fail to reach 0 °C, although with increasing daylength this is a rare event, with only two such occurrences on record – 6 March 1942 was the coldest March day, with a maximum temperature of only -0.6 °C (part of a three-day cold spell), while 1 March 1986 reached only -0.1 °C. March 1965 saw a very wide range of daytime temperatures, from close to the lowest on record (the maximum temperature on 4 March 1965 was just 0.0 °C) to the highest on record less than 4 weeks later. Occasionally temperatures go the other way, too – in March 1928 the temperature reached 18.2 °C on 4th (described by the observer as 'a warm sunny day'), but only a week later the maximum struggled to reach 0.8 °C (a 'bright and cloudy day with snow showers').

Sharp frosts are not uncommon in March, although the coldest March night (-11.3 °C on 7 March 1947) was much colder than any other March night on the record, and came towards the end of a bitterly cold and snowy spell of weather that had persisted since late January of that year. March 1965 makes a third appearance in the March extreme temperatures (Table 6.1), with the fourth-coldest March night recorded on 3rd (-7.2 °C). More recently, -5.5 °C was recorded as late as 23 March in 2008. Grass minimum temperatures below -10 °C have been recorded several times in March, even quite late into the month – notably -13.2 °C on 20 March 1985 and -13.1 °C on 22 March 1980. The second half of March 2013 was the coldest such period since 1883 on local records, and grass minimum temperatures as low as -11.0 °C occurred on 29 March and -11.9 °C on 31 March – both very late in the year for such low temperatures. Air frost occurred on 19 nights in March 1924, 17 in March 1955 and 1962 and 16 in March 2013, and ground frost on 26 mornings in each of the March months of 1962, 1973 and 1976. Air frosts during Easter 1975 at the end of March led to orchard blossom damage locally – and there were to be more air frosts during early April: blossom had arrived early after one of the mildest winters in the Reading record. In contrast, March 1959 and March 1960 were both free of air frost.

Table 6.1 Highest and lowest maximum and minimum temperatures in March, 1908-2015. Records are from the (slightly milder) London Road site 1908-67, and from Whiteknights 1968-2015: no corrections for site differences have been applied.

Rank	Warmest days	Coldest days	Mildest nights	Coldest nights
1	22.8 °C, 29 Mar 1965	-0.6°C, 6 Mar 1942	12.4 °C, 30 Mar 1998	-11.3 °C, 7 Mar 1947
2	22.3 °C 24 Mar 1918	-0.1°C, 1 Mar 1986	11.8 °C, 19 Mar 1990	-7.5 °C, 3 Mar 1909
3	22.1 °C 28 Mar 1965	0.0°C, 4 Mar 1965	11.0 °C, 27 Mar 2006	-7.4 °C, 5 Mar 1909
4	21.9 °C 28 Mar 1929	0.2 °C, 9 Mar 1931	10.8 °C, 2 Mar 1999 and 26 Mar 2006	-7.2 °C, 3 Mar 1965
5	21.9 °C 29 Mar 1968	0.4 °C, 5 Mar 1947	10.6 °C 8 Mar 1981, 9 Mar 2000 and 22 Mar 2006	-6.8°C, 10 Mar 1931

The lowest temperature of the (calendar) year has occurred in March in eight years since 1908 – namely 1909, 1931, 1950, 1965, 2001, 2004, 2006 and most recently 2011.

Very large daily ranges in air temperature can result during clear weather in late March, when the ground is still cold and frosts are likely, and yet the strength of the Sun is the same as that in late September. Four of the ten largest daily ranges in temperature yet recorded (Chapter 22, Table 22.6) occurred in March, more than in any other month: notable amongst these was the 22.7 degC on 28 March 2012 (minimum temperature -1.3 °C, maximum temperature 21.4 °C), and 22.5 degC on 25 March 1953 (-2.0 °C to 20.5 °C). One of the largest ranges in temperature in any month of the year occurred in March 1965, 30.0 degC between -7.2 °C on 3rd and 22.8 °C on 29th.

Warm and cold months

March 1917 was the coldest March in the record. Each month in winter 1916/17 had similar mean temperatures; indeed it was a winter of seemingly continuous cold that extended across north-western Europe at a time of trench warfare. The coldest conditions arguably continued well into March and April, as 1917 saw the coldest of both months in the Reading record. March 1962 and March 2013 were almost as cold – the latter a dull month with persistent winds from the east and north-east. There is little to choose between the March warmth of 1938 and 1957, although in both years April was to be colder than March.

Surprisingly perhaps, it is not that uncommon for March to be colder than February or even January; March has been colder than February in 11 years since 1908, most recently in 1995, and colder than January in a surprising 15 years, most recently in 2013. March 1937 was 2.3 degC cooler than February of that year, while March 1916 was 3.2 degC colder than January that year.

Table 6.2 March temperatures at the University of Reading, 1908-2015. In March the London Road site (1908-67) is about 0.4 degC warmer than the Whiteknights site (1968 onwards) due to its location closer to the town centre. The observed mean temperatures at the London Road site (shown in brackets) have been adjusted by this amount to facilitate comparison between the two records.

March mean temperature 7.1 °C (average 1981-2010)

Mildest months			Coldest months		
Mean temperature, °C	Departure from 1981-2010 normal degC	Year	Mean temperature, °C	Departure from 1981-2010 normal degC	Year
9.5 (9.9)	+2.4	1957	3.0 (3.4)	-4.1	1917
9.5 (9.9)	+2.4	1938	3.3 (3.7)	-3.7	1962
9.2	+2.1	1997	3.4	-3.7	2013
9.0	+1.9	2012	3.7 (4.1)	-3.4	1909, 1916
8.8 (9.2)	+1.7	1948	4.1	-3.0	1970

PRECIPITATION

March is, on average, one of the driest months of the year – its monthly mean precipitation is higher than February only because it has three more days. Snow can be expected on one or two days, and thunder on about one year in two. Heavy falls of rain in a day are very rare, although rainfall can be persistent at times. March 1947 saw probably the most severe flooding of the River Thames in the twentieth century in Reading, a result of the sudden thaw of melting snow coinciding with still-frozen soil conditions. The Mayor of Reading and the Town Council produced a book to commemorate the event, *The Thames in flood: a pictorial record*, from which the photographs on the following pages are taken. Profits from the sale of the book went to the Flood Distress Fund.

Table 6.3 March precipitation at the University of Reading, 1901-2015 (London Road 1901-1967, Whiteknights 1968-2015).

March mean precipitation 44.4 mm (average 1981-2010)

Wettest months			Driest months			Wettest days	
Total fall, mm	Per cent of normal	Year	Total fall, mm	Per cent of normal	Year	Daily fall, mm	Date
122.8	277	1916	1.3	3	1929	34.5	14 Mar 1964
119.8	270	1947	5.0	11	1961	27.4	27 Mar 1916
119.0	268	1919	5.3	12	1931	26.7	19 Mar 1919
111.4	251	1981	5.5	12	1944	23.9	4 Mar 1949
106.0	239	1979	5.7	13	1938	23.8	23 Mar 1984

The wettest and driest months in March all occurred before 1968. March 1929 was a remarkably dry month with just a trace of rainfall in the first 20 days, followed by no rainfall in the final five days: the wettest days (21st and 24th) contributed just 0.5 mm each. In March 1961 just a trace fell in the first 17 days of the month. The wettest March was in 1916, with 123 mm of precipitation, of which 119 mm fell in the 23 days commencing 6 March. Daily rainfall totals exceeding 25 mm in March have occurred only three times in Reading between 1908 and 2015: the wettest day was 14 March 1964, when 34.5 mm fell: 56 mm fell in the three days 13-15th, during which time it rained for 42 hours with some snow also falling.

The second-longest spring drought on record, one of 31 consecutive days during which just 0.1 mm precipitation fell, commenced on 25 March 1997. Only the 34 day dry spell commencing in February 1953 was of longer duration at this time of year.

Snowfall and lying snow

Snowfall can be expected on one or two days in an average March, while snow covers more than half the ground at 0900 GMT only once every 2-3 years. Many falls of sleet or snow tend to be slight in March, often in short-lived wintry showers, and the awareness of the observers as to the conditions can be crucial in obtaining accurate statistics. In March 1937, snow or sleet was observed on 11 days, and nine days in March 1970. Snowfall in March has tended to become less prevalent in recent years, although the very cold March 2013 saw an abrupt reversal of that trend, with an equal-record 11 days with snow falling. Nowadays lying snow rarely occurs on more than one morning in March; three mornings with snow cover occurred in March 1970 and March 1987, and two days in March 1995. The greatest depth of snow on the ground yet recorded during the month was 20 cm on the morning of 4 March 1965; this remained more than 10 cm deep for more than two days, and some lasted for five days. Other notable March snowfalls have included 10 cm lying on 30 March 1952 (very late in the year for this depth of snow, and yet the greatest depth of that 'extended winter'), 8 cm on 4 March 1970 (some of this was still lying on the 6th), 7 cm on 17 March 1979 and 8 cm on 7 March 1987. The cold, snowy March of 2013 produced only one morning with snow cover – 23 March, depth 2.5 cm.

Thunderstorms

Thunder is heard in less than one year in two in March, often associated with a cold front and of the 'one or two rumbles' variety. Thunder was heard on three days in both March 1923 and March 1995.

SUNSHINE

The duration of bright sunshine in March averages 109 hours, about 3½ hours daily, although five or six days in the month can be expected to remain sunless.

Table 6.4 March sunshine duration at the University of Reading, 1957-2015 (London Road 1957-1967, Whiteknights 1968-2015).

March mean sunshine duration 108.9 hours, 3.52 hours per day (average 1981-2010)

Possible daylength: 368 hours. Mean sunshine duration as percentage of possible: 29.6

Sunniest months			Dullest months			Sunniest days	
Duration, hours	*Per cent of possible*	*Year*	*Duration, hours*	*Per cent of possible*	*Year*	*Duration, hours*	*Date*
178.7	48.5	2007	57.5	15.6	1992	11.4	31 Mar 1997
177.2	48.1	1995	59.1	16.0	1984	11.4	31 Mar 2003
176.0	47.8	2012	60.6	16.4	2001	11.4	28 Mar 2012
174.5	47.4	2003	63.1	17.1	1996	11.3	30 Mar 1997
173.8	47.2	2009	63.3	17.2	1964	11.2	27 Mar 2012

Since 1957, sunshine totals in March have varied by a factor of three - from over 175 hours in 1995, 2007 and 2012 (values more typical of early summer) to under 60 hours in 1984 and 1992 (more appropriate to November or January). Increasing daylength during the month means that the sunniest days are much more likely towards the end of the month, when the maximum possible duration of sunshine just exceeds 12 hours per day. Four-day sunny spells, with each day logging more than 10 hours of bright sunshine, occurred in March 1997, 2003 and 2012. In March 1969, a sunless spell commencing on 12th lasted 10 consecutive days, the longest March sunless spell on record, although March 2013 recorded 15 sunless days in all. Not surprisingly, March has never been the sunniest month of the year, although in 2001 (with just 61 hours of sunshine) it was the dullest.

Figure 6.1 *Thames flooding at Caversham, Reading and Pangbourne, March 1947, described at the time as 'Reading's worst disaster in 300 years'.*

Upper photograph: *Aerial view of the flood. The railway is to the left, and Reading Bridge and its causeway cross the centre of the photograph. The submerged Fry's Island (or De Montfort Island) and Caversham Bridge are beyond. Photograph by Eagle Aerophotos: it appeared as plates 17 and 18 in the book,* The Thames in Flood

Middle: *Cars and vans plough through the flood water under the railway bridges in Vastern Road, Reading. The bridge of the Southern Railway is nearest the camera, with that of the Great Western Railway beyond, and the end of Reading Bridge can be seen in the distance*

Bottom: *The flooded Swan at Pangbourne.*

(Reading Central Library: top image 1254 009, middle 1372 725, bottom plate 16 in The Thames in Flood*)*

WINTER the tyrant, having held the land so long in his dictator's grip of ice and snow, and resentful at the approach of his more welcome successor, Spring the Liberator, suddenly and viciously struck back. And no war-time resistance group or dam-busting aircraft could have been more successful. Throughout the country, wherever there was a river or low-lying land the story was the same-communities isolated, houses inundated, streets turned into canals, families taking refuge in upper rooms and many evacuated.

You remember the background-long weeks of snow and frost, which, from January right into the beginning of March, precipitated the fuel and industrial crisis. We eked out our coal to vanishing point, cut our electricity consumption, put out our street lights, staggered our working hours, and lost something like £100,000,000 in exports. Then the snow stopped falling and the frost relaxed its hold. We sighed in relief and warmed at the thought of spring, and of Easter sunshine. But we were wrong. Stealthily, swiftly, the enemy moved. Every thawing field swelled his armies. Every hedge, tree and brimming ditch sent its quota of reinforcements. The ditches ran into the streams, the streams to the tributaries and the tributaries into the Thames.

On the night of Friday, 14 March, the river rose 15 inches [38 cm], and on the morning of Saturday, 15 March, residents in Lower Caversham who went downstairs to make their early cup of tea found Old Father Thames quietly in possession of the ground floor and basement. Then, to help things along, the wind took a hand. On the night of Sunday, 16 March, there was a howling gale which uprooted trees and, to quote a local newspaper, "tossed them like matchsticks against the weir at the Clappers."

After an anxious week, at the beginning of which it looked as if Caversham might be completely cut off from Reading, the floods subsided, but it was to be more than a week before the households could return to normal, and in the meantime the Mayor of Reading had opened a Flood Distress Fund which was to reach nearly £12,000 by the end of May, including a generous grant of £5,000 from the Lord Mayor of London's Fund.

As so often happens, the flood emergency seemed to draw the best out of people. The affected householders forgot their individual troubles by helping each other. The Police, Women's Voluntary Services, Thames Conservancy watermen, lorry drivers and others, with the Mayor's thoughtful example before them, rose magnificently to the occasion, and Reading, which fortunately knew little of the blitzes during the war, developed its own blitz spirit of courage and neighbourliness born, one might say, not of fire, but of flood.

Reading became front-page news in the national newspapers. The *Daily Express* quoted, across two columns, the Mayor's statement that the flood was the town's worst disaster in 300 years, and the *News Chronicle* published a large aerial photograph of the Caversham area. Other papers carried similar items.

It was natural that the situation should evoke comparison with the big flood of November, 1894, and the *Reading Standard* quoted this extract from the files of the *Reading Observer,* its predecessor: "The view from Caversham Bridge was remarkable. As far as the eye could reach there was only water. The islands were completely submerged and only the tops of trees, fences and hedges were visible. The water under Caversham Road and Vastern Road bridges reached the axles of carts going under them." And the report of the 1947 flood adds that the description "could well have been written by *Reading Standard* reporters who all this week have been touring the flooded areas."

Here is the *Reading Standard's* 1947 description : "On Monday Gosbrook Street was knee deep up to the playing fields by Westfield Road, and Gosbrook Road was impassable even to vehicles beyond Mill Road. Punts and rowing boats were taking shoppers from houses beyond this point, and to streets on the north side of Gosbrook Road, where again the water was too deep for lorries. In these roads a fierce current had carried away fences and gates, and in places it was impossible to stand without support.

"Householders who were fortunate enough to have coal found it impossible to get under the depth of water, and those with coke had to watch their precious fuel floating away." Shopkeepers, with their shelves rapidly emptying as people bought anything they could to eat, and with no fresh stocks arriving since the last deliveries on Friday, were viewing the situation with anxiety. Many were further crippled by the fact that reserve stores were in cellars and buildings made inaccessible by the rapid rise of water.

"During the week-end and again on Monday Corporation-contracted lorries were evacuating families with their few necessary belongings to a temporary refuge at Battle Hospital. Other lorries carried those less threatened to and from shops, the thigh-booted drivers and their mates carrying those not so suitably clad up to their front doors."

The number of houses affected was officially estimated at 1,600 - most of them in the Lower Caversham and Caversham Road area - of which nearly 200 were evacuated. Official evacuation facilities were available, and emergency accommodation was prepared at Battle Hospital, but most people preferred to make their own arrangements with their families and friends.

A ferry service of punts, dinghies and high-wheeled lorries was put into operation by the Chief Constable immediately the flood was reported on Saturday morning, 15 March. Later two amphibious army 'ducks' arrived. The School Meals Service proved its worth by providing 100 hot mid-day meals a day at the former British Restaurant in King's Road for those unable to fend for themselves, as well as a smaller number of teas. This again was arranged by the Police, who instituted a system of meal tickets.

The introduction to The Thames in Flood: a pictorial record, *published by the County Borough of Reading following the March 1947 floods*

TEMPERATURE, PRECIPITATION AND SUNSHINE IN GRAPHS – MARCH

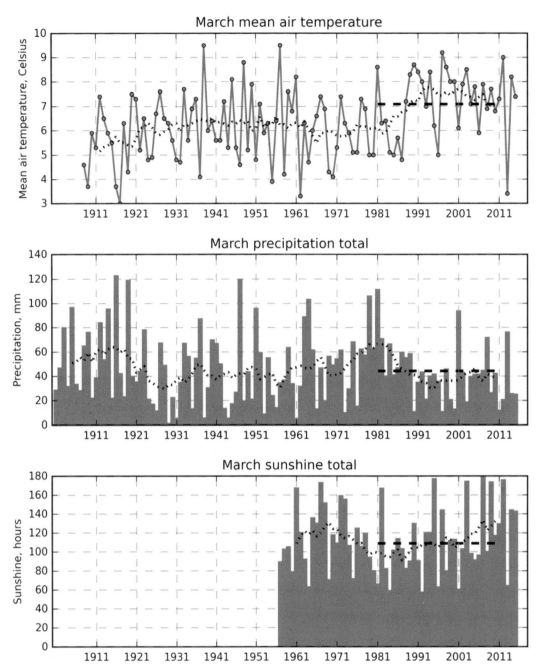

Figure 6.2 *Monthly values of (from top) mean temperature (°C), total precipitation (mm) and sunshine duration (hours) for March at Reading over the available period of record (plots include London Road rainfall records where available 1901-04, with estimates from other Reading stations to 1907 as necessary)*

The mean temperatures as recorded at London Road 1908-67 have been reduced by 0.4 degC to ensure approximate homogeneity with the records from the Whiteknights site, 1968 onwards. No site adjustments have been made for precipitation or sunshine. The 1981-2010 averages are indicated by the thick dashed line, while the 10 year running mean centred on the year shown is indicated by a dashed grey line

7 April

April is one of the driest months of the year, and prolonged spells of wet weather are rare. Snowfall and thunderstorms appear with about equal average frequency in April, but typically occur on only one day each. The frequency of northerly and north-easterly winds reaches a peak in April; winds off the North Sea at this time of year can bring long spells of cold, overcast weather. On the other hand, April's sunshine sees a noticeable increase on March, to an average in excess of 5 hours daily: while not quite up to midsummer levels, as a fraction of the hours of daylight at this time of year they are slightly ahead of June. Increasing daylength brings a continuing rise in temperature, daytime values increasing from 12 °C at the beginning of the month to above 15 °C by the close, but frosts can occasionally still be a hazard for tender outdoor plants beyond the end of April.

TEMPERATURE

Over the 1981-2010 period, the average date for the last air frost of the winter at Whiteknights was 14 April, although with considerable year-to-year variation: in April 1917, the coldest April on Reading's records, frost occurred on 12 mornings, and on nine in 1968. About one April in five remains free of air frost, but ground frosts are still frequent – one night in two on average, but 24 in April 1954 and 21 in 1938 and 1973. Cold nights are more likely in the first ten days of April, after which the risk of sharp frosts diminishes: the lowest grass minimum temperature yet recorded in April was -12.5 °C (on 9 April 2003, following -12.3 °C on the 8th), but -12.1 °C and -12.2 °C were recorded on consecutive nights on 19 and 20 April 1995. The lowest *air* temperature yet recorded in April was -4.2 °C on 2 April 1922 (Table 7.1).

The lowest temperature of the (calendar) year has even occurred once in April. In 1990, the lowest temperature of the three winter months was -3.0 °C; on 5 April, the temperature fell to -3.3 °C (and the grass minimum temperature to -10.0 °C, also the lowest of the calendar year).

Table 7.1 Highest and lowest maximum and minimum temperatures in April, 1908-2015. Records are from the (slightly milder) London Road site 1908-67, and from Whiteknights 1968-2015: no corrections for site differences have been applied.

Rank	Hottest days	Coldest days	Mildest nights	Coldest nights
1	26.2 °C,16 April 1949	1.6 °C, 14 April 1966	12.7 °C, 15 April 1945	-4.2 °C, 2 April 1922
2	26.1 °C, 23 April 2011	2.3 °C, 5 April 1911	12.6 °C, 30 April 2005	-3.6 °C, 6 April 1929
3	25.8 °C, 16 April 1945	2.7 °C, 3 April 1922	12.6 °C, 25 April 2007	-3.5 °C, 3 April 1984
4	25.7°C, 16 April 2003	2.8 °C, 2 April 1968	12.5 °C, 26 April 1975	-3.4 °C, 7 April 2013
5	25.5°C, 16 April 1943	2.9 °C, 6 April 1911	12.0 °C, 11 April 1981	-3.3 °C, 2 April 1970 and 5 April 1990

Occasionally maximum temperatures in April can fail to rise above 3 °C. This has happened five times since 1908, the coldest day being 14 April 1966, when the maximum temperature was a remarkably low 1.6 °C, in a five-day cold spell during which the temperature remained below 7 °C. Perhaps even more noteworthy is cold towards the end of April: on 27 April 1919 the maximum temperature reached only 3.9 °C, the latest date in the first half of the calendar year not to exceed 5 °C.

The earliest date in the year since 1908 when 25 °C has been surpassed is 16 April – and, in another statistical oddity, 25 °C has been reached or exceeded on this date four times since 1908, namely 1943 (25.5 °C), 1945 (25.8 °C), 1949 (26.2 °C, the warmest April day on the record) and 2003 (25.7 °C). In April 1945 the warm spell lasted six days, each of which reached 22 °C, while three consecutive days surpassed 25 °C: in April 1949 three days reached 23 °C. At the slightly cooler Whiteknights site 25.7 °C was recorded on 16 April 2003, the second of four consecutive days reaching 21 °C, while in

2011 26.1 °C was reached on 23 April, the fifth of seven days to reach 20 °C (in a month in which 12 days reached this temperature).

Clear, sunny days and clear, cool nights in dry weather in April can produce some of the largest daily ranges in temperature: the greatest being 22.5 degC on 9 April 1909 and 21.4 degC the following day. More recently, there was a diurnal range of 20.2 degC on 16 April 2003 at Whiteknights. Monthly temperature ranges in April have varied between 14.3 degC in 1961 and 14.7 degC in 1972, and 28.3 degC in 2003. The second-largest reduction in maximum temperature from one day to the next for any month on the record took place over 4-5 April 1946: the maximum temperature on 4th of 24.8 °C was followed next day by a maximum temperature of just 11.3 °C – a day-to-day reduction of 13.5 degC.

As the weather gradually warms during April, at least one night minimum temperature above 10 °C can be expected in about seven Aprils in ten. During the aforementioned warm spell in April 1945, the minimum temperature on 15th was 12.7 °C at the slightly warmer London Road site, the warmest April night on the record, while at the Whiteknights site the warmest April nights to date have been 12.6 °C on both 30 April 2005 and 25 April 2007.

Warm and cold months

April 1917 was the coldest April on Reading's records - following on from the coldest March on record - while April 2011 was the warmest, as a result of a very warm 10 day spell commencing on 16th.

It is not particularly uncommon for April to be colder than March – this has happened eight times since 1908. In 1938, April was 1.8 degC colder than March.

Table 7.2 April temperatures at the University of Reading, 1908-2015. In April the London Road site (1908-67) is about 0.5 degC warmer than the Whiteknights site (1968 onwards) due to its location closer to the town centre. The observed mean temperatures at the London Road site (shown in brackets) have been adjusted by this amount to facilitate comparison between the two records.

April mean temperature 9.1 °C (average 1981-2010)

Warmest months			Coldest months		
Mean temperature, °C	Departure from 1981-2010 normal degC	Year	Mean temperature, °C	Departure from 1981-2010 normal degC	Year
13.0	+3.9	2011	5.8 (6.3)	-3.3	1917
12.3	+3.2	2007	6.1 (6.6)	-3.0	1962
11.1 (11.6)	+2.0	1943	6.3 (6.8)	-2.8	1908
10.8 (11.3)	+1.7	1945	6.5	-2.6	1986
10.6	+1.5	1987	6.8 (7.3)	-2.3	1918, 1936
			6.8	-2.3	1978

PRECIPITATION

Until recent years, April has been a reliably dry month – the first 90 years of the record saw only one April with more than 100 mm of precipitation, and that being 1908, also one of the coldest. In recent years though, Reading has experienced three very wet Aprils – 1998 (107 mm), 2000 (133 mm, the wettest on record) and 2012 (120 mm). Not to be outdone, we have also seen the two of the three driest Aprils in the same period – 2007 (0.9 mm, by a whisker the second-the driest April on record, and to that date the warmest) and 2011 (1.7 mm, the third driest and the warmest). So in recent years April's rainfall has become much more variable than it was in most of the 20th century. The driest April of all, however, was in 1912 – the month of the *Titanic* disaster – with a mere 0.8 mm. Only two days had measurable rainfall in April 1912 and again in April 2007.

Table 7.3 April precipitation at the University of Reading, 1901-2015 (London Road 1901-1967, Whiteknights 1968-2015).

April mean precipitation 48.0 mm (average 1981-2010)

Wettest months			Driest months			Wettest days	
Total fall, mm	*Per cent of normal*	*Year*	*Total fall, mm*	*Per cent of normal*	*Year*	*Daily fall, mm*	*Date*
132.6	276	2000	0.8	2	1912	37.3	25 April 1908
119.8	250	2012	0.9	2	2007	30.6	29 April 1991
106.8	223	1998	1.7	4	2011	22.6	26 April 1940
103.9	216	1908	1.8	4	1954	22.4	3 April 2000
96.1	200	1983	3.4	7	1938	22.0	9 April 1993

Only two days in April in the period 1908-2014 have received more than 25 mm in 24 hours – 37.3 mm fell on 25 April 1908 and 30.6 mm on 29 April 1991 (when rain fell for 19.5 hours in the 24). One of the coldest and wettest spells in April was in 1908: during the three day-period commencing 23 April, exactly 50 mm fell, while the temperature did not exceed 5 °C; most of this fell as snow. Based on contemporary photographs (Figure 7.1, upper) probably 20-25 cm of snow fell in Reading, but a little further west Newbury received 46 cm and Yattendon 51 cm, 'with great damage to trees and shrubs'. Great flooding resulted on the Thames and Kennet as the snow thawed (see 'On this date').

Figure 7.1 Two heavy April snowstorms, 100 years apart.

Upper photograph: *Clappers footpath over the weir between Reading and Caversham following the exceptional snowstorm of 25-26 April 1908. (Reading Central Library, image 1204 928)*

Lower: *A late heavy snowfall covers spring blossom; Stratfield Mortimer, 6 April 2008, when 11 cm fell in an early-morning snowstorm, accompanied by thunder (6 cm fell at the university). Photograph © Stephen Burt*

Snowfall and lying snow

Snow or sleet can be expected on one day in a typical April, but many falls are slight or in showery conditions; snowfall in April is tending to become less prevalent, and in the ten years ending 2014 only three Aprils saw any at all. In contrast, the very cold April of 1917 recorded nine days with snowfall, and there were seven days each in April 1970 and April 1975.

Lying snow is rare in April, and since 1968 has only been reported twice – namely 1 cm on the morning of 5 April 1989 (continuous moderate snow was falling at 0900 GMT) and a surprise 6 cm of snow in just a couple of hours early on 6 April 2008 (Figure 7.1, lower). In April 1981, there was an unusual late spring snowfall on 25-26th. Snow fell at Reading but was not reported lying at Whiteknights, although over higher ground in west Berkshire motorists became stranded in deep snow on the M4. Around Reading some 6000 homes lost power during the snowfall. The latest date yet on record for a morning snow cover was 15 April 1966, when the snow depth at 0900 GMT was 3 cm at London Road.

Thunderstorms

Thunder can be expected on one day in April, often in showery conditions. In the cool and wet April of 1998, thunder was heard on six days, and five each in April 1951 and April 1965.

SUNSHINE

The duration of bright sunshine in April averages 160 hours, or about 5 hours 20 minutes per day: typically just two or three days will remain sunless, although about one April in eight has sunshine every day.

The sunniest Aprils on record were 1984 (234 hours) and 2007 (233 hours - following a very sunny March). Both months were also very dry. These sunshine totals are more typical of a sunny summer month, and are the first in the year to surpass more than 50 per cent of the possible monthly sunshine duration. In 2002 and 2011, April was the sunniest month of the year.

Most Aprils include at least one day with 12 hours or more sunshine: in 1984 there were ten such days, including eight consecutively 23-30 April. In April 2011, six days saw 12 hours or more of sunshine, five of these in an 11 day spell from 20 April totalling 112 hours. Long spells without sunshine are rare in April – only four spells of four consecutive days or more have been recorded since sunshine records commenced at the university in April 1956, the longest such being 5 days commencing 31 March 1964, although the Aprils of 1956, 1966 and 1978 had as many as eight sunless days during the month.

Table 7.4 April sunshine duration at the University of Reading, 1956-2015 (London Road 1956-1967, Whiteknights 1968-2015).

April mean sunshine duration 160.3 hours, 5.34 hours per day (average 1981-2010)

Possible daylength: 416 hours. Mean sunshine duration as percentage of possible: 38.5

Sunniest months			Dullest months			Sunniest days	
Duration, hours	*Per cent of possible*	*Year*	*Duration, hours*	*Per cent of possible*	*Year*	*Duration, hours*	*Date*
234.0	56.2	1984	77.4	18.6	1966	13.9	27 April 1977
232.5	55.9	2007	84.9	20.4	1961	13.7	28 April 1999
228.7	55.0	2011	100.0	24.0	1998	13.6	25 April 1972
225.9	54.3	2015	113.5	27.3	1993	13.6	30 April 2007
223.9	53.8	2010	114.3	27.5	1978	13.4	21 April 2015

TEMPERATURE, PRECIPITATION AND SUNSHINE IN GRAPHS – APRIL

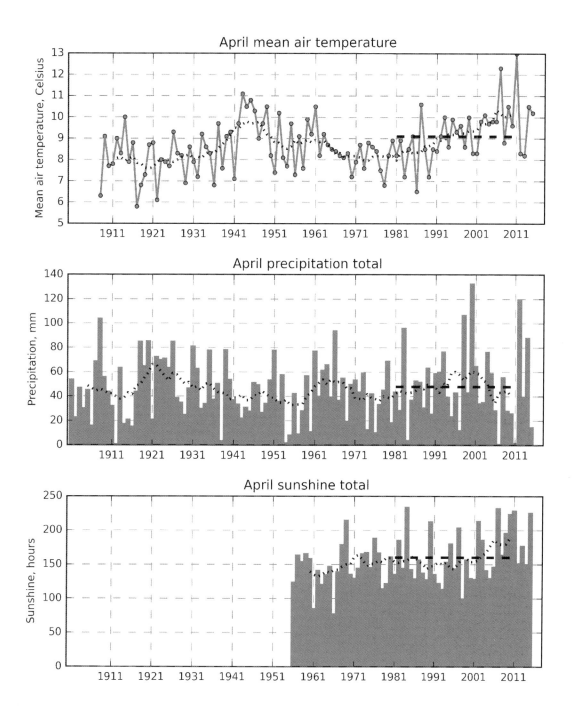

Figure 7.2 *Monthly values of (from top) mean temperature (°C), total precipitation (mm) and sunshine duration (hours) for April at Reading over the available period of record (plots include London Road rainfall records where available 1901-04, with estimates from other Reading stations to 1907 as necessary)*

The mean temperatures as recorded at London Road 1908-67 have been reduced by 0.5 degC to ensure approximate homogeneity with the records from the Whiteknights site, 1968 onwards. No site adjustments have been made for precipitation or sunshine. The 1981-2010 averages are indicated by the thick dashed line, while the 10 year running mean centred on the year shown is indicated by a dashed grey line

8 **May**

May is another transition month – it can bring cool spring days and damaging night frosts, early summer heatwaves, and sometimes both. Snowfall this late in the year is very rare, but thunderstorms are not uncommon and can be heavy. Sunshine can be expected on all but one or two days in May, averaging around 6 hours per day.

TEMPERATURE

There is a fairly steady rise in temperatures, both by day and by night, in Reading throughout May: daytime temperatures rise from around 16 °C at the start of the month to 18 or 19 °C during the closing days, while over the same period average night minimum temperatures increase from 6 °C to 9-10 °C. The mean temperature for the month as a whole over the period 1981-2010 was 12.4 °C.

Air frosts occur at the Whiteknights site in about one May in five, and since 1908 30 have been recorded. Ground frosts can be expected on an average seven nights in a typical May, and can cause considerable damage to tender plants. The coldest May night on record was 9 May 1980, when the minimum temperature was -2.0°C (the grass minimum was -9.1 °C, also the May record), closely followed by -1.9 °C on 17 May 1935 and 8 May 1938 at the (slightly milder) London Road site. Three air frosts occurred in the cold May of 1941, and 15 ground frosts in May 1968 and 1990. The latest air frost on record occurred on 31 May 1975, when the air minimum was -0.1 °C and the grass minimum -7.3 °C. In May 1944 there were two consecutive air frosts on 7th and 8th; these late spring frosts caused problems for local fruit growers as blossom was damaged, yet only three weeks later temperatures reached record high levels (Figure 8.1). More recently, at Whiteknights the highest May minimum temperature since records commenced in 1968 was 15.3 °C on 25 May 2012. But throughout May the maximum temperature can fail to reach 10 °C – on 1 May 1979 only 7.2 °C, and 7.9°C on 2 May 1954. Even as late as the final week, the maximum temperature has remained as low as 8.9 °C on 24 May (in 2013) and on 26 May (in 1962).

Table 8.1 Highest and lowest maximum and minimum temperatures in May, 1908-2014. Records are from the (slightly milder) London Road site 1908-67, and from Whiteknights 1968-2014: no corrections for site differences have been applied.

Rank	Hottest days	Coldest days	Warmest nights	Coldest nights
1	31.9 °C, 29 May 1944	7.2 °C, 1 May 1979	16.6 °C, 25 May 1922 and 30 May 1944	-2.0°C, 9 May 1980
2	31.3 °C, 30 May 1944	7.9 °C, 2 May 1954	16.2 °C, 9 May 1945	-1.9 °C, 17 May 1935 and 8 May 1938
3	31.2 °C, 22 May 1922	8.0 °C, 13 May 1915	15.4 °C, 19 May 1952	-1.6 °C, 1 May 1929 and 16 May 1941
4	30.5 °C, 30 May 1947	8.3 °C, 1 May 1939	15.3 °C, 23 May 1922 and 25 May 2012	-1.2 °C, 4 May 1941
5	30.4 °C, 23 May 1922	8.4 °C, 2 May 1978	15.1 °C, 24 May 1989	-1.1 °C, 10 May 1910, 1 May 1927, 2 May 1945 and 3 May 1967

Literally at the other end of the scale, the earliest date in the year on which 30 °C (summer heatwave level) has been reached is 22 May – this occurred way back in 1922, when the temperature reached 31.2 °C on that date. Temperatures as high as 30 °C have been reached in only four Mays since 1908 – and, at the time of writing, not for over 60 years, the most recent occasion being in 1953. The hottest May days on the record occurred on 29 and 30 May 1944, at 31.9 °C and 31.3 °C, respectively (the intervening night minimum of 16.6 °C being the equal-highest on record for May). Since 1953 the highest May temperature has been 28.5 °C on 28 May 2005; notable also was 27.4 °C as early as 7 May in 1976. Since 1908, there have been three hot spells in May, here defined as five or more consecutive days attaining 25 °C – these have been 25-29 May 1913 (5 days, maximum 27.3 °C on 26th), 21-25 May 1922 (5 days, 31.9 °C on 29th: in the 13 days from the 21st 27 °C or more was reached on nine days) and 23-28 May 2012 (6 days, 26.6 °C on 27th).

May has seen the hottest day of the year in five years since 1908, namely 1920, 1922, 1944, 1965 and 1978. The earliest date in the year to have ended up as the hottest day of the year was 14 May, in 1965 (27.3 °C, in a very cool summer).

The largest reduction in maximum temperature from one day to the next for any month on the record took place in May. On 22 May 1918, a maximum temperature of 29.7 °C was followed next day by a maximum temperature of just 15.7 °C – a day-to-day reduction of 14.0 degC.

Strong sunshine and dry soil conditions can occasionally lead to very large daily ranges in temperature during May, the greatest being 21.9 degC on 20 May 1909 and 21.7 degC on 8 May 1922. More recently, at Whiteknights there was a diurnal range of 19.7 degC on 7 May 1976.

Warm and cold months

Monthly mean temperatures in May can vary between about 14.5 °C (akin to a cool June) and 10 °C (not far different from a very mild March). There was a run of warm Mays during 1917 to 1919, the very warm May of 1917 following the very cold March and April of that year, both of which were the coldest on the record. The cool May of 1975 was followed by the warm and dry conditions that characterised many months from the summer of 1975 to the summer of 1976.

Monthly temperature ranges in May have varied between 16.9 degC in 1972 and 32.8 degC in 1944 – the latter the greatest range in temperature yet observed in any month of the year (Figure 8.1).

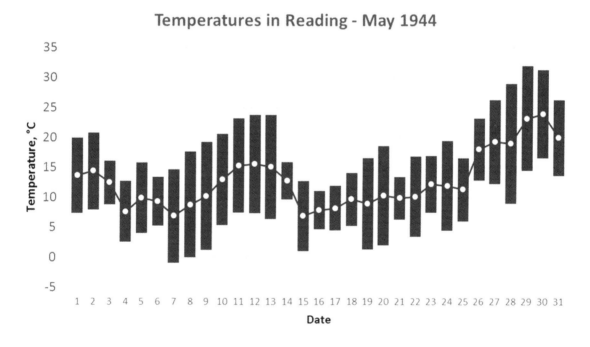

Figure 8.1 Daily maximum and minimum temperatures (top and bottom of daily columns) and daily mean temperature (central circle and connecting line) at the University of Reading in May 1944, the month with the greatest range in air temperatures on Reading's records.

After a warm start to the month, colder conditions quickly became established, and there were two late air frosts on 7 and 8 May before temperatures recovered, reaching almost 24 °C by day on 12 and 13 May. Another sharp reversal then took place, with near-frost once more on 15, 19 and 20 May. Thereafter, temperatures climbed quickly, to 31.9 °C on 29 May (the hottest May day yet recorded), followed by the hottest May night on record with a minimum of 16.6 °C before another very hot day on 30 May, at 31.3 °C

Table 8.2 May temperatures at the University of Reading, 1908-2014. In May the London Road site (1908-67) is about 0.5 degC warmer than the Whiteknights site (1968 onwards) due to its location closer to the town centre. The observed mean temperatures at the London Road site (shown in brackets) have been adjusted by this amount to facilitate comparison between the two records.

May mean temperature 12.4°C (average 1981-2010)

Warmest months			Coldest months		
Mean temperature, °C	*Departure from 1981-2010 normal degC*	*Year*	*Mean temperature, °C*	*Departure from 1981-2010 normal degC*	*Year*
14.5	+2.1	1992	9.6 (10.1)	-2.8	1941
14.3	+1.9	1989, 2008	9.8	-2.6	1996
14.1	+1.7	1998	10.2 (10.7)	-2.2	1955
14.0 (14.5)	+1.6	1917	10.2	-2.2	1975
14.0 (14.5)	+1.6	1952	10.3 (10.8)	-2.1	1962
			10.3	-2.1	1984

PRECIPITATION

May's 1981-2010 monthly mean rainfall in Reading is 46 mm, slightly less than April's average of 48 mm despite one extra day in the month. May's rainfall is less variable than April's, with a lower range in long-term extremes, as can be seen from a comparison of Tables 8.3 and 7.3 for the two months.

Table 8.3 May precipitation at the University of Reading, 1901-2014 (London Road 1901-1967, Whiteknights 1968-2014).

May mean precipitation 46.5 mm (average 1981-2010)

Wettest months			Driest months			Wettest days	
Total fall, mm	*Per cent of normal*	*Year*	*Total fall, mm*	*Per cent of normal*	*Year*	*Daily fall, mm*	*Date*
113.4	245	1967	3.1	7	1990	37.1	21 May 1932
111.4	241	1955	5.1	11	1956	34.3	11 May 1948 *T*
110.2	238	1932	6.1	13	1919	32.5	19 May 1952 *T*
109.4	236	1925	7.0	15	1991	32.0	25 May 1911
103.2	223	1948	7.5	16	1944, 1959	32.0	17 May 1915

T after the date of the heaviest fall indicates thunder was heard on that date.

May 1967 was the wettest May on the record, closely followed by 1955 – although both months still managed several days without measurable precipitation, as falls at this time of year can often be short-lived but heavy, as was the case in both months. Only five Mays to date have exceeded 100 mm of precipitation, while six have received less than 10 mm. Three consecutive Mays from 1989 to 1991 were notably dry – May 1989 and 1990 were relatively warm, while May 1991 was a cool month preceding an unusually cold June.

Daily falls of 25 mm or more occur in about one year in eight in May, the wettest May days being 21 May 1932 (37.1 mm) and 11 May 1948 (34.3 mm, accompanied by thunder). In May 1915 there were two very wet days, 27.7 mm falling on the 13th and 32.0 mm on the 17th – neither day being associated with thunder.

Snowfall and lying snow

Snow or sleet is very rare in May: either has been recorded on only eight days during the month since records commenced in 1908 - namely in May 1935 (sleet on 14th, followed by snow on 17th), snow on both 17 and 18 May 1955, sleet on 1 May 1967 and 4 May 1979, and snow on 3 May 1945 and 6 May 1997. The latest date on which snow has been observed to fall was 18 May, in 1955. Lying snow has never been recorded in May in Reading.

Thunderstorms

Thunder can be expected on one or two days in a normal May, although about one in five remains free of thunder. May 1969 was the most thundery month on record in Reading – thunder was heard on a remarkable 11 days (most of these were affected by thunderstorms more than once during the day), while in May 1924 and May 1967 (the latter the wettest May), thunder was heard on seven days.

SUNSHINE

May's average sunshine duration is 188 hours, just over 6 hours daily, with typically only two days during the month remaining sunless. In about one year in four May is the sunniest month of the year.

Table 8.4 May sunshine duration at the University of Reading, 1956-2014 (London Road 1956-1967, Whiteknights 1968-2014).

May mean sunshine duration 188.1 hours, 6.07 hours per day (average 1981-2010)

Possible daylength: 484 hours. Mean sunshine duration as percentage of possible: 38.9

Sunniest months			Dullest months			Sunniest days	
Duration, hours	*Per cent of possible*	*Year*	*Duration, hours*	*Per cent of possible*	*Year*	*Duration, hours*	*Date*
295.1	61.0	1989	118.7	24.5	1991	15.5	30 May 1966
261.8	54.1	1990	119.8	24.8	1981	15.5	30 May 1985
259.5	53.6	1992	128.7	26.6	1983	15.1	27 May 1977
252.6	52.2	1956	140.5	29.0	1994	15.1	29 May 2009
247.4	51.1	1997	144.6	29.9	1984	14.9	23 May 1966, 22 May 1977 and 26 May 1978

With daylength still increasing, the sunshine duration of 295.1 hours in May 1989 was remarkable (61% of the possible duration, one of only a very few months to exceed 60 per cent). The month recorded more than an hour's sunshine per day than the next sunniest – which occurred the following year, May 1990. May 1992 was also very sunny, making three very sunny May months in four years – although the intervening May 1991 was the dullest May on the university's record.

Since 1956 notable sunny spells during May (consecutive days with 9 hours or more sunshine) have included the 12 days commencing 18 May 1977 (154 hours in total, average 12.83 hours daily), 12 days commencing 16 May 1992 (141 hours in total, average 11.75 hours daily), and 11 days commencing 27 April 1990 (136 hours in all, average 12.36 hours daily - the first nine days each enjoying over 12 hours).

Sunless days are infrequent in May. Since 1956 there have been only three spells of four or more sunless days - in the Mays of 1960, 1984 and 2004.

TEMPERATURE, PRECIPITATION AND SUNSHINE IN GRAPHS – MAY

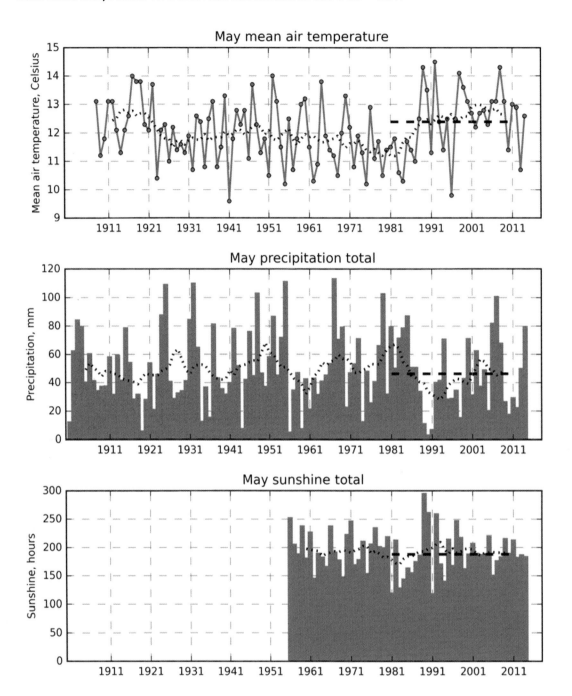

Figure 8.2 *Monthly values of (from top) mean temperature (°C), total precipitation (mm) and sunshine duration (hours) for May at Reading over the available period of record (plots include London Road rainfall records where available 1901-04, with estimates from other Reading stations to 1907 as necessary)*

The mean temperatures as recorded at London Road 1908-67 have been reduced by 0.5 degC to ensure approximate homogeneity with the records from the Whiteknights site, 1968 onwards. No site adjustments have been made for precipitation or sunshine. The 1981-2010 averages are indicated by the thick dashed line, while the 10 year running mean centred on the year shown is indicated by a dashed grey line

9 June

June is the first of the three summer months, and (on average) the driest, although the occasional heavy thunderstorm can deposit as much in a few hours as falls in the average month. Temperatures continue to rise quite steadily throughout the month. The first week or two can be rather cool: the short nights can still be on the chilly side, and ground frosts are not uncommon, although average daytime temperatures reach 19 °C or so. The second half of the month is usually warmer, the days averaging 22 °C by the end of the month: 30 °C is reached in around one June in five. The average temperature for the month is 15.3 °C and, in the 100 years ended 2014, June became the warmest month of the year seven times. Over the period 1981-2010, June's average daily duration of sunshine was 6 hours and 20 minutes.

TEMPERATURE

The beginning of June can be cool – often cooler than the end of May, and ground frosts are not uncommon at this time of year. No air frost has yet been recorded in June, although some mornings have been close to that level – the coldest June nights on record to date being 0.6 °C on 3 June 1923 and 1.5 °C on 2 June 1991 (the latter with a grass minimum temperature of -5.7 °C, and air frost in rural districts around the town). Ground frosts can be expected on two nights in an average June, but occurred on seven mornings in June 1975 and on eight mornings in the Junes of 1972 and 1996. As late as 9 June in 2001 the grass minimum temperature fell to -5.4 °C. During 1981-2010 the average date of the last spring/early summer ground frost was 17 June.

Cold June days are most often associated with prolonged rainfall on a cyclonic northerly or north-easterly flow. The lowest maximum temperatures yet recorded in June were 10.6 °C on 3 June 1953 (following a maximum of just 12.8 °C the previous day – Coronation Day of Queen Elizabeth II in London) and 11.1 °C on 4 June 1932 and 1 June 1964. More recently, 11.5 °C was the maximum on 6 June 1989.

Table 9.1 Highest and lowest maximum and minimum temperatures in June, 1908-2014. Records are from the (slightly milder) London Road site 1908-67, and from Whiteknights 1968-2014: no corrections for site differences have been applied.

Rank	Hottest days	Coldest days	Warmest nights	Coldest nights
1	34.0 °C, 26 June 1976	10.6 °C, 3 June 1953	18.9 °C, 29 June 1949	0.6 °C, 3 June 1923
2	33.9 °C, 17 June 1917	11.1 °C, 4 June 1932 and 1 June 1964	18.5 °C, 27 June 1976	1.5 °C, 2 June 1991
3	33.8 °C, 27 June 1976	11.3 °C, 4 June 1909	18.1 °C, 20 June 2005	2.0 °C, 9 June 2001
4	33.5 °C, 28 June 1976	11.4 °C, 5 June 1932	17.8 °C, 25 June 1935	2.2 °C, 2 June 1962
5	32.3 °C, 29 June 1957	11.5 °C, 6 June 1989	17.7 °C, 27 June 2011	2.6 °C, 1 June 1962

June can also see great heat, and is the first month of the year in which temperatures of 30 °C have been recorded at Whiteknights since records commenced in 1968. The hottest June day on record was 26 June 1976, maximum temperature 34.0 °C, part of a remarkable heatwave lasting into the first week of July which saw temperatures reach 30 °C every day for a fortnight (see also 'Seasons' in Chapter 17): it was also the hottest day of that hot summer. Not far behind was 33.9 °C recorded at the London Road site on 17 June 1917. June 1976 also saw the longest spell of consecutive days reaching or exceeding 25 °C on Reading's records – namely, 18 days commencing 22 June that year, half as long again as the next-longest prolonged hot spell in June, namely the 12 days commencing 30 June 1934. The warmest nights in June were 18.9 °C at London Road on 29 June 1949, in a spell of 10 consecutive days reaching 25 °C by day, and 18.5 °C at Whiteknights on 27 June 1976, immediately following the June record temperature (see above). Minimum temperatures of 15 °C or above occur on average about once each June.

A remarkable turnaround from winter to summer took place in just over a week in June 1975. Following the latest air frost on record on 31 May that year, the minimum temperature remained below 5 °C on each of the first four nights, with three ground frosts (grass minimum temperatures down to -4.6 °C on 1st and 4th). Despite 13.4 hours sunshine on 3 June, the maximum temperature reached only 14.6 °C. Just three days later, the temperature reached 24.4 °C, and 26.0 °C on 7 June, giving a range in temperature of 26.1 degC in eight days (see also 'On this date' for 2 June 1975.)

Large daily ranges in temperature during June have included 21.5 degC at London Road on 3 June 1923 (following the coldest June night on record, the temperature reached 22.1 °C later that afternoon), and 20.3 degC on 30 June 1995 at Whiteknights.

Warm and cold months

Allowing for the temperature difference between the two sites, it can be seen that June 1976 was easily the warmest June on record in Reading – about 1 degC warmer than June in 1940, 1950, 1970 and 2006. The very hot weather towards the end of June 1976 continued into the first half of July. After a dry start to the year, the hot, dry conditions led to widespread forest and woodland fires in Berkshire and many other places in southern and south-eastern England. The 66 day period 22 June-26 August was persistently dry (just 47 mm of rain in over 2 months), sunny (679 hours of bright sunshine) and hot (average temperature 19.4 °C). The summer also saw the culmination of a prolonged drought which had started in April 1975.

June 1916 was the coldest June on record (again, after making allowances for site differences). The temperature reached 20 °C on only three days (it had reached 27.3 °C in the preceding May).

It is not unknown for June to be colder than May, although this has not happened for almost 100 years: both the Junes of 1916 and 1918 were colder than the Mays of those years.

Monthly temperature ranges in June have varied between 13.8 degC in 1972 and 29.1 degC in 2001.

Table 9.2 June temperatures at the University of Reading, 1908-2014. In June the London Road site (1908-67) is about 0.7 degC warmer than the Whiteknights site (1968 onwards) due to its location closer to the town centre. The observed mean temperatures at the London Road site (shown in brackets) have been adjusted by this amount to facilitate comparison between the two records.

June mean temperature 15.3°C (average 1981-2010)

Warmest months			Coldest months		
Mean temperature, °C	Departure from 1981-2010 normal degC	Year	Mean temperature, °C	Departure from 1981-2010 normal degC	Year
18.1	+2.8	1976	11.6 (12.3)	-3.7	1916
17.1	+1.8	2006	12.0	-3.3	1972
17.0 (17.7)	+1.7	1940	12.1 (12.8)	-3.2	1909
16.9 (17.6)	+1.6	1950	12.4	-2.9	1977
16.9	+1.6	1970	12.9 (13.6)	-2.4	1923
			12.9	-2.4	1991

PRECIPITATION

The monthly mean rainfall for June in Reading is just under 45 mm. Only one June during the period 1908-2014 has exceeded three times the normal rainfall – June 1971, which was very cool in addition to being very wet. More than one-third of this total fell on one day (10 June, 54.7 mm - during a spell of almost 21 hours of rain) while 10 mm or more fell on another four days. June 2012 was part of a wet 12 months that began in April that year while in June 1910 about half of the rain fell in just two days (68 mm fell on 7th and 9th, although the 8th remained dry).

Table 9.3 June precipitation at the University of Reading, 1901-2014 (London Road 1901-1967, Whiteknights 1968-2014).

June mean precipitation 44.6 mm (average 1981-2010)

Wettest months			Driest months			Wettest days	
Total fall, mm	Per cent of normal	Year	Total fall, mm	Per cent of normal	Year	Daily fall, mm	Date
155.3	348	1971	0.5	1	1925	60.5	11 June 1970 *T*
134.9	302	1903	3.2	7	1962	54.7	10 June 1971
123.5	277	1910	7.9	18	1975	47.8	28 June 1917
123.2	276	2012	8.3	19	1921	42.7	9 June 1910
120.2	270	1998	8.9	20	1996	42.4	13 June 1998 *T*

T after the date of the heaviest fall indicates thunder was heard on the same date

With just 0.5 mm rainfall during the month, June 1925 remains the driest month of any name on the university's records to date. It was, perhaps surprisingly, the only dry month from April to October that year, and all the measurable rain fell on one day – 26 June. June 1962 was also another very dry June with two-thirds of the month's total of 3.2 mm falling in three days, 9-11th.

Falls of 25 mm or more in 24 hours occur in about one year in six in June; roughly one-third of these occur on a day when thunder is heard. The wettest June day was 11 June 1970 when 60.5 mm fell in a torrential afternoon thunderstorm, following a maximum temperature of 29.1 °C. All but 6 mm fell within an hour, including 34 mm in the 27 minutes commencing 1619 GMT, the heaviest short-period rainfall on the university's record. Hail as large as peas fell during the storm, and there was flooding on the university campus and along Pepper Lane in the afternoon.

Other notable rainstorms in Reading in June have included 47.8 mm on 28 June 1917 (part of an almost unprecedented heavy rainfall event extending across the whole of southern England, including the highest known daily rainfall for the United Kingdom to that time – namely 243 mm at Bruton in Somerset) and 54.7 mm on 10 June 1971 (a long dreary spell of almost unbroken precipitation – rain fell for 21 hours out of 24 that day).

A tremendous rain- and hailstorm affected Reading, particularly the Caversham area, on 9 June 1910 (Figure 9.1). Hailstones larger than 12 mm in diameter caused considerable damage around the town, and the accompanying heavy rainfall converted several of the streets in the northern and western parts of the town into rivers, although there was comparatively little rain in the east and south. Caversham primary school and the telegraph equipment at Caversham post office were struck by lightning, and the Oxford Road was badly flooded. According to *The Times*, the hail did great damage to flowers, crops and glasshouses: "The workhouse master at Reading estimates that the damage to the glass and grounds of the workhouse will exceed £500. At a residence in St Peter's Avenue, Caversham Heights, £300 damage was done to large conservatories. Several nurserymen have suffered to a considerable extent. Mrs Phippen, who has a big range of glass in the Oxford Road, Reading, where the full force of the storm was felt, has suffered damage estimated at £1,000."

The university site in London Road was only on the periphery of the storm, but even so 42.7 mm was recorded that day, which today, more than a century later, still remains as the fourth-wettest June day on record. At Forbury Gardens, only 700 m north of the London Road site, the day's total was 57.7 mm, while in Caversham, 77 mm fell at Hemdean Road. More than 100 mm fell in south Oxfordshire, much of that within an hour. Although the university's report for June 1910 makes no mention of thunder on 9 June, it was noted every day from 5-8 June (25.9 mm of thundery rain also fell on 7 June).

Snowfall
Snowfall has never been recorded in Reading between mid-May and mid-October.

***Figure 9.1**. Flooding in Oxford Road, Reading, following an intense thunderstorm on 9 June 1910. A horse-drawn fire engine heads westwards through the spray. A tramcar, a cart and a small crowd of people have been stopped by the flood on the other side of the bridge. (Reading Central Library, image 1372 726)*

***Figure 9.2**. Cracked earth at Lands End pool, Twyford, during the intense hot spell in late June 1976. (Courtesy and Copyright © getreading.co.uk)*

Thunderstorms

Most Junes will see at least one thunderstorm. In June 1963, thunder was heard on seven days, and six days in June 1933. Two of the five heaviest daily rainfalls yet observed in June were associated with thundery rain.

SUNSHINE

The average sunshine duration in June is 189 hours, or an average of 6 hours and 19 minutes daily – very similar to May in monthly total (although with a slight reduction in the percentage of possible sunshine, from 39% in May to 38% in June), and only slightly less than in July and August. The monthly figure hides a surprising amount of variation in the day-to-day averages, but over the period 1981-2010 the sunniest day of the year was 15 June, with an average of 8 hours, 18 minutes.

June 1975 was the sunniest of any month on the Reading record, the only one to exceed 300 hours (a daily average of 10 hours, 11 minutes sunshine), and one of only four months to surpass 60 per cent of possible sunshine since the university's sunshine records began in 1956. It also included the highest number of days in any month with 12 hours or more sunshine duration – 15. The following year, June 1976, was not quite as sunny – but still marked the start of three months of prolonged sunshine in a remarkable summer. Oddly enough, the two dullest Junes were also consecutive – 1990 and 1991, while in preceding years both 1987 and 1988 were also rather dull.

Table 9.4 June sunshine duration at the University of Reading, 1958-2014 (London Road 1958-1967, Whiteknights 1968-2014).

June mean sunshine duration 189.4 hours, 6.31 hours per day (average 1981-2010)

Possible daylength: 496 hours. Mean sunshine duration as percentage of possible: 38.2

Sunniest months			Dullest months			Sunniest days	
Duration, hours	*Per cent of possible*	*Year*	*Duration, hours*	*Per cent of possible*	*Year*	*Duration, hours*	*Date*
305.6	61.6	1975	109.4	22.1	1990	16.0	30 June 1976
279.5	56.3	1976	110.3	22.2	1991	15.7	24 June 1976
278.3	56.1	1970	127.4	25.7	2012	15.5	14 June 1959
274.1	55.3	1969	132.6	26.7	1997	15.5	16 June 1959
266.4	53.7	1996	135.6	27.3	1987	15.5	29 June 1976

Sunny days and spells

Daylength reaches its maximum at the summer solstice on 21 June: in Reading, midsummer day is 16 hours and 37 minutes long (sunrise at 0347 GMT, sunset 2024 GMT). Allowing for the limited response of the sunshine recorder to very low-angle sunshine, the longest possible duration of sunshine in a day is very close to 16 hours, and then only on the clearest of days at midsummer. The sunniest day on record was 30 June 1976, with 16.0 hours. Only 14 days have recorded 15 hours or more bright sunshine since records commenced at Whiteknights in 1968. Daily sunshine durations of 15.5 hours or more occurred three times in one week in June 1976 (15.7 hours on 24 June, 15.5 hours on 29 June and 16.0 hours on 30 June). At London Road, daily totals of 15.5 hours were noted on both 14 and 16 June 1959.

The sunniest spells recorded in June (each day with at least 12 hours of sunshine) have been the 10 days commencing 23 June 1976 (147.2 hours – a daily mean of 14.7 hours), eight days commencing 7 June 1969 (total 110.0 hours, daily mean 13.75 hours) and 6 June 1975 (total 113.2 hours, daily mean 14.15 hours) and the seven days commencing 12 June 1996 (total 97.7 hours, daily mean 13.96 hours). Despite the long hours of daylight, sunless days are not uncommon in June – typically one or two per year, but eight such days in the Junes of 1977 and 1988. In 1977, a remarkable eight days in nine commencing 13 June remained sunless – only 16 June saw any sunshine (9.6 hours) and a maximum daily temperature of 15 °C or more.

TORNADO IN LOWER EARLEY

On 13 June 1998, a tornado was observed in Lower Earley during a thunderstorm. According to *The Independent* newspaper:

> " ... garden walls were flattened and fencing panels tossed into the air when the tornado swept through Lower Earley, near Reading. One motorist had a lucky escape when a fir tree was torn in two, blown across the road and sent spearing through his passenger window. He careered off the road as other cars swerved to avoid him. Les Wise, 50, watched from his kitchen window as a 30 metre long garden wall linking five terraced homes was brought crashing down. 'It just went over all in one go as if someone had grabbed hold of both ends and just twisted it,' he said. He described how trees were bent double by the high winds, but said the drama was over within 15 or 20 seconds. Police and emergency services were called to the scene and removed rubble and fencing from the middle of the road, and firefighters made roofs safe."

At the university, however, the highest wind gust recorded that day as only 19 knots (22 mph), although the 42.4 mm of rainfall that fell during the storm remains the fifth wettest June day on record. The university site caught three times as much rainfall as fell not far to the south-west of Lower Earley.

ONE HUNDRED YEARS OF READING WEATHER

TEMPERATURE, PRECIPITATION AND SUNSHINE IN GRAPHS – JUNE

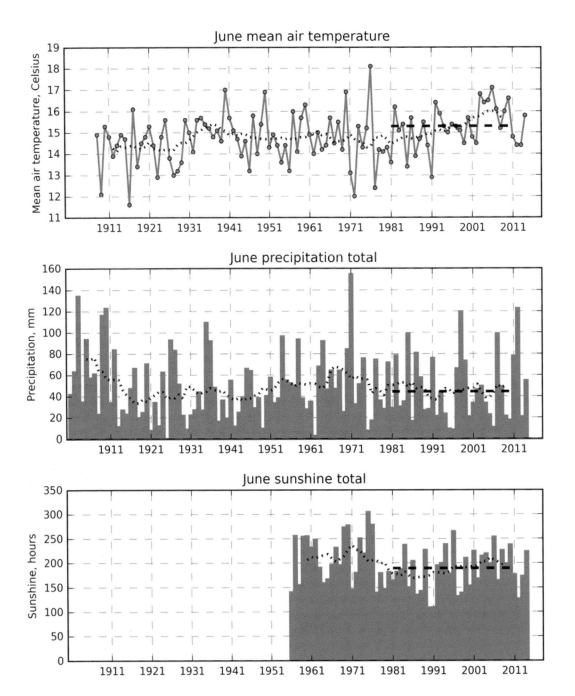

Figure 9.3 *Monthly values of (from top) mean temperature (°C), total precipitation (mm) and sunshine duration (hours) for June at Reading over the available period of record (plots include London Road rainfall records where available 1901-04, with estimates from other Reading stations to 1907 as necessary)*

The mean temperatures as recorded at London Road 1908-67 have been reduced by 0.7 degC to ensure approximate homogeneity with the records from the Whiteknights site, 1968 onwards. No site adjustments have been made for precipitation or sunshine. The 1981-2010 averages are indicated by the thick dashed line, while the 10 year running mean centred on the year shown is indicated by a dashed grey line

10 July

July is, on average, both the sunniest and warmest month of the year in Reading, and also the most thundery. The average temperature is 17.6 °C (mean daily minimum 12.7 °C, maximum 22.4 °C, over the period 1981-2010), and mean daily sunshine 6 hours and 22 minutes, 3 minutes per day more than June and 12 minutes per day more than August.

Over the 100 years ending in 2014, July was the warmest month of the year in 54 years, and August in 37 (June was warmest in seven years, and September once: June and July tied in one year). Average temperatures tend to rise as July progresses, with daily mean maximum temperatures around 22 °C at the start of the month to 23 °C towards the end. Minimum temperatures increase more slowly, from about 12 °C in the first week to 13 °C at the end of the month (see daily averages plotted in Chapter 3). Although there is of course much year-to-year variation, the warmest day of the year is, on average, 29 July – mean minimum 13.4 °C, mean maximum 23.7 °C, and a resultant mean temperature of 18.6 °C. No air frosts have ever been recorded during July in Reading, but ground frosts occur in about one year in three.

July's mean rainfall is 46 mm – but the mean daily rainfall is almost identical to June, the very slightly higher monthly mean arising solely from July's 31 days compared with June's 30. Wet days are infrequent, but occasional downpours – often accompanied by thunder – can deposit more than a month's average rainfall in just a few hours.

TEMPERATURE

During the period 1908-2014, July temperatures in Reading have ranged from 4.9 °C to 35.3 °C.

The coldest July night was 25 July 1978, when the temperature fell to 4.9 °C; four other July nights have fallen below 5.5 °C since 1908. Slight ground frosts are not uncommon in July at Whiteknights, occurring about one year in three on average: the lowest grass minimum temperatures were those of -2.2 °C on 18 July 1971, -2.1 °C on 22 July 1970 and -2.0 °C on 16 July 2001. In both July 1977 and July 1993, ground frosts occurred twice.

The coldest July days barely surpass a mild January day. The maximum temperature attained just 13.3 °C on 7 July 1910, 8 July 1917 and 31 July 1917, and only 13.4 °C on 5 July 1920. The occurrence of two of the equal-coolest July days in July 1917 is noteworthy, coming so soon after the great heatwave in June of that year, culminating in 33.9 °C on 17 June. Since the Whiteknights record commenced in 1968, the coolest July day has been 14.2 °C on 6 July 1969.

Since 1908, only four days have reached 35 °C in Reading, and only one of these was in July – that was 19 July 2006, when the temperature reached 35.3 °C at Whiteknights (Figure 10.1). In July 1923, 34 °C was surpassed on two consecutive days (12th and 13th, 34.7 °C and 34.3 °C respectively): this has only occurred twice on Reading's record, the other being 80 years later in August 2003. Several deaths in Reading were attributed to heatwave conditions and glaring sunshine in July 1923, while in July 1948, 34.6 °C was recorded on 29th – the opening day of the London Olympics.

By far the longest notable hot spells extending into July, in which the maximum temperature reached 30 °C or above each day, occurred in the 14 days commencing 25 June 1976, when the highest temperature reached was 34.0 °C on 26 June. The next-longest spells by this measure were just six days long (commencing 11 July 1983, maximum temperature 31.6 °C on 16 July) and five days (commencing 9 July 1921, maximum temperature 32.7 °C on 10 July, and commencing 30 July 1995, maximum temperature 33.6 °C on 1 August). Only three Julys have seen eight days in the month attain 30 °C or more – 1921, 1976 and 2006 – while July 1983 managed seven such days.

Table 10.1 Highest and lowest maximum and minimum temperatures in July, 1908-2014. Records are from the (slightly milder) London Road site 1908-67, and from Whiteknights 1968-2014: no corrections for site differences have been applied.

Rank	Hottest days	Coldest days	Warmest nights	Coldest nights
1	35.3 °C, 19 July 2006	13.3 °C, 7 July 1910, 8 July 1917 and 31 July 1917	19.9 °C, 29 July 1948	4.9 °C, 25 July 1978
2	34.7 °C, 12 July 1923	13.4 °C, 5 July 1920	19.2 °C, 23 July 1921	5.1 °C, 4 July 1965
3	34.6 °C, 29 July 1948	13.8 °C, 23 July 1930	19.1 °C, 13 July 1941	5.2 °C, 11 July 1993
4	34.3 °C, 13 July 1923	13.9 °C, 1 July 1919	19.0 °C, 4 July 1976	5.3 °C, 1 July 1924
5	33.5 °C, 3 July 1976	14.0 °C, 7 July 1919	18.9 °C, 13 July 1923 and 1 July 1968	5.4 °C, 22 July 1970

Lowering the threshold to 25 °C or more each day, the longest hot spells were 18 consecutive days long (commencing 18 July 1921 and 22 June 1976), with 15 consecutive days commencing 15 July 2006. In July 2014, 25 °C was reached on 10 consecutive days 17-26th, yet the highest maximum was 'only' 28.6 °C (on 24th). In July 1983, 22 days during the month reached or exceeded 25 °C (Figure 10.1), while the Julys of 1911, 1934 and 2006 all reached this threshold on 20 days. Only five calendar months since 1908 have reached at least 20 °C on every day of the month: four of these were Julys (1934, 1983, 2006 and 2010). In July 1934, the lowest daily maximum temperature was 21.4 °C (on 24th), the highest 'lowest daily maximum' on record for any month.

Hot, airless and often humid nights can be a problem in summer heatwaves, with night-time temperatures remaining above 15 °C at least once in most Julys. The warmest July nights on record were 19.1 °C on 13 July 1941, 19.2 °C on 23 July 1921 and 19.9 °C on 29 July 1948 – all recorded at the slightly warmer London Road site. The warmest July night at Whiteknights was on 4 July 1976 – a

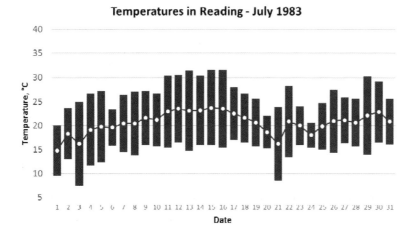

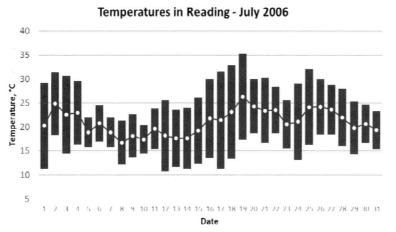

Figure 10.1 Daily maximum and minimum temperatures, °C (top and bottom of daily columns) and daily mean temperature (central circle and connecting line) at the University of Reading in July 1983 (top) and July 2006 (bottom), the two hottest months on Reading's records

minimum temperature of 19.0 °C. Spells of minimum temperatures above 15 °C each night for six or more consecutive nights occurred in July in 1923, 1955, 1983 and 1989. In 1983, a spell of seven consecutive nights from 14 July saw minimum temperatures ranging from 15.3 °C to 17.0 °C, followed by a nine-day spell 23-31 July with seven of these nine nights also remaining above 15 °C.

Diurnal temperature ranges in July have been as large as 20.8 degC at London Road on 10 July 1921. At Whiteknights, the largest daily range was 20.3 degC on 17 July 2006.

Warm and cold months

The Julys of 2006 and 1983 (Figure 10.1) were the hottest months yet recorded in Reading, and the only months to record a mean daily temperature above 20 °C. There is little to choose in mean temperature between July 1921, 1976, 1989, 1995 and 2013, once allowance has been made for the relative warmth of the inner-town London Road site. The three coolest Julys all occurred in the four years between 1919 and 1922, and yet July 1921 was the warmest on record until beaten by July 1976.

Monthly temperature ranges in July have varied between 14.1 degC in 1988 and 27.3 degC in 1948.

Table 10.2 July temperatures at the University of Reading, 1908-2014. In July the London Road site (1908-67) is about 0.6 degC warmer than the Whiteknights site (1968 onwards) due to its location closer to the town centre. The observed mean temperatures at the London Road site (shown in brackets) have been adjusted by this amount to facilitate comparison between the two records.

July mean temperature 17.6°C (average 1981-2010)

Warmest months			Coldest months		
Mean temperature, °C	*Departure from 1981-2010 normal degC*	*Year*	*Mean temperature, °C*	*Departure from 1981-2010 normal degC*	*Year*
21.1	+3.5	2006	14.1 (14.7)	-3.5	1922
20.6	+3.0	1983	14.2 (14.8)	-3.4	1919, 1920
19.6	+2.0	1989	14.3 (15.0)	-3.3	1910, 1954
19.5	+1.9	1976, 1995, 2013	14.5 (15.1)	-3.1	1965
19.3 (19.9)	+1.7	1921	14.8	-2.8	1980

PRECIPITATION

The monthly mean rainfall for July in Reading is 46 mm. Table 10.3 gives the extremes of monthly and daily rainfall recorded since 1901.

Table 10.3 July precipitation at the University of Reading, 1901-2014 (London Road 1901-1967, Whiteknights 1968-2014).

July mean precipitation 45.8 mm (average 1981-2010)

Wettest months			Driest months			Wettest days	
Total fall, mm	*Per cent of normal*	*Year*	*Total fall, mm*	*Per cent of normal*	*Year*	*Daily fall, mm*	*Date*
154.7	337	1920	4.0	9	1921	50.3	25 July 1941
143.5	313	1918	4.3	9	1955	46.7	22 July 1967 *T*
143.0	312	1917	8.9	19	1935	42.5	2 July 1999
130.3	284	1915	9.0	20	1911	42.5	20 July 2007 *T*
120.5	263	1950	9.5	21	1990	38.4	30 July 1917

T after the date of the heaviest fall indicates thunder was heard on that date

The run of very wet Julys at the beginning of the record is notable: in the six years ended 1920, four had over 130 mm. Since 1920 no July has recorded as much as 125 mm: July 2007, with 116 mm, was not wet enough to qualify for the monthly table (see also Figure 10.4). July 1917 was a wet month following a very wet end to June: the wet state of the land, coupled with a lack of farm labourers due to the war, caused severe problems on local farms at this critical time of the year. In July 1918 the first eight days were dry - no hint of the rains that were to follow: and in July 1920, there were four days with over 10 mm in a day.

Daily falls of 25 mm or more of rain occur in about one year in four in July – and about 40 per cent of those falls occur on days with thunderstorms. During thundery activities rainfall can be very heavy and short-lived. The wettest July day was 25 July 1941, when 50.3 mm fell. On 22 July 1967 lightning struck an elm tree in Whiteknights Park: 46.7 mm of rain fell at London Road - 20.3 mm of that in 48 minutes commencing 0136 GMT on 23 July. On 20 July 2007, 42.5 mm was recorded during the 'rainfall day' (i.e. 0900-0900 GMT), but this was part of a longer fall bridging two rain days – 69.0 mm fell across the two days 19-20 July 2007, most of that in about 15 hours during a spell of prolonged heavy thunderstorms accompanied by extreme 'day darkness' for much of the morning. Enormous flooding resulted on many local rivers, a most unusual occurrence during the summer half-year (Figure 10.2).

Figure 10.2 *The Kennet in flood through The Oracle shopping centre in Reading, late on 20 July 2007 following 69 mm of rainfall in about 15 hours. Photograph © Stephen Burt*

At the opposite hydrological extreme, July/August 1976 holds the record for longest spell of consecutive days without measurable rainfall. The 37 days commencing 21 July 1976 saw only a 'trace' of rainfall recorded, equalling the record set in August/September 1959.

Thunderstorms

Thunderstorms can be expected on one or two days in a typical July, but occurred on seven days in July 1925 and six days in July 1934, 1947, 1962 and in the hot July of 1983.

SUNSHINE

July is, on average, the sunniest month of the year in Reading with 197.5 hours of bright sunshine, although August has the highest percentage of possible daylight hours (July 40%, August 42%).

No July has yet surpassed 300 hours of sunshine, although two have come close - July 1959 recorded 298.2 hours at the London Road site, just shy of 60% of the maximum possible, while July 2013 came very close with 297.6 hours: July 2006 was also very sunny. July 1976 was the second of three very sunny summer months. In contrast, July 1965 could muster only 110.6 hours of bright sunshine at London Road (this total has been exceeded three times in February!); July 1962 was little better, recording just 116.8 hours.

By early July, the daylength is beginning to decrease – ever so slowly at first, but more noticeably by the end of the month. Even so, 15 hours of bright sunshine is possible during the first week or so of July, and there have been seven such days at Whiteknights in the period 1968-2014, the sunniest July day on record there being 15.7 hours on 3 July 1968. In July 1959 there were five days (4-8 July) that each recorded at least 14.0 hours of sunshine, including 15.8 hours on 4 July. July 2006 had the highest number of days with 12 hours or more of sunshine recorded (13) for any month except June 1975 (15); there were also 12 such days in July 1959.

Table 10.4 July sunshine duration at the University of Reading, 1956-2014 (London Road 1956-1967, Whiteknights 1968-2014).

July mean sunshine duration 197.5 hours, 6.37 hours per day (average 1981-2010)

Possible daylength: 499 hours. Mean sunshine duration as percentage of possible: 39.6

Sunniest months			Dullest months			Sunniest days	
Duration, hours	*Per cent of possible*	*Year*	*Duration, hours*	*Per cent of possible*	*Year*	*Duration, hours*	*Date*
298.2	59.8	1959	110.6	22.2	1965	15.8	4 July 1959
297.6	59.7	2013	116.8	23.4	1962	15.7	3 July 1968
291.8	58.5	2006	135.1	27.1	1988	15.4	6 July 1959
282.5	56.6	1976	136.5	27.4	1992	15.3	1 July 1986
269.3	54.0	1983	140.5	28.2	1956	15.2	9 July 1967

Long sunny spells of 12 hours or more daily and lasting at least seven days that have encompassed July were limited to a ten-day spell from 23 June to 2 July 1976 (147.2 hours of sunshine was recorded in this spell, a daily average of 14.72 hours) and a seven-day spell 7-13 July 2013 (95.3 hours, daily average 13.61 hours). Spells with a minimum of nine hours sunshine per day have included 12 consecutive days from 22 June 1976 (169.2 hours total, daily average 14.10 hours) and nine consecutive days commencing 18 July 1990 (112.8 hours in all, 12.53 hours daily).

A typical July will see only one sunless day, and about one year in four has no sunless days in July – but in 1968 there were eight sunless days, while both July 1956 and July 1977 recorded six sunless days each. A rare prolonged sunless spell in July occurred in 1956, with no sunshine for four consecutive days 18-21 July.

Sea breezes ... in Reading?

Reading experiences around half a dozen sea breezes per year, more in warmer summers. Most originate from the south coast, although one or two per year can be traced back to the Thames estuary. They can often be felt as a sudden gust of cooler, damper air accompanied by a freshening breeze and an increase in cloud, typically between about 6 p.m. and 8 p.m. on warm, sunny evenings between May and August – very occasionally as early as late March or as late as early September. Figure 10.3 shows the rapid jump in humidity experienced during the passage of a marked sea breeze at 1815 GMT on 5 July 2013 (7.15 p.m. British Summer Time). Much important theoretical and practical work on sea breezes was undertaken within the Department of Meteorology in the 1970s.

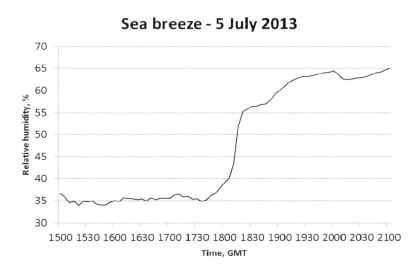

Figure 10.3 Relative humidity record at the University of Reading for the evening of 5 July 2013, showing the rapid increase in relative humidity at the passage of a sea breeze around 1815 GMT (7.15 p.m. British Summer Time). This plot is from 5 minute AWS data

TEMPERATURE, PRECIPITATION AND SUNSHINE IN GRAPHS – JULY

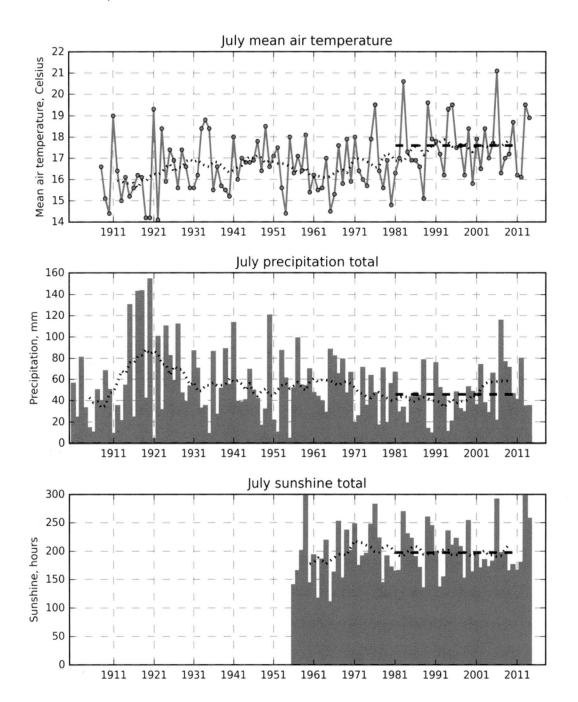

Figure 10.4 *Monthly values of (from top) mean temperature (°C), total precipitation (mm) and sunshine duration (hours) for July at Reading over the available period of record (plots include London Road rainfall records where available 1901-04, with estimates from other Reading stations to 1907 as necessary)*

The mean temperatures as recorded at London Road 1908-67 have been reduced by 0.6 degC to ensure approximate homogeneity with the records from the Whiteknights site, 1968 onwards. No site adjustments have been made for precipitation or sunshine. The 1981-2010 averages are indicated by the thick dashed line, while the 10 year running mean centred on the year shown is indicated by a dashed grey line

11 **August**

August is the typical month of high summer in most people's minds – long school holidays, sunny days at the beach, light and warm evenings – and yet the decline into autumn is already apparent in mean temperatures, which are a few tenths lower than July, and in sunshine totals – the latter an average of 12 minutes per day less than in July. The monthly mean temperature is 17.3 °C, and yet August holds the crown for both of the hottest days on record, with 36 °C recorded twice since 1908, and the hottest night. August also tends to be a wetter month than July, and heavy thundery rains are not uncommon, when once again a month's normal rainfall can fall in the space of just a few hours.

TEMPERATURE

The warmest days of the year tend to be reached around late July, after which there is a fairly gentle decline in mean daily maximum temperatures throughout August, from around 23 °C in the first week or so to 20-21 °C by the end of the month. There is a slower and more irregular fall in mean minimum temperatures, from about 13 °C to 12 °C over the same period.

The July chapter makes mention that only four days since 1908 have reached 35 °C in Reading: three of those four were in August, two of which reached 36 °C. The hottest day on the entire record was 10 August 2003, when 36.4 °C was reached at Whiteknights: the other '36' was 92 years earlier, on 9 August 1911, at 36.0°C. The former came at the start of a warm month when 30 °C was measured on six out of eight days – the eight days had an average maximum temperature of 32.4 °C. The latter occurrence was in a very warm August during a spell when 30 °C was reached on five days out of seven.

Table 11.1 Highest and lowest maximum and minimum temperatures in August, 1908-2014. Records are from the (slightly warmer) London Road site 1908-67, and from Whiteknights 1968-2014: no corrections for site differences have been applied.

Rank	Hottest days	Coldest days	Hottest nights	Coldest nights
1	36.4 °C, 10 Aug 2003	13.5 °C, 19 Aug 1977	20.8 °C, 2 Aug 1995	2.9 °C, 31 Aug 1934
2	36.0 °C, 9 Aug 1911	13.6 °C, 19 Aug 1954	19.9 °C, 11 Aug 2003	3.4 °C, 28 Aug 1979
3	35.5 °C, 3 Aug 1990	13.8 °C, 24 Aug 1931	19.4 °C, 23 Aug 1977 and 9 Aug 2004	3.9 °C, 31 Aug 1921 and 26 Aug 1922
4	34.2 °C, 9 Aug 2003	13.9 °C, 4 Aug 1974 and 3 Aug 1986	19.2 °C, 18 Aug 1947, 5 Aug 1975, 13 Aug 1997 and 24 Aug 2003	4.7 °C, 26 Aug 1931
5	33.8 °C, 19 Aug 1932	14.1 °C, 6 Aug 1962	19.0 °C, 22 Aug 1997	4.8 °C, 18 Aug 1970 and 28 Aug 1974

The warmest nights tend to occur during the first half of the month – the warmest being 2 August 1995, when the temperature did not fall below 20.8 °C (following a maximum of 33.6 °C the previous afternoon, and one of 32.7 °C later that day). This is one of only two 24 hour periods ending at 0900 GMT to have remained above 20 °C (the other in early September 1949), although 11 August 2003 came very close (minimum temperature 19.9 °C, after the record hot day 36.4 °C mentioned above).

The most intense hot spells during August – five consecutive days reaching 30 °C – occurred in August 1947 (five days commencing 15th, maximum temperature 33.5 °C on 16 August) and August 1995 (five days commencing 30 July, maximum temperature 33.6 °C on 1 August). In August 2003, eight consecutive days exceeded 29 °C. Prolonged hot spells, in which the maximum temperature reached at least 25 °C each day for at least 12 consecutive days encompassing August, have occurred five times on Reading's records. The longest such spell was 26 days, commencing 11 August 1947 – an unusually long and late warm spell; the next longest spells were 'only' 14 days, commencing 7 August 1911 and 3 August 1944.

Only one August since 1908 has reached at least 20 °C on every day of the month: this was in 1933, when the lowest daily maximum temperature was 20.1 °C on 17 August.

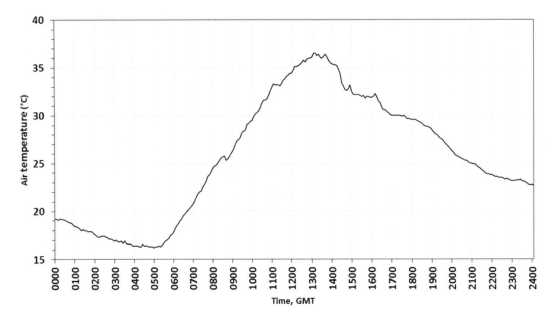

Figure 11.1 *Air temperatures recorded at the University of Reading on Sunday 10 August 2003, the hottest day on the university's records: the highest temperature reached was 36.4 °C between 1305 and 1310 GMT. This plot is from 5 minute AWS data*

The longest spell of extremely warm nights, each with minimum temperatures above 18 °C, occurred in August 1997: for three nights 22-24 August the temperature did not fall below 18.9 °C (minimum temperatures of 19.0 °C, 19.4 °C and 18.9 °C respectively). This spell occurred towards the end of a run of nine nights each of which had minimum temperatures above 15 °C (August 1997 also holds the record for the highest mean minimum temperature for any month, at 15.2 °C). Nine-night spells of 15.0 °C and above minima also occurred 15-23 August 1947 and 5-13 August 2003.

Cool August days tend also to be wet. Maximum temperatures below 14 °C have occurred on five August days since 1908 – the coldest being 13.5 °C on 19 August 1977, which was a sunless day at the end of a six-day spell during which 84 mm of rain fell.

The coldest nights tend to occur towards the end of August as summer slides into autumn, sometimes all too quickly. All August minimum temperatures below 5 °C since 1908 have occurred after mid-month – and an August ground frost can be expected in about one year in two, although as many as seven were logged in August 1993 (the earliest on 13th). The coldest nights are most likely when the ground is very dry after a warm, dry summer and are often accompanied by ground frost. In the middle of the very hot and dry summer of 1976, a grass minimum temperature of -2.6 °C was recorded on 1 August. The coldest August night on the record was 31 August 1934, when the screen minimum temperature was 2.9 °C. On 31 August 1921, again following a warm and dry summer, a grass minimum temperature of -5.0 °C was recorded at London Road – very low for the time of year.

Daily temperature ranges in August have been as large as 21.6 degC at London Road on 29 August 1936, and 21.0 degC on 12 August 1911. At Whiteknights, the daily range was 20.2 degC on 10 August 2003, the hottest day on the record.

Warm and cold months
The Augusts of 1947, 1995 and 2003 were very warm and contained some of the hottest August nights and days, while those of 1920 and 1922 were very cool with average temperatures similar to those

expected in late May or late September. August 1985 and 1986 both produced a poor end to summer. In August 1933 the lowest maximum temperature was 20.1 °C on the 17th – one of only five months when 20 °C was reached every day.

Monthly temperature ranges in August have varied between 15.5 degC in 1952 and 30.0 degC in 2003.

Table 11.2 August temperatures at the University of Reading, 1908-2014. In August the London Road site (1908-67) is about 0.5 degC warmer than the Whiteknights site (1968 onwards) due to its location closer to the town centre. The observed mean temperatures at the London Road site (shown in brackets) have been adjusted by this amount to facilitate comparison between the two records.

August mean temperature 17.3°C (average 1981-2010)

Warmest months			Coldest months		
Mean temperature, °C	Departure from 1981-2010 normal degC	Year	Mean temperature, °C	Departure from 1981-2010 normal degC	Year
20.1	+2.8	1995	13.8 (14.3)	-3.5	1920
20.0	+2.7	2003	13.8 (14.3)	-3.5	1922
20.0 (20.5)	+2.7	1947	13.9 (14.4)	-3.4	1912
19.8	+2.5	1997	14.2 (14.7)	-3.1	1956
19.3 (19.8)	+2.0	1911	14.8 (15.3)	-2.5	1963
19.3	+2.0	1990	14.9	-2.4	1986

PRECIPITATION

The monthly mean rainfall for August in Reading is 52 mm, 14% higher than July's average.

Table 11.3 August precipitation at the University of Reading, 1901-2014 (London Road 1901-1967, Whiteknights 1968-2014).

August mean precipitation 52.3 mm (average 1981-2010)

Wettest months			Driest months			Wettest days	
Total fall, mm	Per cent of normal	Year	Total fall, mm	Per cent of normal	Year	Daily fall, mm	Date
136.3	261	2004	1.0	2	1940	59.5	18 Aug 2011
131.9	252	1977	3.3	6	1995	55.6	20 Aug 1932 *T*
128.4	246	1999	7.2	14	1947	52.6	9 Aug 1999
127.0	243	2011	8.6	16	1991	50.8	14 Aug 1980 *T*
118.4	226	1916	10.9	21	1936	44.2	9 Aug 2004

T after the date of the heaviest fall indicates thunder was heard on that date.

August rainfall totals have ranged from 136 mm in August 2004 to just 1 mm in August 1940. In the latter month, all the rain fell on a single day – the 18th: apart from this, there was no measurable rain in a 41 day period beginning on 28 July 1940. In August 2004 over half the rain fell on two days (30.6 mm on the 5th and 44.2 mm on the 9th) while during 19-22 August another 39 mm fell – much of the month was, in fact, relatively dry.

Daily rainfall totals of 25 mm or more of rain occur in about one year in four in August, although since 1908, only four August days have recorded 50 mm or more rainfall — the wettest being 18 August 2011 when 59.5 mm fell in 7.5 hours. This fall was not associated with thunder.

At the opposite extreme, the month of August has featured in both equal-longest spells of consecutive days without measurable rainfall. In 1959, the 37 days commencing 15 August saw only a 'trace' of rainfall recorded; the same duration and total occurred in 1976, commencing 21 July. In 1947, just a trace of rainfall fell in the 33 days commencing 5 August.

Figure 11.2

Upper photograph: *Mortimer fire brigade in attendance at a field fire at Mortimer, south of Reading, following the heatwave of late July and early August in 1990; the temperature reached 35.5 °C at the university on 3 August, at that time the second-hottest day on record. This photograph was taken on 4 August 1990*

Lower photograph: *Desiccated fields and parched livestock at Great Park Farm, Mortimer, during the hot, dry August of 1995 (photographed on 14 August). Both photographs © Stephen Burt*

Thunderstorms
One or two days with thunder can be expected in a typical August, although there were six such days in the Augusts of 1931, 1960 and 2004. About one August in four remains free of thunder.

SUNSHINE
Although August is slightly less sunny than July in average sunshine duration (on average, 191 hours of bright sunshine, just 12 minutes per day less than July, making it the second-sunniest month of the year), it is the sunniest month of the year when considered as a percentage of the possible, at 42 per cent, compared to July's 40 per cent. Not unconnected is that August has the lowest average cloud amount at 0900 GMT of any month of the year – 68 per cent.

August 1976 and 1995 stand out as the two sunniest Augusts on the record, and in 1976 all three summer months were remarkably sunny. August 1976 (Figure 11.3) also achieves the double distinction of having the lowest average cloud cover at 0900 GMT of any month since complete daily records began in 1960 (just 39 per cent average cover), and being the sunniest month of any name on record, when considered as a percentage of the possible daylight hours, achieving a remarkable 62.2 per cent (281 hours out of 451). August 1995 was only a whisker behind 1976, at 61.9 per cent. Both were sunnier by this measure than the month with the highest total sunshine duration, June 1975, which although it amassed 306 hours of sunshine, that was 'only' 61.6 per cent of possible.

In 1958, however, August managed only 115.4 hours of sunshine at the London Road site – with 1968 and 2008 being almost as dull. This figure has been surpassed twice in February; and in 2008, February's daily mean sunshine duration was 34 minutes per day greater than August's!

The length of daylight in August decreases noticeably, by around 3½ minutes per day, and so it is only to be expected that the sunniest August days occur at the beginning of the month, when more than 14 hours sunshine is still possible. On 2 August 1981, 14.5 hours of sunshine was recorded, 94% of possible (although there is some doubt about this value as it is 0.8 hours more than on any other August day).

Table 11.4 August sunshine duration at the University of Reading, 1956-2014 (London Road 1956-1967, Whiteknights 1968-2014).

August mean sunshine duration 191.3 hours, 6.17 hours per day (average 1981-2010)

Possible daylength: 451 hours. Mean sunshine duration as percentage of possible: 42.4

Sunniest months			Dullest months			Sunniest days	
Duration, hours	*Per cent of possible*	*Year*	*Duration, hours*	*Per cent of possible*	*Year*	*Duration, hours*	*Date*
280.9	62.2	1976	115.4	25.6	1958	14.5	2 Aug 1981
279.4	61.9	1995	116.9	25.9	1968	13.7	11 Aug 1972
254.1	56.3	1959	117.9	26.1	2008	13.7	4 Aug 1976
246.0	54.5	1998	132.6	29.4	2010	13.7	8 Aug 2005
245.6	54.4	1989	133.8	29.6	1977	13.7	5 Aug 2007

The longest sunny spells in August – runs of consecutive days each with 9 hours or more sunshine – have included the 12 days commencing 15 August 1976 (total sunshine total 143.6 hours, daily average 11.97 hours), ten days commencing 2 August 2003 (total sunshine 118.0 hours, daily average 11.80 hours) and nine days commencing 4 August 1998 (total sunshine 110.8 hours, daily average 12.31 hours).

A typical August will see sunshine on 30 of its 31 days, although about one year in four has sunshine every day during the month. August 1968 saw an unenviable eight days without any sunshine, while both August 1956 and August 1977 saw six sunless days. In August 1968, four of the sunless days occurred consecutively (commencing 6 August): the 3rd and 4th were also sunless. In fact the first nine days received just 6.7 hours of sunshine – an unusually dull spell for any summer month.

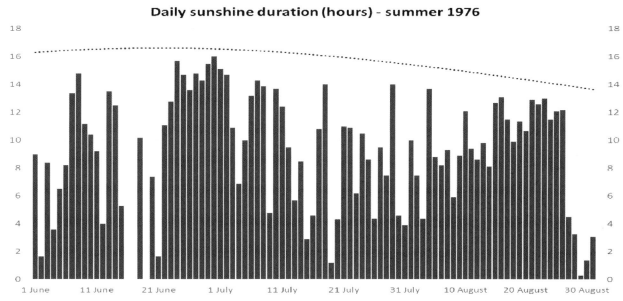

Daily sunshine duration (hours) - summer 1976

***Figure 11.3** Daily sunshine duration (in hours) at the University of Reading during the summer of 1976. The dotted line gives the length of daylight on each day (sunrise to sunset, hours). Even after almost four decades, each month of 'the summer of '76' remains in the 'Top five' sunniest for the respective month on Reading's records – June second-sunniest, July fourth-sunniest and August sunniest*

TEMPERATURE, PRECIPITATION AND SUNSHINE IN GRAPHS – AUGUST

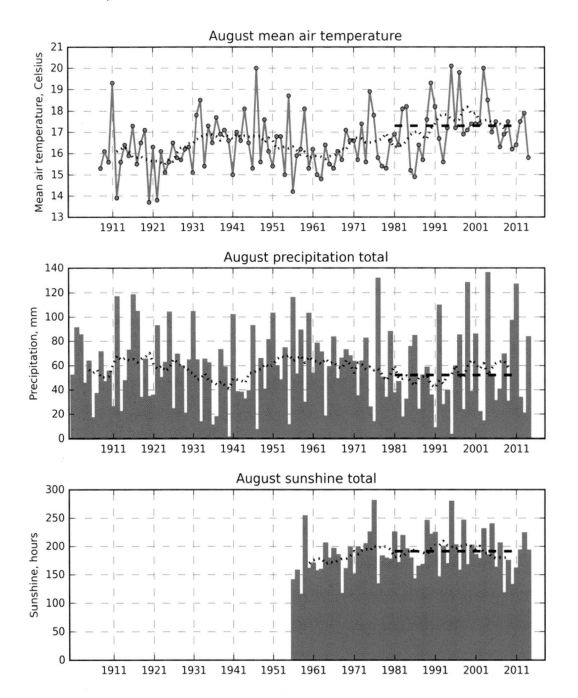

Figure 11.4 *Monthly values of (from top) mean temperature (°C), total precipitation (mm) and sunshine duration (hours) for August at Reading over the available period of record (plots include London Road rainfall records where available 1901-04, with estimates from other Reading stations to 1907 as necessary)*

The mean temperatures as recorded at London Road 1908-67 have been reduced by 0.5 degC to ensure approximate homogeneity with the records from the Whiteknights site, 1968 onwards. No site adjustments have been made for precipitation or sunshine. The 1981-2010 averages are indicated by the thick dashed line, while the 10 year running mean centred on the year shown is indicated by a dashed grey line

12 September

September is another 'transition month'. Most Septembers include at least a few warm, sunny days seemingly left-over from high summer – indeed, in some years summer continues well into September – but autumn usually shows its hand in cooler, cloudier and windier conditions by the end of the month. There is a steady and fairly rapid decline in mean temperatures, with average maximum temperatures dropping from 20-21 °C in early September to near 17 °C by the end; there is a similar decrease in minimum temperatures over the same period, from about 12 °C to about 9.5 °C, although both are subject to considerable year-to-year and day-to-day variability at this time of year. September's average temperature over the period 1981-2010 was 14.6 °C.

September sees a noticeable reduction in the duration of bright sunshine, partly due to declining daylength (almost 4 minutes per day), but mainly due to increased cloud cover – the percentage of possible sunshine in September declines sharply, from August's 42% to September's 36%, while September's mean cloud cover at 0900 GMT is 71 per cent, up from 68 per cent in August. The average monthly sunshine duration for the month is 138 hours, or 4 hours 37 minutes per day. In terms of rainfall, September is almost indistinguishable from August – the monthly mean (50 mm) is lower than August only because September has fewer days. One September day in 1992 holds the dubious honour of the wettest day yet recorded on the university's long record.

TEMPERATURE

Not surprisingly, the highest temperatures in September tend to occur towards the beginning of the month, although 25 °C can still be exceeded well into October. The hottest September day on the record was 7 September 1911, when 31.7 °C was reached: in September 1929 30 °C was reached three times in the first eight days, including 31.2 °C on 4 September. However, only five years have exceeded 30 °C in September in Reading — 1911, 1919, 1929, 1940 and 1949 (all at the slightly warmer London Road site). At the time of writing, the highest since 1949 has been 29.6 °C on 11 September 2006 at Whiteknights.

The hottest day of the year has been recorded in September twice since 1908 – in 1929 (31.2 °C on 4 September, the latest date in the year to achieve this distinction) and 1954 (28.0 °C on 1 September).

Table 12.1 Highest and lowest maximum and minimum temperatures in September, 1908-2014. Records are from the (slightly warmer) London Road site 1908-67, and from Whiteknights 1968-2014: no corrections for site differences have been applied.

Rank	Hottest days	Coldest days	Warmest nights	Coldest nights
1	31.7 °C, 7 Sept 1911	9.6 °C, 27 Sept 1993	20.3 °C, 5 Sept 1949	-1.1 °C, 30 Sept 1919
2	31.2 °C, 4 Sept 1929	10.0 °C, 29 Sept 1918	18.0 °C, 5 Sept 2006	-0.8 °C, 29 Sept 1919
3	30.6 °C, 8 Sept 1929	10.4 °C, 15 Sept 1986	17.6 °C, 12 Sept 1945 and 5 Sept 2005	-0.3 °C, 23 Sept 1914 and 30 Sept 1914
4	30.5 °C, 3 Sept 1911	10.5 °C, 15 Sept 1994	17.5 °C, 3 Sept 1939	0.1 °C, 20 Sept 1919
5	30.3 °C, 11 Sept 1919 and 5 Sept 1929	10.6 °C, 30 Sept 1952	17.2 °C, 3 Sept 1932 and 6 Sept 1951	0.4 °C, 27 Sept 1927

The longest spells of warm days at this time of year, those when the maximum temperature reached at least 25 °C for at least six consecutive days, were in 1947 (26 days commencing 11 August 1947; maximum temperature in September 25.9 °C) and eight days commencing 2 September 1929 – three of which surpassed 30 °C. In September 1959, the seven days commencing 6 September all exceeded

25 °C, the highest maximum being 28.1 °C on 11 September. In 2011, a remarkably late hot spell commenced on 28 September and lasted six days (see also October's chapter).

High minimum temperatures are not uncommon in early September, particularly following warm summers when the ground temperature is close to its highest. The warmest September night occurred on 5 September 1949, when the minimum temperature was 20.3 °C, following a hot day (maximum temperature of 30 °C on the 4th): even the grass minimum temperature was a high 16.8 °C. The next warmest September night was 5 September 2006, at 18.0 °C.

Cold, wet conditions more typical of mid-autumn are not uncommon towards the end of the month. The coldest September days on the record have been 27 September 1993 (maximum temperature just 9.6 °C) and 29 September 1918 (10.0 °C: also 10.8 °C on the 27th and 11.4 °C on the 30th).

During 1981-2010 the average date of the first autumn ground frost was 8 September. A typical September will see ground frosts on three or four nights, most likely in the second half of the month. Air frosts during September are very rare in the town, although not unknown in the surrounding rural areas. September air frosts occurred at the London Road site in 1914 (on 23rd, the earliest air frost on the record, and again on 30th) and in 1919 (on both 29th and 30th – the minimum of -1.1 °C on 30 September 1919 being the coldest September night on the record). Since 1968, the coldest September night at Whiteknights has been +0.8 °C on 30 September 1969.

The largest daily temperature range on any day in the year was 22.8 degC at London Road on 7 September 1911. At Whiteknights, a daily range of 20.4 degC was recorded on 9 September 2012.

Warm and cold months
The warmest September on record in Reading was September 2006, with 1929 and 1949 not far behind. Each of these months had some unusually warm days and nights. Only two days in the first 26 in September 2006 had maximum temperatures below 20 °C, and most nights remained above 10 °C in this period.

Table 12.2 September temperatures at the University of Reading, 1908-2014. In September the London Road site (1908-67) is about 0.5 degC warmer than the Whiteknights site (1968 onwards) due to its location closer to the town centre. The observed mean temperatures at the London Road site (shown in brackets) have been adjusted by this amount to facilitate comparison between the two records.

September mean temperature 14.6°C (average 1981-2010)

Warmest months			Coldest months		
Mean temperature, °C	*Departure from 1981-2010 normal degC*	*Year*	Mean temperature, °C	*Departure from 1981-2010 normal degC*	*Year*
18.0	+3.4	2006	11.0 (11.5)	-3.8	1912
17.3 (17.8)	+2.7	1949	11.4 (11.9)	-3.2	1952
17.1 (17.6)	+2.5	1929	11.7 (12.2)	-2.9	1925, 1931
16.3	+1.7	2005	11.8	-2.8	1986
16.0 (16.5)	+1.4	1947, 1959	12.0 (12.5)	-2.6	1909

September 1912 was the coldest September on record, followed by 1952. In September 1912 no day reached 20 °C – following a maximum temperature of just 20 °C in August of that year. More recently, September 1986 was a remarkably cool month, with 12 ground frosts, although the lowest air temperature was 2.1 °C on 20th. There were ten ground frosts in September 2003, including a grass minimum temperature of -6.7 °C on 24th – the air minimum that morning was 1.4 °C, with a sharp air frost outside the town. The lowest September grass minimum temperature on record was -7.6 °C on 30 September 1969.

September is, occasionally, warmer than August. This last happened in 2006, but before that also in 1956 and 1929.

Monthly temperature ranges in September have varied between 15.5 degC in 1988 and 31.4 degC in 1919. September 1919 is one of only three months in the entire record to feature in both the 'hottest days' and 'coldest nights' tables for that month – the others being March 1965 and November 2010.

PRECIPITATION

The monthly mean rainfall for September in Reading is 50 mm. Mean daily rainfall increases quite sharply after the first week of the month (see annual plot, Chapter 3).

Table 12.3 September precipitation at the University of Reading, 1901-2014 (London Road 1901-1967, Whiteknights 1968-2014).

September mean precipitation 50.3 mm (average 1981-2010)

Wettest months			Driest months			Wettest days	
Total fall,	*Per cent of*		*Total fall,*	*Per cent of*		*Daily fall,*	
mm	*normal*	*Year*	*mm*	*normal*	*Year*	*mm*	*Date*
145.7	290	1974	0.8	2	1959	76.3	22 Sep 1992
137.4	273	1968	3.3	7	1941	50.9	20 Sept 1980 *T*
125.3	249	1918	5.0	10	2003	50.0	11 Sept 1921 *T*
125.0	249	1927	6.3	13	1997	49.8	15 Sept 1968
115.7	230	1965	6.6	13	1910	43.0	13 Sept 1975 *T*

T after the date of the heaviest fall indicates thunder was heard on that date.

The September months of 1968 and 1974 were the wettest in the Reading record. In September 1968, 70.1 mm fell in two days 14-15th, while in September 1974 six days had daily falls exceeding 10 mm: in all, 79 mm fell in the six days commencing 22 September 1974.

September 1959 saw a prolonged period of summer weather, lasting even into October. This was one of the driest months yet recorded in Reading: less than 1 mm of rain fell, all on 21st.

Daily falls of 25 mm or more of rain occur in about one year in six in September – occasionally more than 50 mm, as on the thundery days of 11 September 1921 (50.0 mm) and 20 September 1980 (50.9 mm). However, the wettest day of any month in the Reading record was 22 September 1992, when 76.3 mm of rain fell in 13 hours, mostly during the evening and overnight.

Figure 12.1 Dusty ploughing at Grazeley, south of Reading, during the very dry September of 2003. Photograph © Stephen Burt

Snowfall

Snowfall has never been reported in September in Reading.

Thunderstorms

Thunder is heard on at least one day in most Septembers. In September 1974 thunder was heard on five days, and in 1976 on six days.

SUNSHINE

The transition from August to September sees a reduction in mean sunshine by more than 90 minutes per day; and on average, two or three September days can be expected to remain sunless.

Table 12.4 September sunshine duration at the University of Reading, 1956-2014 (London Road 1956-1967, Whiteknights 1968-2014).

September mean sunshine duration 138.2 hours, 4.61 hours per day (average 1981-2010)

Possible daylength: 380 hours. Mean sunshine duration as percentage of possible: 36.4

Sunniest months			Dullest months			Sunniest days	
Duration, hours	*Per cent of possible*	*Year*	*Duration, hours*	*Per cent of possible*	*Year*	*Duration, hours*	*Date*
224.6	59.2	1959	85.8	22.6	1993	12.6	2 Sept 1982
203.9	53.7	1964	93.8	24.7	1994	12.0	3 Sept 1977
179.3	47.2	1971	98.7	26.0	1956	12.0	2 Sept 1994
178.3	47.0	2004	105.9	27.9	1984	12.0	4 Sept 2003
177.5	46.8	2003	107.0	28.2	1969	11.9	3 Sept 1976,
							4 Sept 2004,
							7 Sept 2006

September 1959 was an exceptionally sunny month, recording 224.6 hours, 59% of the possible duration. This month saw a spell of six days each with 9.5 hours or more of sunshine from 8-13 September, and notably even the final four days of the month each recorded over 9 hours.

At the opposite extreme, the two consecutive Septembers of 1993 and 1994 were exceptionally dull – more reminiscent of late autumn. Indeed, September 1993's sunshine total has been bettered in two Januarys.

Daylength falls below 12 hours after the autumnal equinox, but 12 hours sunshine is still possible at the beginning of the month: the sunniest September day on record was 2 September 1982, with 12.6 hours. During 1968-2014 only seven September months had sunshine every day, while in 1963 and 2010 September had seven sunless days. The dull September of 1969 had a spell of five consecutive sunless days commencing 12 September, with just 4.7 hours recorded in the preceding five days.

TEMPERATURE, PRECIPITATION AND SUNSHINE IN GRAPHS – SEPTEMBER

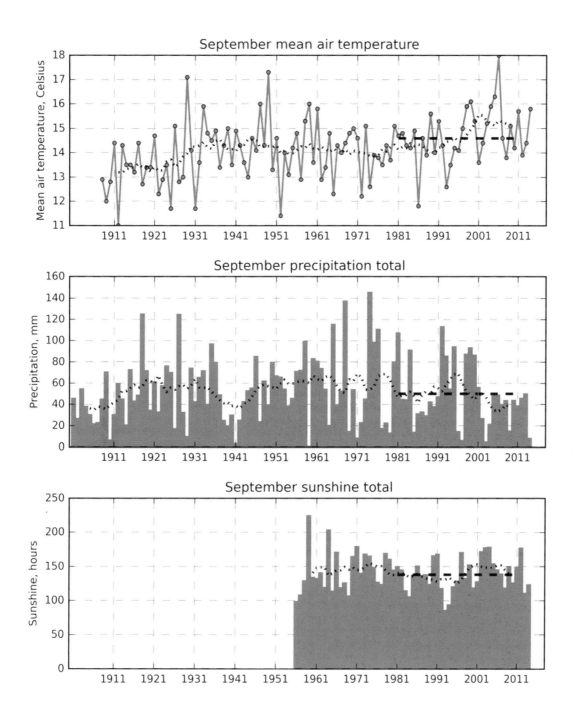

Figure 12.2 *Monthly values of (from top) mean temperature (°C), total precipitation (mm) and sunshine duration (hours) for September at Reading over the available period of record (plots include London Road rainfall records where available 1901-04, with estimates from other Reading stations to 1907 as necessary)*

The mean temperatures as recorded at London Road 1908-67 have been reduced by 0.5 degC to ensure approximate homogeneity with the records from the Whiteknights site, 1968 onwards. No site adjustments have been made for precipitation or sunshine. The 1981-2010 averages are indicated by the thick dashed line, while the 10 year running mean centred on the year shown is indicated by a dashed grey line

13 **October**

October is, on average, the wettest month of the year in Reading, with rainfall almost half as much again as a typical September: three of the six wettest months on the entire record have been Octobers. Although the beginning of the month can still produce summer-like heat, there are further noticeable decreases in both temperature and sunshine duration as the month progresses: the mean daily maximum temperature falls from about 16.5 °C at the start of the month to 13.5 °C by month's end, while mean daily minimum temperatures fall from about 9 °C to 5.5 °C. The first air frost of autumn can normally be expected during the second half, and even the occasional but rare October snowfall. The average temperature for the month as a whole is 11.2 °C. October's mean daily sunshine is more than an hour down on September's, and the percentage of possible is also further reduced from 36% to 32%, indicating increased cloudiness as well as shorter days. October can also produce occasional very severe gales – most notably the 'Great Storm' of 16 October 1987, which produced one of the highest wind gusts on record in Reading.

TEMPERATURE

Temperatures during October in Reading in the period 1908-2014 ranged from 28.2 °C in 1921 to -4.7 °C in 1931.

Early October is still capable of producing remarkably late summer heat: temperatures above 27 °C were recorded in October in 1921 and more recently in 2011. The hottest October days on the record were 28.2 °C on 4 October 1921 (maximum temperatures on 4th, 5th and 6th of that month were 25.7 °C, 28.2 °C and 27.7 °C respectively), and 27.8 °C on 1 October 2011 (followed by 27.0 °C on 2 October). The 1 October 2011 reading is all the more remarkable as it was within half a degree of the hottest day of the year at Whiteknights that year (28.2 °C on 1 August), and it featured in the latest hot spell of the year on record (six consecutive days, each of which reached 25 °C or more) – namely, the six consecutive days commencing 28 September 2011.

Table 13.1 Highest and lowest maximum and minimum temperatures in October, 1908-2014. Records are from the (slightly milder) London Road site 1908-67, and from Whiteknights 1968-2014: no corrections for site differences have been applied.

Rank	Hottest days	Coldest days	Warmest nights	Coldest nights
1	28.2 °C, 5 Oct 1921	4.4 °C, 31 Oct 1934	16.6 °C, 12 Oct 2005	-4.7 °C, 28 Oct 1931
2	27.8 °C, 1 Oct 2011	5.3 °C, 29 Oct 1922	16.5 °C, 4 Oct 2013	-4.6 °C, 19 Oct 1926
3	27.7 °C, 6 Oct 1921	5.6 °C, 30 Oct 1909	16.4 °C, 4 Oct 1921	-4.4 °C, 29 Oct 1997
4	27.0 °C, 2 Oct 2011	5.7 °C, 30 Oct 1974	15.6 °C, 9 Oct 1967, 3 Oct 1985 and 1 Oct 1997	-3.9 °C, 27 Oct 1931 and 30 Oct 1997
5	26.5 °C, 3 Oct 1959	6.2 °C, 28 Oct 1926	15.5 °C, 10 Oct 2011	-3.6 °C, 24 Oct 1926 and 22 Oct 1931

With ground temperatures still high in early October, warm nights are not uncommon – three October nights have remained above 16 °C, the warmest being 12 October 2005 (16.6 °C).

Given the fairly rapid decline in temperatures during October, it is no surprise that the lowest temperatures all occur towards the end of the month. The coldest October day was 31 October 1934, when the maximum temperature reached just 4.4 °C (not until the following January was there a colder day); more recently, at Whiteknights the lowest maximum temperature in October has been 5.7 °C on 30 October 1974. As an indication of the temperature contrasts possible in late October, contrast these chilly days with the maximum temperature of 21.7 °C attained on 31 October 2014, the warmest Halloween day on record and an exceptionally high reading so late in the year.

The first air frost of the winter can normally be expected towards the end of October (the average date for the first air frost of the winter at Whiteknights over the period 1981-2010 was 4 November, but 2-3 weeks earlier than this in Reading's rural surroundings). There were seven air frosts in the Octobers of 1926 and 1931, and six in 1997. Ground frosts are more frequent – averaging eight mornings in October. Since ground frost measurements began in 1920, only October 1945 has been free of ground frost, while in October 1992 19 were recorded at Whiteknights, and 18 in October 2003.

Minimum temperatures occasionally fall below -3 °C in October; the lowest temperatures on record were noted on the mornings of 19 October 1926 (-4.6 °C), 28 October 1931 (-4.7 °C) and 29 October 1997 (-4.4 °C). The reading in 1926 was part of a four-night spell of air frosts, while the cold spell in 1997 ran into early November with air frost on seven out of eight mornings from the 25th.

The largest fall in minimum temperature from one day to the next for any month on the record took place over 15-16 October 1955: the minimum temperature on 15th of 11.0 °C was followed next day by a minimum temperature of -1.7 °C – a day-to-day fall of 12.7 degC.

The largest daily range in temperature during October was 19.9 degC, on 25 October 1951; at Whiteknights since 1968 the largest daily range was 18.7 degC on 7 October 1971. October 1997 features in both the highest and lowest minimum temperatures table for October, namely 15.6 °C on 1st and -3.9 °C on 30th.

Warm and cold months

Allowing for the warmth of the London Road site relative to Whiteknights, the years 1995, 2001 and 2005-6 were the warmest October months in the period 1908-2014 – and October 2011 was also a mild month. October 1919 was the coldest October in the same period – a month with five air frosts. In October 2014 mild conditions continued for much of the month with little sign of the normal seasonal decline in temperature: the remarkable maximum temperature of 21.7 °C attained on 31st has already been commented upon.

The sharp seasonal decline in mean temperatures during the autumn means that no October has ever been warmer than the preceding September, although in both 1986 and 2001 October was only 0.1 degC cooler than September.

Monthly temperature ranges in October have varied between 13.5 degC in 1974 and 29.1 degC in 1977.

Table 13.2 October temperatures at the University of Reading, 1908-2014. In October the London Road site (1908-67) is about 0.3 degC warmer than the Whiteknights site (1968 onwards) due to its location closer to the town centre. The observed mean temperatures at the London Road site (shown in brackets) have been adjusted by this amount to facilitate comparison between the two records.

October mean temperature 11.2°C (average 1981-2010)

Warmest months			Coldest months		
Mean temperature, °C	Departure from 1981-2010 normal degC	Year	Mean temperature, °C	Departure from 1981-2010 normal degC	Year
14.1	+2.9	2006	7.1 (7.4)	-4.1	1919
13.9	+2.7	2005	7.7	-3.5	1974
13.5	+2.3	1995, 2001	8.0 (8.3)	-3.2	1917
13.3	+2.1	2014	8.1 (8.4)	-3.1	1912
13.2 (13.5)	+2.0	1921	8.2 (8.5)	-3.0	1922

PRECIPITATION

October is, on average, the wettest month of the year in Reading, and the monthly average fall is 72 mm. The third week of October is, again on average, the wettest week of the year (see annual plot, Chapter 3), although there is of course much variation from year-to-year.

Table 13.3 October precipitation at the University of Reading, 1901-2014 (London Road 1901-1967, Whiteknights 1968-2014).

October mean precipitation 72.0 mm (average 1981-2010)

Wettest months			Driest months			Wettest days	
Total fall, mm	*Per cent of normal*	*Year*	*Total fall, mm*	*Per cent of normal*	*Year*	*Daily fall, mm*	*Date*
179.6	249	1903	3.8	5	1969	49.3	29 Oct 2000
174.3	241	1960	4.1	6	1978	35.6	16 Oct 1967
165.0	229	1949	10.5	15	1947	33.0	21 Oct 1982
154.5	214	1987	12.9	18	1931	32.0	31 Oct 1915
153.2	212	2000	13.0	18	1950	31.7	9 Oct 1987

The five wettest Octobers since records commenced in 1901 have each received over 150 mm of precipitation, with October 1903 being the wettest of any calendar month on Reading's records. In October 1960, the second-wettest month of any name, 111 mm of the month's total 174 mm fell during the final 13 days of the month – with five days seeing more than 10 mm. In October 1949 117 mm of the month's total 165 mm total fell in the nine days commencing 18 October – also with five days having at least 10 mm.

The two driest Octobers occurred in 1969 and 1978. In October 1969 (3.8 mm total) the wettest day of the month (18th) recorded just 1.3 mm, while in October 1978 (4.1 mm) the wettest day was 17th, with 2.9 mm.

Daily falls of 25 mm or more were recorded on 21 occasions between 1908 and 2014, or about one year in five, and yet only one October day has recorded even as much as 40 mm. That was 29 October 2000, when 49.3 mm of rain fell in 16 hours, much of it overnight. None of the five wettest October days were associated with thunderstorms.

Figure 13.1 The Fox and Horn (now The Cinnamon Tree) in Stratfield Mortimer flooded out on 30 October 2000 following over 50 mm of rainfall locally in about 16 hours. The pub remained shut for flood-related repairs for eight months after this event and was eventually sold. Photograph © Stephen Burt

October 1906 (at Forbury Gardens) and October 1916 (at London Road) both recorded 27 days with 0.2 mm or more of precipitation during the month – the highest frequency of rainfall for any month except December 1934, which had 30 such days at London Road (October 1903 also recorded 30 rain days at Forbury Gardens).

Snowfall and lying snow

Snow or sleet is very rare in October; snow or sleet has been recorded on only 11 days in all since 1908 (in six Octobers — 1921, 1922, 1933, 1934, 1941 and 2008). In October 1922 there were four days with snow falling (28th-31st). The earliest dates when *sleet* has been observed have been 15 October 1934 (when sleet fell 2-3 pm, the observation confirmed by local observations from Ascot and Warfield) and 23 October 1921. The earliest date with *snow* observed to fall was 27 October, in 1933. In 2008, heavy snow fell during the evening on 28 October (rainfall equivalent 14.5 mm during the day), resulting in a 1 cm cover the following morning (Figure 13.2) – the earliest occurrence of a winter snow cover at 0900 GMT on local records since 1880, and the only instance of a morning snow cover in October on the university record. The previous instance of snow cover was on 6 April that year – making 2008 the shortest 'snow-free' season on the record, just 6 months and 22 days between mornings with snow cover.

Figure 13.2 Lying snowfall in October – the first in the Reading area since 1880: Stratfield Mortimer, on the morning of 29 October 2008. Photograph © Stephen Burt

SUNSHINE

October averages 107 hours of sunshine at Whiteknights, a decline of more than an hour a day on September, and only 32% of the possible. On average, five days remain sunless during October.

The Octobers of 1997 and 1999 were the sunniest on record, while 1976 (following a memorable summer) was unusually dull with a sunshine duration more typical of a winter month.

The reduction in daylength during October means that 10 hours of sunshine in a day is possible only at the beginning of the month, and this has occurred on four October days since sunshine records began in Reading – the sunniest being 1 October 1973 with 10.3 hours. In October 1972, four days received 9.5 hours or more (including the 3rd-5th).

A typical October will see around five sunless days, although in 1973 there were ten (ironically, the first day of that month was the sunniest October day on record). In October 2012, there were five consecutive sunless days commencing 21 October; spells of four consecutive sunless days in October occurred on six other occasions between 1956 and 2014.

Table 13.4 October sunshine duration at the University of Reading, 1956-2014 (London Road 1956-1967, Whiteknights 1968-2014).

October mean sunshine duration 106.6 hours, 3.44 hours per day (average 1981-2010)

Possible daylength: 331 hours. Mean sunshine duration as percentage of possible: 32.2

Sunniest months			Dullest months			Sunniest days	
Duration, hours	*Per cent of possible*	*Year*	*Duration, hours*	*Per cent of possible*	*Year*	*Duration, hours*	*Date*
162.0	48.9	1999	58.2	17.6	1976	10.3	1 Oct 1973
154.1	46.5	1997	65.2	19.7	1982	10.2	4 Oct 1957
149.4	45.1	1971	72.4	21.9	1966	10.2	2 Oct 1997
143.8	43.4	2003	73.7	22.2	1968	10.0	4 Oct 1994
140.3	42.4	2011	75.7	22.9	1960	9.9	5 Oct 1972, 7 Oct 1975 and 6 Oct 1999

THE 'GREAT STORM' OF OCTOBER 1987

The 'Great Storm' of 16 October 1987 caused immense damage and disruption across much of southern England. Hundreds of trees (most were still in leaf), probably thousands, were felled or badly damaged around Reading, although there were few injuries as the worst part of the storm occurred during the early hours of the morning, and thus before the roads had a chance to fill with traffic. However, several people had narrow escapes as trees fell on to their houses – including two families in Caversham. The strongest wind gust recorded at the university during this storm – and the highest on record for October – was 67 knots (77 mph). Two years later, a storm on 21 October 1989 gave a gust of 56 knots (64 mph). A lesser storm on 28 October 2013 brought down some trees, although the highest gust on that occasion was only 41 knots (47 mph) – the so-called 'St Jude's Storm'.

Figure 13.3 The Street in Mortimer Common blocked by fallen trees on the morning of Friday 16 October 1987 – the 'Great Storm'. Photograph © Stephen Burt

TEMPERATURE, PRECIPITATION AND SUNSHINE IN GRAPHS – OCTOBER

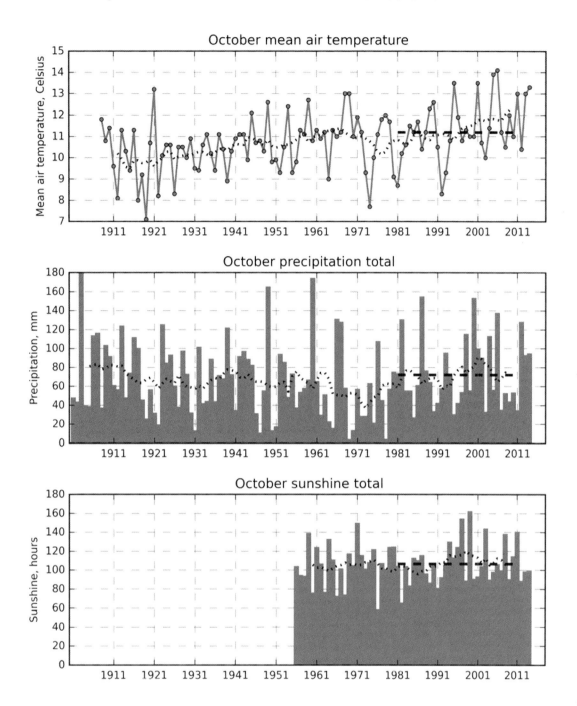

Figure 13.4 *Monthly values of (from top) mean temperature (°C), total precipitation (mm) and sunshine duration (hours) for October at Reading over the available period of record (plots include London Road rainfall records where available 1901-04, with estimates from other Reading stations to 1907 as necessary)*

The mean temperatures as recorded at London Road 1908-67 have been reduced by 0.3 degC to ensure approximate homogeneity with the records from the Whiteknights site, 1968 onwards. No site adjustments have been made for precipitation or sunshine. The 1981-2010 averages are indicated by the thick dashed line, while the 10 year running mean centred on the year shown is indicated by a dashed grey line

14 **November**

The rapid decline in temperatures at this time of year, together with normally-abundant moisture following on from October's rainfall and the migration of the time of sunrise towards the morning rush hour, means that foggy mornings become particularly evident in November. However, the decrease in air pollution since the introduction of the Clean Air Act in 1956 has dramatically reduced both the frequency of fogs and their thickness in recent decades.

Warm summer-like days are very rare in November, although 18 °C has occurred on a few occasions, while nights towards the end of the month can occasionally drop below -5 °C. Precipitation – usually rain, but very occasionally snow - occurs on about one day in two in a typical November. Although amounts are on average slightly less than in October, four of the ten wettest months on the record have been Novembers. Sunshine duration continues its seasonal decline, to average a little over two hours daily; around nine of November's 30 days are likely to remain sunless.

TEMPERATURE

Average daytime maximum temperatures continue their seasonal decline throughout November, falling from a little above 13 °C at the beginning of the month to 9 °C at the close of the month, while average night minimum temperatures follow a slightly more irregular pattern from 5-6 °C at the beginning to below 3 °C during the final week of the month. The average temperature for the month is 7.5 °C.

Although a maximum temperature of 21.7 °C was reached on the last day of October in 2014, only one November day has ever surpassed 20 °C – that was on 5 November 1938, when 20.4 °C was recorded at the London Road site (part of a four-day spell commencing 4th, in which the temperature remained above 10 °C throughout). Other warm November days included 4 and 5 November 1946, when the temperature reached 18.2 °C and 18.7 °C respectively, while more recently 18.1 °C was reached at Whiteknights on 4 November 2010. During the first five days of November 2010, the maximum temperature was never lower than 14 °C while three nights had minimum temperatures of 12 °C or above.

Table 14.1 Highest and lowest maximum and minimum temperatures in November, 1908-2014. Records are from the (slightly milder) London Road site 1908-67, and from Whiteknights 1968-2014: no corrections for site differences have been applied.

Rank	Warmest days	Coldest days	Mildest nights	Coldest nights
1	20.4 °C, 5 Nov 1938	-1.9 °C, 25 Nov 1923	14.2 °C, 3 Nov 1996	-8.3 °C, 23 Nov 1983
2	18.7 °C, 5 Nov 1946	-1.8 °C, 26 Nov 1923	14.0 °C, 5 Nov 2010	-6.7 °C, 26 Nov 1923 and 27 Nov 1923
3	18.2 °C, 4 Nov 1946	-0.1 °C, 28 Nov 2010	13.8 °C, 5 Nov 1938	-6.4 °C, 24 Nov 1983 and 26 Nov 1989
4	18.1 °C, 4 Nov 2010	0.1 °C, 23 Nov 1993	13.7 °C, 20 Nov 1994	-6.2 °C, 17 Nov 1930
5	17.9 °C, 1 Nov 1984	0.2 °C, 22 Nov 1956	13.4 °C, 12 Nov 1947	-5.8 °C, 27 Nov 1915, 28 Nov 1915 and 28 Nov 2010

November nights can also be very mild, although these are much more likely at the beginning of the month than at the end. November nights milder than the average for midsummer have occurred on numerous occasions; the mildest November nights on record were 3 November 1996, when the minimum temperature was 14.2 °C, and 5 November 2010, at 14.0 °C.

As the days become shorter with the approach of the winter solstice, fog becomes more prevalent and can be slow to clear. Occasionally, maximum temperatures in November fail to rise above 0 °C, and often this is because the weak winter Sun fails to clear overnight freezing fog. The coldest November days on the record were 25 and 26 November 1923, when the maximum temperatures were -1.9 °C and -1.8°C respectively – both days were very foggy and followed by very cold nights. More recently, the maximum temperature on 28 November 2010 reached only -0.1 °C in a spell of cold northerly winds, despite 3 hours sunshine.

During 1981-2010 the average date of the first autumn air frost was 4 November (median date 3 November). The winter season began suddenly in 1985 – the first air frost of the season that year came in at -5.0 °C (grass minimum temperature -11.0 °C) on 3 November, while in 1978 the first air frost did not arrive until 27 November, but was similarly sharp at -4.2 °C (grass minimum temperature -12.7 °C).

Since 1968 there have been seven Novembers without an air frost at Whiteknights; previously there had only been two air frost-free November months at London Road in the 60 years to 1967, suggesting that November months have become milder. Ground frosts have occurred in every November since grass minimum temperatures were first recorded in 1920, although in 1946 and 2011 there were only two. In November 1910 there were 18 air frosts, 16 in November 1915 and 15 in November 1923 – the three frostiest Novembers in the entire record, while 26 ground frosts occurred in November 1923 and 23 in November 1969.

A minimum temperature of -5 °C or lower can be expected in slightly less than one November in five. The lowest November minimum was -8.3 °C, logged on 23 November 1983, while the next coldest occurred sixty years previously, namely -6.7 ° on both 26 and 27 November 1923 – following the two coldest November days on record (see above).

The coldest night of the calendar year has been recorded in November eight times since 1908: in 1915, 1921, 1923, 1930, 1937,1983, 1988, and 1989.

The second-largest rise in maximum temperature from one day to the next for any month on the record took place over 26-27 November 1950: the maximum temperature on 26th of 1.8 °C was followed next day by a maximum temperature of 13.1 °C – a day-to-day increase of 11.3 degC.

The largest daily temperature ranges recorded in November have been 19.4 degC on 24 November 1983 and 17.5 degC on 11 November 1908. Unique in the records for *any* month, November 2010 features in all four of the daily temperature record tables – the maximum temperature varying from 18.1 °C on 4th to -0.1 °C on 28th, the minimum from 14.0 °C on 5th to -5.8 °C, also on 28th.

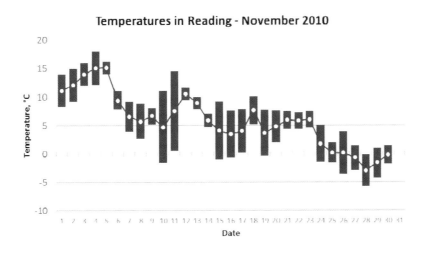

Figure 14.1 Daily maximum and minimum temperatures (top and bottom of daily columns) and daily mean temperature (central circle and connecting line) at the University of Reading in November 2010, the only month on record with entries in all four highest and lowest maximum and minimum temperatures – see text for details. The cold weather at the end of the month ushered in the extremely cold month of December 2010

Warm and cold months

The Novembers of 1910, 1915 and 1923 were the coldest on record, even allowing for the fact the London Road site is a little milder on average than Whiteknights. When it is considered that four of the five coldest Novembers occurred between 1910 and 1952, and only one of the five has occurred since 1968 at the Whiteknights site, November appears to have become a lot milder in recent decades. At the other end of the temperature scale, the mildness of the Novembers of 1994 and 2011 at Whiteknights is also remarkable.

In 1939, November's mean temperature was 0.2 degC above October's; this is the only time on the record that November has been milder than October.

Monthly temperature ranges in November have ranged from 12.8 degC in 1974 and 13.6 degC in 1958, to 24.5 degC in 1983 and 23.9 degC in 2010.

Table 14.2 November temperatures at the University of Reading, 1908-2014. In November the London Road site (1908-67) is about 0.4 degC warmer than the Whiteknights site (1968 onwards) due to its location closer to the town centre. The observed mean temperatures at the London Road site (shown in brackets) have been adjusted by this amount to facilitate comparison between the two records.

November mean temperature 7.5°C (average 1981-2010)

Mildest months			Coldest months		
Mean temperature, °C	Departure from 1981-2010 normal, degC	Year	Mean temperature, °C	Departure from 1981-2010 normal, degC	Year
10.7	+3.2	1994	2.8 (3.2)	-4.7	1910, 1915, 1923
10.1	+2.6	2011	3.4 (3.8)	-3.1	1919
9.4 (9.8)	+1.9	1938	4.0 (4.4)	-3.5	1921
9.4	+1.9	2009	4.1 (4.5)	-3.4	1925, 1952
9.2	+1.7	2002	4.4	-3.1	1985

PRECIPITATION

The monthly mean rainfall for November in Reading is 66 mm. Rain can be expected on about one day in two.

Table 14.3 November precipitation at the University of Reading, 1901-2014 (London Road 1901-1967, Whiteknights 1968-2014).

November mean precipitation 66.1 mm (average 1981-2010)

Wettest months			Driest months			Wettest days	
Total fall, mm	Per cent of normal	Year	Total fall, mm	Per cent of normal	Year	Daily fall, mm	Date
169.0	255	1951	4.7	7	1945	38.4	5 Nov 1951
167.0	252	1929	11.2	17	1901	30.2	13 Nov 1940
163.0	246	1970	14.7	22	1909	30.0	17 Nov 1974
158.7	239	1940	14.9	22	1917	29.5	3 Nov 1940
143.5	216	1974	15.9	24	1956	28.7	22 Nov 2003

November is a consistently wet month – for only once since the record commenced in 1908 has less than 10 mm been recorded, and that was back in 1945 when just 4.7 mm of precipitation fell, less than half of the amount recorded in the next-driest November (1901, 11.2 mm). In contrast, a monthly total of 150 mm or more has occurred four times in the same period, the wettest being 169 mm in November 1951. Almost all of this fell in the first 24 days of the month – a spell that gave in excess of 10 mm on five days, including the wettest November day on record (38.4 mm on 5 November 1951). Daily falls of 25 mm in November or more occur less than once per decade on average, and only two other November days have recorded 30 mm or more since 1908. Two of the five wettest November days occurred just ten days apart in 1940.

Snowfall and lying snow

Snowfall is uncommon in November – only about one November in three sees any snow or sleet, although in 1919 there were six days. Since 1969, no November has seen snowfall on more than three days.

Lying snow at 0900 GMT is very rare in November in Reading, and has occurred just twice in 99 years of records – on 9 November 1921 (depth unknown) and 30 November 2010 (depth 2 cm).

SUNSHINE

November is much less sunny than October, owing to greater cloudiness (average 74 per cent at 0900 GMT, compared with 70 per cent in October) and sharply reduced daylength (almost 20 per cent less daylight hours). The combination reduces the monthly average duration of bright sunshine to 63 hours, or around 2 hours and 7 minutes daily, 23.7 percent of possible (down from October's 32.2 per cent). There are, however, large variations from year-to-year.

Table 14.4 November sunshine duration at the University of Reading, 1956-2014 (London Road 1956-1967, Whiteknights 1968-2014).

November mean sunshine duration 63.1 hours, 2.11 hours per day (average 1981-2010)

Possible daylength: 267 hours. Mean sunshine duration as percentage of possible: 23.7

Sunniest months			Dullest months			Sunniest days	
Duration, hours	Per cent of possible	Year	Duration, hours	Per cent of possible	Year	Duration, hours	Date
107.0	40.0	1971	32.6	12.2	1962	8.5	5 Nov 1970
96.9	36.3	1977	34.6	12.9	1994	8.4	10 Nov 1979
95.6	35.8	1989	38.2	14.3	2014	8.3	1 Nov 1969
90.4	33.8	1965	41.6	15.6	1987	8.3	6 Nov 1973
89.9	33.6	1973	42.7	16.0	1983	8.2	11 Nov 1973 and 6 Nov 1986

The sunniest November was in 1971, with 107 hours of bright sunshine, and the dullest 1962, with less than 33 hours – a factor of three different. Despite the association of November with foggy conditions, in both the two dullest Novembers (1962 and 1994) there were only three mornings with fog at 0900 GMT.

The low total of 38 hours in November 2014 may possibly be partly due to the fact that much of the sunshine that month occurred in spells either at the beginning or end of the day. It is known that since 1997 nearby tree growth has reduced sunshine totals at either end of the day in winter – in 2014 the sunshine measured by another sensor in the enclosure was 20% higher, at 46.5 hours, while only 10 km distant at Stratfield Mortimer the sunshine total for that month was just under 62 hours, 60 per cent greater.

The duration of daylight during November in Reading decreases from 9.69 hours on the first day of the month to 8.24 hours on the last, an average decrease of just under 3 minutes per day. The sunniest November days at the beginning of the month can record a little over 8 hours sunshine, and this has been recorded on 13 November days during the period 1956 to 2014, the sunniest being 5 November 1970, with 8.5 hours. During the 12 days 3-14 November 1971, four days reached or exceeded 8 hours sunshine - helping to make that month the sunniest November on record.

On average, about nine November days remain sunless, although both 1977 and 2006 were fortunate in seeing only two; this compares to 17 sunless days in the Novembers of 1962 and 1994, and 16 in 1968. November 1958 recorded 15 sunless days, including a long dull spell of 13 consecutive days commencing 17 November.

TEMPERATURE, PRECIPITATION AND SUNSHINE IN GRAPHS – NOVEMBER

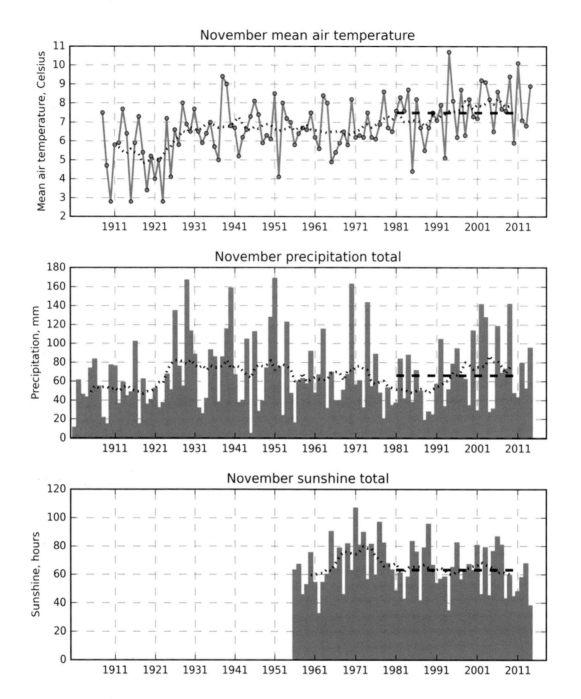

Figure 14.2 *Monthly values of (from top) mean temperature (°C), total precipitation (mm) and sunshine duration (hours) for November at Reading over the available period of record (plots include London Road rainfall records where available 1901-04, with estimates from other Reading stations to 1907 as necessary)*

The mean temperatures as recorded at London Road 1908-67 have been reduced by 0.4 degC to ensure approximate homogeneity with the records from the Whiteknights site, 1968 onwards. No site adjustments have been made for precipitation or sunshine. The 1981-2010 averages are indicated by the thick dashed line, while the 10 year running mean centred on the year shown is indicated by a dashed grey line

15 **December**

December has the unenviable distinction of being, on average, the dullest month of the year, with a daily quota of just under 90 minutes daily: in a typical December, almost half of the month's days will remain sunless. Temperatures continue to fall during the month, but more slowly as the winter solstice is reached. December is, on average, less wet than October or November, and rain can be expected on almost one day in two: the first snowfalls of winter normally occur in December.

TEMPERATURE

Average daytime temperatures range from above 9 °C during the first week to below 7 °C during the final week, while average night minimum temperatures are more variable, from 3-4 °C early in the month to below 2 °C from mid-month. The average temperature for the month is 5.0 °C.

The highest December temperatures are normally reached in deep, mild south-westerly airstreams, which can bring very mild conditions irrespective of the time of day. Temperatures have reached 15 °C three times in December, and minimum temperatures have exceeded 12 °C twice, since 1908. The highest December temperature attained was 15.8 °C at Whiteknights on 2 December 1985; this temperature was reached in the late evening, well after sunset. On Boxing Day in 1911, 15.1 °C was recorded at London Road, while in December 1931, the temperature exceeded 13 °C on each of three consecutive days, including 15.4 °C on 4 December. In December 1994, 14 °C was reached on three consecutive days 10-12th, the highest being 14.8 °C on 10th.

Table 15.1 Highest and lowest maximum and minimum temperatures in December, 1908-2014. Records are from the (slightly milder) London Road site 1908-67, and from Whiteknights 1968-2014: no corrections for site differences have been applied.

Rank	Mildest days	Coldest days	Mildest nights	Coldest nights
1	15.8 °C, 2 Dec 1985	-5.0 °C, 29 Dec 1908	12.4 °C, 3 Dec 1985	-13.4 °C, 13 Dec 1981
2	15.4 °C, 4 Dec 1931	-3.1 °C, 28 Dec 1908	12.0 °C, 5 Dec 1986 and 28 Dec 1994	-12.8 °C, 30 Dec 1908
3	15.1 °C, 26 Dec 1911	-2.8 °C, 20 Dec 1938	11.9 °C, 15 Dec 1998	-11.9 °C, 31 Dec 1908
4	14.8 °C, 10 Dec 1994	-2.3 °C, 19 Dec 1938 and 6 Dec 1962	11.8 °C, 14 Dec 1918	-9.8 °C, 14 Dec 1981
5	14.6 °C, 5 Dec 1979, 12 Dec 1994, 6 Dec 2007	-2.2 °C, 31 Dec 1978	11.7 °C, 11 Dec 1961, 12 Dec 1961, 23 Dec 1991, 12 Dec 2000	-9.4 °C, 20 Dec 2010

Minimum temperatures above 10 °C in December are not particularly uncommon - about one December in two will see at least one 24 hour period remaining at or above this level. The mildest December night followed the record December temperature reached late on 2 December 1985, when the minimum temperature was 12.4 °C: this was the second of four consecutive nights that remained above 10 °C.

Between 1908 and 2014, 19 Decembers (35 occasions in total) recorded at least one day when the maximum temperature failed to reach 0 °C: there were five such days in December 1981 and four in the Decembers of 1927 and 1962. The two coldest December days occurred in the first year of the record: on 28 December 1908 the maximum temperature was only -3.1 °C, followed by -5.0 °C the following day. Maximum temperatures for the three days 18-20 December 1938 were a bitter -1.5 °C, -2.3 °C and -2.8 °C respectively, in a bitter easterly wind. A spell of persistent fog in early December 1962 saw maximum temperatures of -1.7 °C, -1.1 °C and -2.3 °C from 4th to 6th, respectively. The coldest December days at the Whiteknights site since 1968 have been 31 December 1978 (maximum temperature -2.2 °C, with the next day also remaining below 0 °C) and 14 December 1991 (-2.0 °C). A spell of four consecutive 'ice days' commenced on 31 December 1996, which briefly saw the River Thames freeze over at Pangbourne.

Minimum temperatures of -10 °C have been recorded on 26 occasions in Reading since 1908, but only three of these have been in December. The coldest December night was 13 December 1981, which fell to -13.4 °C, by more than a fortnight the earliest date in the winter on which -10°C has been reached and the equal second-coldest night on the entire record. Snow lay 14 cm deep that morning, following heavy snowfalls in previous days. Aside from December 1981, the coldest December nights are dominated by the cold spell late in 1908 (-12.8 °C on 30 December and -11.9 °C on 31 December) and the cold December of 2010 (minimum temperature -9.4 °C on 20th).

The largest rise in maximum temperature from one day to the next for any month on the record took place 6-7 December 1962: the maximum temperature on 6th of -2.3 °C in freezing fog was followed next day by a maximum temperature of 9.4 °C – a day-to-day increase of 11.7 degC. Similarly, the largest rise in minimum temperature from one day to the next for any month on the record took place during 22-23 December 1909: the minimum temperature on 22nd of -5.0 °C was followed next day by a minimum temperature of 9.6 °C – a day-to-day rise of 14.6 degC. This latter is also the greatest change in any temperature extreme from one day to the next on the record.

The largest daily temperature ranges during the month have been 18.2 degC on 13 December 1981 (the coldest December night was followed by a maximum of 4.8 °C) and 17.5 degC on 29 December 1964.

Mild and cold months

Table 15.2 December temperatures at the University of Reading, 1908-2014. In December the London Road site (1908-67) is about 0.4 degC milder than the Whiteknights site (1968 onwards) due to its location closer to the town centre. The observed mean temperatures at the London Road site (shown in brackets) have been adjusted by this amount to facilitate comparison between the two records.

December mean temperature 5.0°C (average 1981-2010)

Mildest months			Coldest months		
Mean temperature, °C	*Departure from 1981-2010 normal degC*	*Year*	*Mean temperature, °C*	*Departure from 1981-2010 normal degC*	*Year*
8.1	+3.1	1974	0.7	-4.3	2010
8.1 (8.5)	+3.1	1934	0.8	-4.2	1981
7.6	+2.6	1988	1.2 (1.6)	-3.8	1933
7.2	+2.2	1985	1.3 (1.7)	-3.7	1916
7.1 (7.5)	+2.1	1953	1.3 (1.7)	-3.7	1950

The Decembers of 1981 and 2010 were significantly colder than any other on the record. December 1981 was particularly cold in the second week, remarkably early for severe cold in the winter. December 2010 was the coldest December locally since 1890: the month's highest temperature was just 8.5 °C, and there were 24 mornings with air frost.

December 1934 and 1974 tie as the mildest Decembers on the Reading record. In both Decembers only a single air frost was recorded, while the coldest day reached at least 5 °C. Remarkably, December 1974 (with a mean temperature of 8.1 °C, tying as the mildest December on the record) was milder than both the preceding *October* (mean temperature 7.7 °C, the second-coldest on record) *and November* (mean temperature 7.5 °C). In December 2002 the minimum temperature for the month was just -0.1 °C; the previous year saw 22 air frosts. In December 1933 there were 28 ground frosts, while four December months have recorded 27.

It is not uncommon for December to be a milder month than November – since 1908, this has occurred on almost 20 occasions. In 1910, December was 3.2 degC milder than November.

Monthly temperature ranges in December have varied from 12.1 degC in 1922 and 12.7 degC in 1933, to 24.9 degC in 1908 and 23.1 degC in 1981.

PRECIPITATION

The monthly mean rainfall for December in Reading is 63 mm, falling on around 15 days.

Although only the third-wettest month of the year (after October and November), December is rarely dry – only two Decembers have received less than 20 per cent of normal rainfall since records began in 1908: the driest was December 1988, with just 9.9 mm or 16 per cent of normal (and 7.0 mm of this fell on one day - 3rd). In contrast, monthly totals in excess of 150 mm have occurred three times. Parts of Reading along the Thames were flooded as a result of the wet December of 1914. December 1934 was by some margin the wettest December on record in Reading with 165 mm of precipitation: five days received 10 mm or more precipitation, while 0.2 mm or more fell on 30 of the month's 31 days – the highest number of rain days yet recorded in any calendar month on the entire record.

Table 15.3 December precipitation at the University of Reading, 1901-2014 (London Road 1901-1967, Whiteknights 1968-2014).

December mean precipitation 63.0 mm (average 1981-2010)

Wettest months			Driest months			Wettest days	
Total fall,	*Per cent of*		*Total fall,*	*Per cent of*		*Daily fall,*	
mm	*normal*	*Year*	*mm*	*normal*	*Year*	*mm*	*Date*
165.4	263	1934	9.9	16	1988	43.2	8 Dec 1954
151.2	240	1914	10.5	17	1926	35.8	20 Dec 1989
150.7	239	1989	12.3	20	1991	33.5	1 Dec 1919
145.2	230	1911	13.2	21	1933	31.3	19 Dec 1995
141.3	224	1929	14.3	23	1953	29.0	23 Dec 2013

Daily falls of 25 mm or more in December can be expected a little more often than once per decade. The wettest December days were 8 December 1954 (43.2 mm) and 20 December 1989 (35.8 mm). Unusually for December, thunderstorms were reported on both days. In December 1989, the first ten days of the month remained dry, while the second ten days saw 129 mm fall, including the second-highest December daily fall on record. More recently, 29.0 mm fell on 23 December 2013, the first of a number of very wet days during the exceptionally wet winter of 2013/14.

Figure 15.1 Flooding on the Foudry Brook at the Tun Bridge in Stratfield Mortimer on 20 December 1989, following two weeks of heavy rainfall. Photograph © Stephen Burt

Snowfall and lying snow

An average December will see two days with snow falling, although there are wide variations from year-to-year – about one in three Decembers are snowless, and many snowfalls in December are slight. The Decembers of 1950 and 1969 each had 11 days with snow observed to fall, and December 1981 nine.

The arithmetic mean number of days with lying snow is very skewed towards the occasional snowy month. Although two in three Decembers do not experience any snow cover (i.e. at least 50 per cent lying snow at 0900 GMT), the average is 1.8 mornings with snow lying. How does this come about? In December 1981 there with 15 mornings with snow cover, in December 2009 nine, and December 2010 12 mornings. These three Decembers alone account for 36 mornings with snow cover. When averaged over 30 years, these three account for 1.2 mornings of snow cover per year (36/30) - two-thirds of the average 1.8 mornings with snow lying over the 1981-2010 period.

Figure 15.2 Snowdrifts on the A340 between Theale and Pangbourne, following the Boxing Day snowstorm of 1927. (Reading Central Library, image 1399 881)

December 1981 and January 1982 had spells of heavy, disruptive snow and low temperatures. On 8 December snow began in Reading around 0700 GMT, and was 7 cm deep at Whiteknights at 0900 GMT. Another heavy fall on 11 December increased the level depth to 15 cm. Travel was disrupted during the week and diesel froze in lorry tanks as the temperature fell to -13.4 °C on 13 December (see above). Further snow fell just before Christmas and lay for a few days; after a mild spell over New Year further snowfall in January led to more severe conditions.

The greatest snow depths at 0900 GMT in December have been 15 cm, 18 cm and 14 cm on 11, 12 and 13 December 1981, respectively, and 21 cm and 22 cm on 30 and 31 December 1962. The latter event marked the beginning of the bitter winter of 1962/63.

Thunderstorms
Thunder is quite rare in December, with less than 20 occurrences since 1908. In the Decembers of 1919, 1959 and 1989 thunder was heard on two days (in 1959 those two days were Christmas Day and Boxing Day: thunder was also heard on Christmas Day in 1947).

SUNSHINE
December has the unenviable distinction of being, on average, the dullest month of the year, with a daily quota of just under 90 minutes. The short measure is a result of the combination of short daylight hours (the shortest day of the year, the winter solstice on 21 December, sees just 7.84 hours of daylight) and high average cloud amounts – over the period 1981-2010, December had the highest mean cloud amount at 0900 GMT (6.1 oktas or 76% cover – a smidgeon ahead of January's 75% average) and the lowest percentage of possible sunshine in any month – less than one hour in five seeing sunshine.

Table 15.4 December sunshine duration at the University of Reading, 1956-2014 (London Road 1956-1967, Whiteknights 1968-2014).

December mean sunshine duration 46.1 hours, 1.49 hours per day (average 1981-2010)

Possible daylength: 246 hours. Mean sunshine duration as percentage of possible: 18.7

Sunniest months			Dullest months			Sunniest days	
Duration, hours	*Per cent of possible*	*Year*	*Duration, hours*	*Per cent of possible*	*Year*	*Duration, hours*	*Date*
74.6	30.3	2001	7.8	3.2	1956	7.1	3 Dec 1976
73.3	29.8	1962	13.4	5.4	2010	7.1	4 Dec 1976
72.5	29.5	1961	21.8	8.9	1998	7.0	5 Dec 1976
69.6	28.3	1967	25.3	10.3	1969	6.9	2 Dec 1961
67.1	27.3	1976	27.2	11.1	1958	6.9	9 Dec 1973, 31 Dec 1973 and 20 Dec 1986

December is also the month when year-to-year variations in sunshine are at their most pronounced. Since sunshine records commenced in 1956, December's sunshine total has varied by almost a factor of ten – from less than 8 hours in 1956 (only 3% of possible, and the dullest of any month on the record), and 13 hours in the very cold and cloudy 2010, to almost 75 hours in 2001. Only three days saw more than an hour of sunshine during December 1956, the sunniest day (29th) a mere 3.0 hours; 24 days remained sunless. The shortfall was due to general cloudiness and frequent winds from the south-west; there were only six days with fog reported at 0900 GMT that month.

It is rare for any day in December to receive more than 6.5 hours of bright sunshine, and 7.0 hours or more has been recorded only three times – on three consecutive days in December 1976. The daily total amounted to 7.1 hours on both 3 and 4 December that year, while 5 December added a further 7.0 hours. These three days accounted for about one-third of the month's total sunshine.

In a typical December, 13 days will remain sunless – almost one day in two. In December 1956 there were 24 sunless days (the highest such frequency for any month on the record), and in the Decembers of 1968 and 1998 there were 20, but in the sunny December of 2001 there were only six.

Between 1956 and 2014 there were nine spells of at least seven consecutive sunless days in December, the longest such spells being one of 13 days commencing 3 December 1968, and ten days commencing 12 December 1956.

Although December is, on average, the dullest month of the year, occasionally it has been sunnier than November. Between 1956 and 2014, this happened eight times, the most extreme example being in 1962, when December (73.3 hours) had more than twice as much sunshine as November (32.6 hours).

GALES

The strongest wind gusts on record during December have been those of 17 December 1989 (59 knots, 68 mph) and 9 December 1993 and 24 December 2013 (both 58 knots, 67 mph). The windy conditions either side of midnight on 23-24 December 2013 led to widespread Christmas travel disruption in Reading and beyond, and were exacerbated by widespread flooding resulting from heavy and prolonged rainfall - in Reading 29.0 mm of rain accompanied the near-gale.

TEMPERATURE, PRECIPITATION AND SUNSHINE IN GRAPHS – DECEMBER

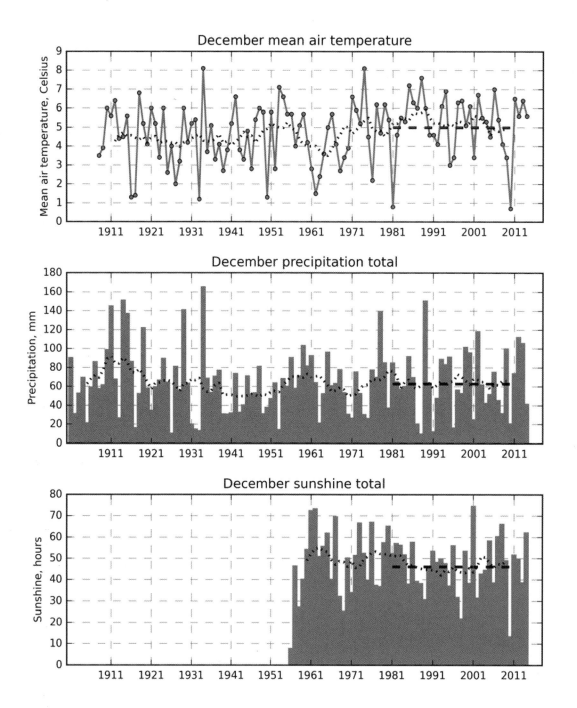

Figure 15.3 *Monthly values of (from top) mean temperature (°C), total precipitation (mm) and sunshine duration (hours) for December at Reading over the available period of record (plots include London Road rainfall records where available 1901-04, with estimates from other Reading stations to 1907 as necessary)*

The mean temperatures as recorded at London Road 1908-67 have been reduced by 0.4 degC to ensure approximate homogeneity with the records from the Whiteknights site, 1968 onwards. No site adjustments have been made for precipitation or sunshine. The 1981-2010 averages are indicated by the thick dashed line, while the 10 year running mean centred on the year shown is indicated by a dashed grey line

16 Annual

Located as it is in the Thames Valley in southern England, Reading has a fairly equitable climate with few extremes of weather (see Chapter 1). It is one of the warmest parts of the British Isles, with the nearby continent providing the potential for heatwaves in summer but also occasionally very cold spells in winter. Reading lies in one of the driest parts of the country – but can still be subjected to prolonged falls of frontal rainfall in autumn or winter, or intense thundery downpours in summer. Snowfall amounts tend to be small while ground frost can occur in any month of the year. Sunshine amounts in the summer averages out to something over six hours daily.

TEMPERATURE

Since 1908, air temperatures in Reading have ranged from -14.5 °C (on 14 January 1982) to 36.4 °C (on 10 August 2003). The ten highest and lowest daily maximum, minimum and mean air temperatures are listed in Chapter 22, 'Top ten extremes'; more details on these events can be found in the monthly sections.

The largest daily temperature ranges recorded were 22.8 degC on 7 September 1911 and 22.7 degC on 28 March 2012 (Table 22.6 in Chapter 22).

There were several years when the highest temperature of the year was not recorded during the three summer months: the highest temperature of the year occurred in May in 1920, 1922, 1944, 1965 and 1978, and in September in 1929 and 1954. The lowest temperature of the calendar year was recorded outside of the three winter months 17 times between 1908 and 2014; in 1990 the lowest temperature occurred in April, while March and November each had the lowest temperature in eight years during this period.

Over the available period of record, annual mean temperatures in Reading have varied between 11.8 °C (in 2006) and 8.6 °C (in 1917), a range of 3.2 degC. The five warmest and five coldest years are shown in Table 16.1.

Mild and cold years

Table 16.1 Mean annual temperatures at the University of Reading, 1908-2014. Averaged over the year as a whole, the London Road site (1908-67) is about 0.5 degC milder than the Whiteknights site (1968 onwards) due to its location closer to the town centre. The observed mean temperatures at the London Road site (shown in brackets) have been adjusted by this amount to facilitate comparison between the two records.

Annual mean temperature 10.6°C (average 1981-2010)

Warmest years			Coldest years		
Mean temperature, °C	*Departure from 1981-2010 normal degC*	*Year*	*Mean temperature, °C*	*Departure from 1981-2010 normal degC*	*Year*
11.8	+1.2	2006	8.6 (9.1)	-2.0	1917
11.6	+1.0	2014	8.7 (9.2)	-1.9	1909, 1919, 1963
11.5	+0.9	2011	8.8 (9.3)	-1.8	1922, 1962
11.4	+0.8	1990	9.2	-1.4	1979
11.4	+0.8	2003	9.4	-1.2	1985, 1986

Warm days and nights

Table 16.2 shows the annual variation in the number of hot days (25 °C or more) and heatwave days (30 °C or more) during 1918-2014[*]; while 1947 had by far the largest number of hot days, 1976 was a hot summer due to a 14 day period in June-July when 30 °C was reached every day.

The greatest number of heatwave days in a month (eight days) occurred in July 1921, July 1976 and July 2006, with seven days in July 1983.

The greatest number of hot days in an individual month was 25 days in August 1947, followed by 22 days in July 1983.

There have been five months in the period 1908-2014 when every day reached a temperature of at least 20 °C. These were August 1933, July 1934 (when the lowest maximum temperature was 21.4 °C on 24 July), July 1983, July 2006 and July 2010.

Table 16.2 Highest and lowest calendar year totals of 'hot days' (25.0 °C or more) and 'heatwave days' (30.0 °C or more) at the University of Reading, 1918-2014. No corrections have been attempted for site differences.

Highest and lowest calendar year totals of hot days

	'Hot days' (25.0 °C or more) Annual average 1981-2010 18 days				'Heatwave days' (30.0 °C or more) Annual average 1981-2010 2 days	
Rank	Highest annual totals	Year	Lowest annual totals	Year	Highest annual totals	Year
1	53	1947	1	1931, 1962, 1974	14	1976
2	46	1976	2	1920, 1965, 1972	10	1947
3	45	1933	3	1927	9	1921
4	42	1989			9	1995
5	39	1921, 1959			8	1933, 2003, 2006

In 1974, the warmest day of the year (16 June) reached just 25.0 °C, the lowest annual maximum temperature in the series. In 1962, the hottest day reached only 25.6 °C, and in 1931, 25.9 °C. Each of these years reached 25 °C on only a single day.

Table 16.3 shows the incidence of warm nights (minimum air temperature 15 °C or more).

Table 16.3 Highest monthly and highest and lowest calendar year totals of 'warm nights' (15.0 °C or more) at the University of Reading, 1917-2014. No corrections have been attempted for site differences.

	'Warm nights' (15.0 °C or more) Annual average 1981-2010 14 nights					
Rank	Highest monthly frequency	Month and year	Highest annual frequency	Year	Lowest annual frequency	Year
1	19	July 1983	36	2006	1	1920, 1924, 1940
2	17	July 2006	31	1947	2	1922
3	16	Aug 1997	26	1983, 1995, 2003	3	1931, 1965, 1968

Large temperature changes in 24 hours

Temperature changes can be quite large from day-to-day at any time of the year. The largest changes observed during 1908-2014 are shown in Table 16.4.

---

[*] *1918 to 2014 rather than 1908, as daily records are missing for some months between 1908 and 1917.*

Table 16.4 Extreme temperature changes in 24 hours at the University of Reading, 1908-2014.

Element		Temperature change, degC	Dates
Maximum temperature	*Fall*	14.0	22-23 May 1918
		13.5	4-5 Apr 1946
	Rise	11.7	6-7 December 1962
		11.3	26-27 November 1950
Minimum temperature	*Fall*	12.7	15-16 October 1955
		12.5	9-10 January 1933
	Rise	14.6	22-23 December 1909
		14.2	31 Dec 1908-1 Jan 1909
Mean daily temperature	*Rise*	8.6	31 Dec 1908- 1 Jan 1909
		8.1	4-5 June 1919
	Fall	9.4	10-11 January 1914
		8.9	9-10 January 1933

Frosts

Over the 1981-2010 period, Reading averaged 41 air frosts and 123 ground frosts each year. Table 16.5 shows the frostiest months and Table 16.6 the greatest and least numbers of air and ground frosts in a year since 1925, from when continuous and reliable winter records are available. The longest spells of consecutive days with air frost during 1908-2013 have been a run of 33 days in 1947 (5 February – 9 March) and 28 days in 1986 (5 February - 4 March).

Table 16.5 Frostiest calendar months at the University of Reading, from January 1925, updated to April 2015. No corrections have been attempted for site differences.

Frostiest months

Air frosts	Month and year	Ground frosts	Month and year
27	Jan 1963	30	Jan 1940, Jan 1985
26	Jan 1940, Feb 1947	29	Jan 1979
25	Feb 1942	28	Jan 1929, Dec 1933, Feb 1956, Feb 1979

Table 16.6 Most and least frosty calendar years at the University of Reading for the period 1925-2014. No corrections have been attempted for site differences.

	Most frosty				**Least frosty**			
Rank	Air frosts	Year	Ground frosts	Year	Air frosts	Year	Ground frosts	Year
1	81	1929	160	1973	19	1974, 1990	79	1964
2	72	1963	157	2003	22	1994	81	1939
3	71	1947	151	1970	22	2002	84	1949
4	71	2010	146	1972,	22	2014	85	1927
5	68	1985		1975,	23	1972	86	1945,
				2013				1967

During 1981-2010 Reading averaged 2.0 ice days each year. The greatest number of ice days in a month and a year in the period January 1918 to April 2015 are shown in Table 16.7.

Table 16.7 Greatest number of ice days for months and calendar years at the University of Reading; January 1918 to April 2015. No corrections have been attempted for site differences.

Rank	Most ice days		In a month	Month
	In a year	*Year*		
1	15	1947	12	Jan 1963
2	14	1963	10	Feb 1947
3	12	1985	8	Feb 1929
4	10	1929	6	Feb 1956, Feb 1985, Jan 1987
5	6	1956, 1979, 1986, 1987		

Monthly and annual ranges in temperature

The largest *monthly* ranges in temperature have been 32.8 degC (in May 1944) and 31.4 degC (in September 1919).

During the period 1981-2010 the average *annual* temperature range was 37.4 degC. The largest and smallest annual ranges during 1918-2014 are shown in Table 16.8. A range of 46.1 degC is known to have occurred in 1911 but some observations are missing during 1916-17.

Table 16.8 The highest and lowest annual temperature ranges (calendar years) at the University of Reading, 1918-2014. No corrections have been applied to the London Road records (1918-67).
Average highest maximum 30.3 °C, average lowest minimum -7.1 °C; see also Appendix 1

Mean annual temperature range 37.4 degrees Celsius (average 1981-2010)

Greatest annual ranges				Least annual ranges			
Temperature range, degC	*Annual maximum temp °C*	*Annual minimum temp °C*	*Year*	Temperature range, degC	*Annual maximum temp °C*	*Annual minimum temp °C*	*Year*
45.7	33.5	-12.2	1947	28.3	25.0	-3.3	1974
44.1	31.2	-12.9	1929	31.6	27.4	-4.2	1951
43.0	36.4	-6.6	2003	32.2	26.5	-5.7	1993
42.4	34.0	-8.4	1976	32.4	26.9	-5.5	1977
42.2	27.7	-14.5	1982	32.4	28.2	-4.2	2011

Reversal in month-to-month temperature trends

As the days grow longer, the expectation is that from March to June the monthly mean temperature should be higher in each month when compared to the previous ones. Conversely, into autumn we expect September to be cooler than August, October cooler than September, November cooler than October and December cooler than November.

This is not always the case, as the following details for 1908-2014 reveal. March was colder than February in 11 years, being 2.3 degC colder than February in 1937. In 1916, January (average temperature 7.3 °C) was much milder than March (4.1 °C). April was colder than March in eight years – in 1938 April was 1.8 degC colder than March. May has never been colder than April, but in 1916 and 1918 June was colder than May.

September has been warmer than August in three years – by 0.9 degC in 1929. October has never been warmer than September, but in 1986 and 2001 October was only 0.1 degC colder than September. Only in 1939 was November milder than October. December is milder than November quite frequently – on average once every six years during 1908-2014. In 1974 the average temperatures during the final three months were (October) 7.7 °C, (November) 7.5 °C and (December) 8.1 °C – December being milder than both October and November, for the only time on Reading's long records.

PRECIPITATION

The average annual rainfall in Reading is 634 mm, falling on around 154 days. The wettest and driest years are shown in Table 16.9 (the wettest and driest months on record are given in Chapter 22, Table

22.7, and the wettest days in Table 22.8). Information on droughts and wet spells over various durations from days to years can be found in Chapter 20.

Table 16.9 Highest and lowest annual precipitation at the University of Reading, 1901-2014 (London Road 1901-1967, Whiteknights 1968-2014). *For the 'Top 10' wettest days, see Table 22.8*

Average annual precipitation 634 mm (average 1981-2010)

Wettest years			Driest years		
Total fall, mm	*Per cent of normal*	*Year*	*Total fall, mm*	*Per cent of normal*	*Year*
961.4	151	1903	404.7	64	1921
897.4	141	1951	463.0	73	1990
876.6	138	2014	480.9	76	2005
860.0	136	1927	484.0	76	1947
857.3	135	1915	488.5	77	1996

The wet year of 1903 was the result of both June and October being very wet, October 1903 being the wettest month on the record and June 1903 still the second-wettest June on record. The very wet year of 2014 is placed third in the table – the 12 months commencing December 2013 were even wetter, at 941.0 mm. The wettest 12 month period on record in Reading since 1908 was that commencing 1 April 2000, amounting to 1002.4 mm (Chapter 20, Table 20.2 gives more details of wet spells by duration).

The annual fall in 1921 was less than half of 1903's total, and this was the only year to date to attain less than two-thirds of the annual average rainfall. The driest 12 month period on record in Reading since 1908 was that commencing 21 September 1975, with just 346.4 mm (Chapter 20, Table 20.2).

A 'rain day' is one in which 0.2 mm or more is recorded 0900-0900 GMT. The average number of rain days over 1981-2010 was 154 per annum. The highest and lowest monthly and annual frequency of rain days is given in Table 16.10.

Table 16.10 Highest and lowest monthly and annual precipitation frequency (days with 0.2 mm or more) at the University of Reading, 1908-2014 (London Road 1908-1967, Whiteknights 1968-2014)

Greatest monthly		Fewest monthly		Greatest annual		Fewest annual	
Rain days	*Month and year*	*Rain days*	*Month and year*	*Rain days*	*Month*	*Rain days*	*Month*
30	Dec 1934	1	June 1925, Aug 1940 and Sep 1959	212	1960	126	1990
27	Oct 1909, Oct 1916	2	Apr 1912, Sep 1929, Aug 1947, Apr 1954, Apr 2007, Apr 2011	205	1910	129	1949, 1973, 1996, 2003
26	Dec 1910, Mar 1914, Nov 1951, Nov 1960, Jan 1970, May 1972, Mar 1981, Jan 2014	3	*Numerous months*	194	1916, 1930, 1939	130	1921

Snowfall and lying snow

Snow or sleet falls on 10.9 days on average during the year (1981-2010) and a 50 per cent or more cover of lying snow can be expected on an average 5.9 mornings. The months with the most snowfall days between January 1908 and April 2015 were those of February 1963 (16 days) and January 1963 (15 days). In terms of with lying snow, the snowiest months were also January 1963 (31 days) and February 1963 (17 days).

The snowiest years during 1908-2014 in terms of the number of days with snowfall were 1963 and 1969 (both had 36 days with snowfall). In terms of lying snow, 1963 (with 48 days) was much snowier than 2010 (24 days) and 1979 (23 days) which were the next snowiest.

In 2002 there were no days with falling snow and there was just one day with sleet in 2014. About one year in four had no lying snow during 1908-2014.

During the period 1981-2010 the average date of the last winter/spring snowfall was 1 April while the average date of the first autumn/winter snowfall was 16 December. Snow has fallen as late as 18 May (in 1955) and as early as 15 October (in 1934). Snow has been observed lying as late as 15 April (in 1966) and as early as 29 October (in 2008) – see Chapter 21, 'Earliest and latest' for more details.

The longest periods with lying snow at 0900 GMT have been those of 50 days from 27 December 1963 (31 cm deep on 3 January 1963) and 15 days from 6 February 1986 (18 cm deep on the 6th).

Thunder

Thunder was heard on an average of 9.0 days each year during 1981-2010. The most thundery month on the record was May 1969 (Table 16.11), in which thunder was heard on 11 days: no other month had had more than seven days with thunder. Table 16.11 also lists the greatest and least number of days with thunder in any year since 1908: annual totals are plotted in Figure 16.1. Thunder was heard on 23 days in 1974 and 1983 and 20 days in 1936, 1954 and 1969, but on only two days in 1915 and 1985. More recently, 2014 (19 days of thunder) was the most thundery year since 1983 (23 days) after a seven-year run of below-normal activity (Figure 16.1), with a 'low' of just three days in 2011.

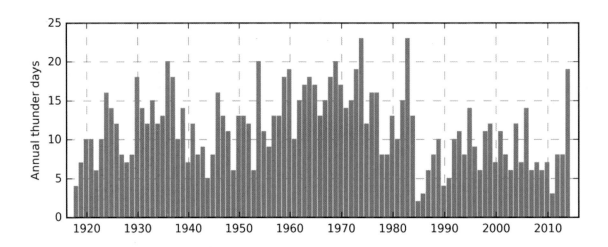

Figure 16.1 *The annual frequency of days with thunder heard, University of Reading, 1918-2014.*

Table 16.11 The most thundery months and years on Reading's records, January 1908 to April 2015

Most thundery months

No of days	Month(s)
11	May 1969
7	May 1924, July 1925, June 1963 and May 1967
6	Aug 1931, June 1933, July 1934, July 1947, Aug 1960, July 1962, May 1972, Sept 1976, May 1983, July 1983, Apr 1998, Aug 2004

Most and least thundery years

Rank	No of days thunder heard	Year	No of days thunder heard	Year
1	23	1974, 1983	2	1915, 1985
2	20	1936, 1954, 1969	3	1909, 1916, 1986, 2011
3	19	1960, 1973, 2014	4	1918, 1990
4	18	1930, 1937, 1959, 1964, 1968	5	1944, 1991

SUNSHINE

The average annual sunshine duration in Reading during 1981-2010 was 1522 hours. The sunniest and dullest years in Reading during 1956-2014 are shown in Table 16.12. Monthly sunshine amounts have varied between 305.6 hours in June 1975 and 7.8 hours in December 1956. The months of May to August have similar average sunshine totals, and in about one year in four the sunniest month of the year occurs outside the three 'summer' months of June, July and August. In about one year in eight the dullest month occurs outside the three 'winter' months (December, January and February).

Table 16.12 Annual sunshine duration at the University of Reading, 1956-2014 (London Road 1956-1967, Whiteknights 1968-2014).

Annual mean sunshine duration 1522 hours, 4.17 hours per day (average 1981-2010)

Possible daylength: 4480 hours (leap-year 4490 hours). Mean sunshine duration as percentage of possible: 34.0

Sunniest years			Dullest years			Sunniest days	
Duration, hours	Per cent of possible	Year	Duration, hours	Per cent of possible	Year	Duration, hours	Date
1917.8	42.8	1959	1307.2	29.2	1958	16.0	30 Jun 1976
1810.1	40.4	2003	1337.8	29.8	1992	15.8	4 Jul 1959
1792.0	39.9	1976	1342.6	30.0	1993	15.7	3 Jul 1968
1732.6	38.7	1989	1350.9	30.2	1991	15.7	24 Jun 1976
1709.9	38.2	1990	1360.9	30.4	1981	15.5	14 & 16 June 1959
							30 May 1966
							29 June 1976
							30 May 1985

Table 16.13 Annual frequency of sunless days at the University of Reading, 1956-2014 (London Road 1956-1967, Whiteknights 1968-2014)

Most sunless days	Year	Least sunless days	Year
92	1968	42	1990
86	2013	45	1967
84	1992	50	2003, 2007

The annual average number of sunless days during the year in the period 1981-2010 was 65 (and thus, perhaps contrary to popular belief, Reading averages 300 days of sunshine per year). The number of sunless days in a year has varied between 42 and 92 days (see Table 16.13). In December 1956 there were 24 sunless days.

The annual average number of days with 12 hours or more of sunshine in the period 1981-2010 was 17, the number varying in individual years from nine in 1986 and 2000 to 36 days in 1976. In June 1975, the sunniest month yet recorded, half of the days (15) in the month recorded at least 12 hours of sunshine.

Fog at 0900 GMT (visibility below 1000 m)
Fog occurred at 0900 GMT on 14 mornings per annum on average during 1981-2010. The months with the most fog days during 1908-2014 were those of October 1908 and December 1958, with 13 days each. Over a year the number of mornings with fog at 0900 GMT has varied between 40 days in 1920 and 34 days in 1908 to nil in 1911 and two days in 1910.

While the occurrence of fog at any time during the 24 hour period is unknown as fog measurements are only made at 0900 GMT, nevertheless an indication of foggy periods can be ascertained by examining consecutive mornings with fog reported. Eight consecutive foggy mornings were noted 24 November-1 December 1948, and seven 22-28 October 1920 and 11-17 February 1934.

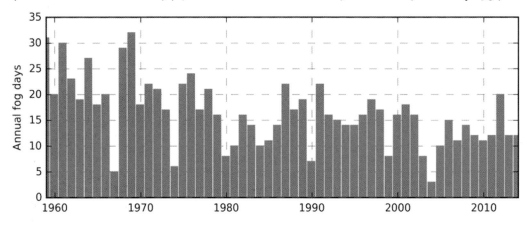

Figure 16.2 *Annual incidence of mornings with fog in Reading, 1959 to 2014. The frequency of fog has halved during this period, owing mainly to 'clean air' legislation.*

BAROMETRIC PRESSURE
Records of barometric pressure at mean sea level (MSL) at 0900 GMT have been kept at the university since 1908, although there are minor gaps in the record (in all, 596 days' data are missing, 1.5% of the record: values for these missing dates have been estimated from a reanalysis dataset). As methods for correcting station-level pressures to mean sea level have varied somewhat over the period of record, manuscript records of station pressure were retrospectively corrected to mean sea level using a standard algorithm when the earlier records were digitised in 2013. Some minor inhomogeneities in the record are still under investigation and adjustment: these arise mainly through changes in the instrument used or its location over the years.

Table 16.14 lists the ten highest and ten lowest daily (0900 GMT) barometer readings, and Table 16.15 the highest and lowest 0900 GMT pressure observations by month. It should be noted that the maximum and minimum values quoted in Tables 16.14 and 16.15 refer only to once-daily 'spot' pressure observations: because barometric pressure changes continuously throughout any 24 hour period, sometimes by 20-30 hPa or more, any single daily observation is unlikely to represent the true highest or lowest value attained in any period.

Monthly averages (over the 1981-2010 period) of MSL barometric pressure at 0900 GMT are given in Table 16.16, together with the highest and lowest monthly means over the period January 1908 to April 2015 (including estimates from a reanalysis dataset where daily values are missing). The average annual MSL pressure at 0900 GMT during 1981-2010 was 1015.9 hectopascals, or hPa (1 hPa = 1 millibar). The mean 0900 GMT MSL pressure for February 2014, 997.6 hPa, was almost certainly the lowest MSL pressure for any month extending back to before 1692 (based on a monthly series assembled for London: Richard Cornes *et al*, A daily series of mean sea-level pressure for London, 1692-2007. *International Journal of Climatology*. 2011, doi: 10.1002/joc.2301).

The highest 0900 GMT value yet recorded, 1049.5 hPa, occurred on 26 January 1932 (Table 16.14). During this prolonged anticyclonic spell, the readings at 0900 GMT remained above 1030 hPa for 20 consecutive mornings commencing 18 January. At the other end of the scale, on 25 February 1989 the barometer continued falling for several hours from its 0900 GMT reading of 962.4 hPa, the lowest on the series; the true minimum, reached around 1700 GMT that day, was just above 952 hPa (Figure 16.3). A similar value prevailed in London, where it was the lowest recorded barometric pressure since 25 December 1821; it is reasonable to assume that the same can be said of Reading's extreme that day.

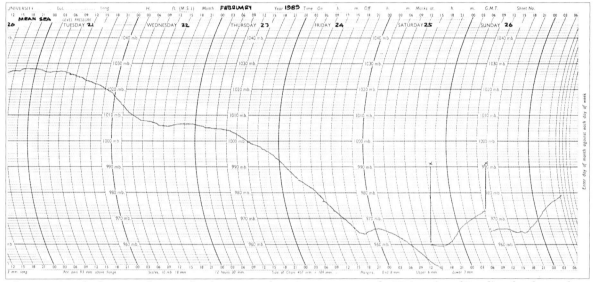

Figure 16.3 *The barograph trace for the Meteorology Department at the University of Reading for the week commencing 20 February 1989. On Saturday 25 February the pressure fell to 952 hPa; the barograph arm required adjustment upwards to ensure it did not drop below the bottom of the chart*

Table 16.14 The highest and lowest observed mean sea level barometric pressures at 0900 GMT: period January 1908 to April 2015, 98.5% data availability (no estimates included for missing daily data). Note that because these observations relate to a single daily observation and not to a continuous 24 hour record, they do not cover the full range of barometric pressure extremes

	Highest 0900 GMT barometric pressures		Lowest 0900 GMT barometric pressures	
Rank	hPa	Date	hPa	Date
1	1049.5	26 Jan 1932	962.4	25 Feb 1989
2	1048.8	15 Feb 1934	964.5	10 Feb 1953
3	1048.4	27 Jan 1932	965.2	26 Feb 1989
4	1048.4	16 Feb 1934	966.0	9 Dec 1954
5	1046.8	31 Jan 1932	966.1	17 Dec 1989
6	1046.8	7 Feb 1964	966.9	1 Jan 1949
7	1046.6	17 Feb 1934	968.2	10 Mar 2008
8	1046.3	15 Jan 1946	969.4	22 Feb 1914
9	1046.1	8 Feb 1964	969.6	19 Nov 1916
10	1046.0	17 Feb 1959	971.6	13 Jan 1969

Table 16.15 Highest and lowest mean sea level barometric pressure at 0900 GMT by month (extremes period January 1908 to April 2015, 98.5% data availability). Note that because these observations relate to a single daily observation and not to a continuous 24 hour record, the values shown here do not represent the full range of barometric pressure extremes during the period

Month	Highest 0900 GMT value		Lowest 0900 GMT value	
	hPa	*Date*	*hPa*	*Date*
Jan	1049.5	26 Jan 1932	966.9	1 Jan 1949
Feb	1048.8	15 Feb 1934	962.4	25 Feb 1989
Mar	1045.3	1 Mar 1929	968.2	10 Mar 2008
Apr	1043.3	11 Apr 1938	978.4	18 Apr 2012
May	1042.4	16 May 1943	977.4	8 May 1943
June	1037.5	7 June 1962, 8 June 2005	989.9	23 June 2004
July	1035.2	10 and 11 July 1911	982.8	29 July 1956
Aug	1034.8	12 Aug 1949	975.4	28 Aug 1917
Sep	1039.5	19 Sep 1986	981.2	26 Sep 1981
Oct	1040.1	23 Oct 1958, 22 Oct 1983	971.8	27 Oct 1959
Nov	1043.9	16 Nov 1922	969.6	19 Nov 1916
Dec	1045.2	22 Dec 2006	966.0	9 Dec 1954
Year	1049.5	26 Jan 1932	962.4	25 Feb 1989

Table 16.16 Mean and highest and lowest monthly mean barometric pressure at mean sea level at 0900 GMT. Extremes period January 1908 to April 2015, 98.5% data availability, 1.5% gaps filled (mostly prior to 1960) using daily NCEP pressure reanalysis. Averages period 1981-2010.

Month	*1981-2010 mean*	Highest monthly mean 1908-2015		Lowest monthly mean 1908-2015	
	hPa	*hPa*	*Year*	*hPa*	*Year*
Jan	1016.6	1030.7	1992	1000.6	1948
Feb	1017.3	1033.2	1932	997.6	2014
Mar	1015.8	1030.1	1929	999.1	1909
Apr	1014.9	1028.5	1938	1002.5	1998
May	1015.9	1024.8	1991	1006.5	1983
June	1017.0	1022.9	1962	1009.2	1997
July	1016.4	1022.4	1911	1010.9	1988
Aug	1016.1	1022.5	1940	1007.4	1917
Sep	1016.4	1024.9	1941	1007.5	1918
Oct	1014.2	1025.0	2007	1003.4	1960 and 1976
Nov	1014.4	1025.5	1942	999.7	2000
Dec	1015.6	1028.5	1991	1001.1	1978
Year	1015.9	1033.2	Feb 1932	997.6	Feb 2014
Annual		1019.5	1921	1011.7	1960
means		1019.0	1949	1012.3	1951
		1018.7	1973, 2005	1012.4	2014

The range in pressure during May 1943 (Table 16.15, a rise of 65 hPa, from 977.4 hPa on 8 May to 1042.4 hPa just eight days later) would be remarkable for any month of the year. In early 1989, the barometer at 0900 GMT ranged from 1044.4 hPa on 29 January to 962.4 hPa on 25 February (and subsequently to 952 hPa later on 25 February, see Figure 16.3 and entry in 'On this date', Chapter 23) – a range in pressure of 92 hPa in less than four weeks.

Gales

Table 16.17 lists the strongest wind gusts on record in Reading, and Table 16.18 the highest gusts by month, over the period of available records (from August 1961; some gaps in the record, data availability 83.1% to April 2015). Since 1970, the anemometer has been at a height of 10 m above ground level. It is particularly noteworthy that in Table 16.17, five of the highest gusts listed occurred within five weeks of each other during the very stormy months of January and February 1990.

Table 16.17 Highest wind gusts recorded at the University of Reading, period August 1961 to April 2015; 83% data availability to April 2015.

	Highest gusts			
Rank	*Gust, knots*	*Gust, mph*	*Gust, m/s*	*Date(s)*
1	76	88	39.1	25 Jan 1990
2	75	86	38.6	2 Jan 1976 *(for wind chart record, see p. 19)*
3	71	82	36.5	26 Feb 1990
4	70	81	36.0	7 Feb 1990
5	67	77	34.5	16 Oct 1987, 8 Feb 1990
6	66	76	34.0	24 Mar 1986
7	65	75	33.4	12 Feb 1990
8	63	73	32.4	12 Nov 1982, 28 Feb 1990

Table 16.18 Highest wind gusts recorded by month at the University of Reading, period August 1961 to April 2015; 83% data availability to April 2015.

	Highest gusts			
Month	*knots*	*mph*	*m/s*	*Date*
Jan	76	88	39.1	25 Jan 1990
Feb	71	82	36.5	26 Feb 1990
Mar	66	76	34.0	24 Mar 1986
Apr	52	60	26.7	1 April 1994
May	43	50	22.1	17 May 1979
June	42	48	21.6	6 June 1974
July	39	45	20.1	22 July 1985
Aug	49	56	25.2	7 Aug 1962
Sep	56	64	28.8	7 Sept 1974
Oct	67	77	34.5	16 Oct 1987
Nov	63	73	32.4	12 Nov 1982
Dec	59	68	30.3	17 Dec 1989
Year	76	88	39.1	25 Jan 1990

TEMPERATURE, PRECIPITATION AND SUNSHINE IN GRAPHS – ANNUAL

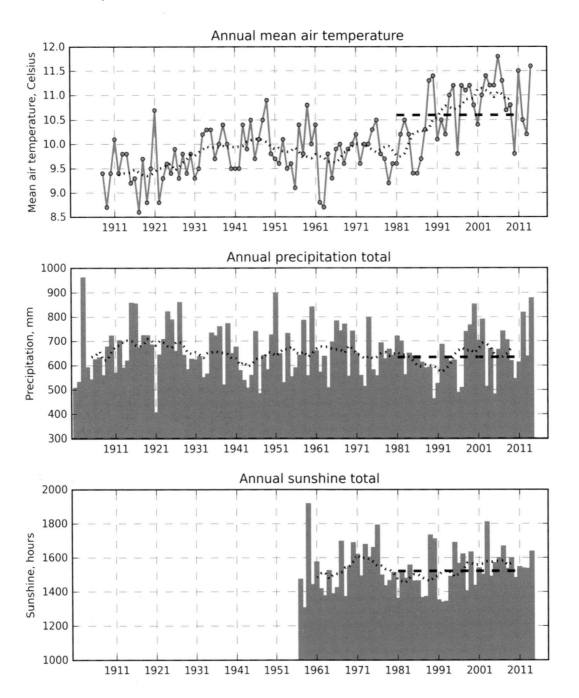

Figure 16.4 *Annual values of (from top) mean temperature (°C), total precipitation (mm) and sunshine duration (hours) in Reading over the available period of record (plots include London Road rainfall records where available 1901-04, with estimates from other Reading stations to 1907 as necessary)*

The mean temperatures as recorded at London Road 1908-67 have been reduced by 0.5 degC to ensure approximate homogeneity with the records from the Whiteknights site, 1968 onwards. No site adjustments have been made for precipitation or sunshine. For temperature and precipitation, the 10 year running mean centred on the year shown is indicated by a dashed grey line

17 The seasons – winter, spring, summer and autumn

By convention, in the UK the year is subdivided meteorologically into four seasons, namely winter (for convenience, this is normally taken as the three calendar months December, January and February), spring (March, April and May), summer (June, July and August) and autumn (September, October and November).

Winter *(December, January and February)*

Winter is the coldest season of the year, and temperatures tend to reach their minimum in early to mid-February, some 7-8 weeks after the winter solstice. Winter air temperatures average 4.9 °C with January having the coldest days (average daily maximum temperature 7.7 °C) and February the coldest nights (averaging daily minimum temperature 1.7 °C).

Winter averages 164 mm precipitation, slightly less than in autumn but considerably wetter (by over 30 mm) than both spring and summer. Some of this falls as snow in winter; snow can be expected to fall on about eight days in an average winter and to cover the ground on about five days. Thunderstorms are rare at this time of year and many consist of just one or two claps of thunder, occurring on about one day every two years.

With daylength being short, sunshine averages just under 2 hours daily (178 hours each winter), although about one day in three (an average of 32 of the 90 or 91 days) will remain sunless.

TEMPERATURE

During the period 1908-2015, winter temperatures in Reading have ranged from -14.5 °C on 14 January 1982 to 17.4 °C on 28 February 1959. The mildest and coldest winter days and nights on record are shown in Table 17.1.

Table 17.1 Highest and lowest maximum and minimum temperatures in winter, 1908/9-2014/5. Records are from the (slightly milder) London Road site 1908/09-Dec 1967, and from Whiteknights Jan 1968-2014/15: no corrections for site differences have been applied.

Rank	Mildest days	Coldest days	Mildest nights	Coldest nights
1	17.4 °C, 28 Feb 1959	-6.8 °C, 12 Jan 1987	12.4 °C, 3 Dec 1985	-14.5 °C, 14 Jan 1982
2	17.0 °C, 23 Feb 1990	-5.6 °C, 24 Jan 1963	12.0 °C, 28 Dec 1984	-13.4 °C, 13 Dec 1981
3	16.8 °C, 13 Feb 1998	-5.0 °C, 29 Dec 1908	12.0 °C, 5 Dec 1986	-13.4 °C, 15 Jan 1982
4	16.7 °C, 14 Feb 1961	-4.5 °C, 16 Jan 1985	11.9 °C, 15 Dec 1998	-12.9 °C, 15 Feb 1929
5	16.7 °C, 29 Feb 1948	-4.5 °C, 23 Jan 1963	11.8 °C, 14 Dec 1918	-12.8 °C, 30 Dec 1908

The mildest winter nights are often in December, as the ground and especially the surrounding seas are warmer than later in the winter. On the other hand, the mildest winter days tend to occur in the second half of February, as the increasing strength of the Sun begins to be felt. The coldest days tend to occur in January, although the coldest nights can be found anytime between mid-December and mid-February. Mild days or nights in winter usually occur when the air flows off the Atlantic Ocean, while low temperatures are favoured by an airflow off the near-continent – and when the continent is cold, something that is most likely in the second half of the season.

Air frosts occur with a similar frequency in each of the three winter months although January is the month most likely to record an ice day.

Warm and cold winters

The winter of 1962/63 was by far the coldest winter in the period 1908/09-2014/15 with an average temperature more than 5 degC below normal – the mean temperature over Central England was the lowest since 1740. Monthly temperatures departures from average ranged from -3.5 degC in December 1962 to -7.3 degC in January 1963, the coldest month on Reading's records.

Early December 1962 was cold and foggy: the maximum temperature of -2.3 °C on 6 December was the third consecutive ice day and the coldest December day since 1938. Fog was very dense at times – the visibility was only 50 metres at the 0900 GMT observations 4-8 December, while the weather diary notes that visibility fell to just 15 metres later on 3 December. After a short milder interlude, persistent cold weather set in just before Christmas 1962, and thereafter north-easterly or easterly winds dominated much of the winter. There was a blizzard across Wales and south-west England on 29-30 December, and on the morning of 30 December the snow depth in Reading was 21 cm: the Reading observer noted that morning "drifts of 75 to 90 cm were present, the strong wind causing considerable drifting and blowing of snow." The snow depth reached 31 cm on the morning of 3 January, the greatest depth of lying snow on Reading's records, while snow remained on the ground (more than 50% cover for 50 consecutive days) from 27 December to 14 February. Altogether, snow fell on 38 days during the three winter months. Once the snowstorms at the end of December/start of January were over, it was a mainly dry winter with just 33 mm of precipitation falling in the first two months of 1963 – about one-third of normal: most of that had fallen by 4 January. On 4 March a mild south-westerly flow finally reached the British Isles and temperatures gradually rose, allowing snow to melt and bringing an end to this harsh winter. Sunny days towards the end of February and in early March helped clear the snow, preventing the severe flooding along the Thames that sometimes occurs after a cold, snowy spell (as in March 1947).

The next-coldest winter (1946/47) was only 2.6 degC below average by the end of January, but February was 6.4 degC below normal; the overall result was a winter 3.8 degC below the current average temperature.

The five coldest winters all occurred before 1965 and four of the five mildest winters have occurred in the past forty years – the only exception being 1934/35. Even so, milder winters struggle to reach average temperatures in excess of 2 degC above normal – reflecting how quickly a cold air outbreak off the near continent can lower the temperature in Reading in winter.

Table 17.2 Winter mean temperatures at the University of Reading, 1908/09-2014/15. In winter the London Road site (1908/09- Dec 1967) is about 0.4 degC milder than the Whiteknights site (Jan 1968 onwards) due to its location closer to the town centre. The observed mean temperatures at the London Road site (shown in brackets) have been adjusted by this amount to facilitate comparison between the two records.

Winter mean temperature 4.9°C (average 1981-2010)

Mildest winters			Coldest winters		
Mean temperature, °C	Departure from 1981-2010 normal degC	Year	Mean temperature, °C	Departure from 1981-2010 normal degC	Year
7.0	+2.1	1989/90 and 2006/07	-0.4 (0.0)	-5.3	1962/63
			1.1 (1.5)	-3.8	1946/47
6.8	+1.9	1974/75	1.2 (1.6)	-3.7	1916/17
6.6	+1.7	1988/89	1.4 (1.8)	-3.5	1939/40
6.5 (6.9)	+1.6	1934/35	1.5 (1.9)	-3.4	1928/29
6.5		2013/14			

Frosts

There have been only three winters with fewer than ten air frosts: 1960/61 and 1974/75, both with nine, and 1989/90 with just eight. Note that two of these occurred at the relatively colder

Whiteknights site. The two coldest winters of 1946/47 (61 days with frost) and 1962/63 (68 days) were the only ones to record over 60 days with air frost.

But winter can also have long spells free from air frost – in 1937/38 the first 45 days of 1938 remained frost-free, and in 1966 the 57 day period 22 January to 19 March also remained frost-free.

PRECIPITATION

The mean precipitation total for winter in Reading is 164 mm, falling on around 43 days. Some of this usually falls as snow – on 7.6 days in an average winter.

Winter's precipitation during the period 1908/09 to 2014/15 varied from well above twice normal in 2013/14 to just less than one third of the average in 1991/92. The occurrence of three wet winters during 1911/12 to 1915/16 is noteworthy (265 mm fell in the latter winter). The winter of 2013/14 began remarkably dry, with less than 5 mm of rainfall in the first fortnight of December, and yet it went on to be much wetter than the previous wettest winters of 1914/15 and 1989/90, with flooding widespread from 23 December well into the spring months. Both the frequency and amount of rainfall in winter 2013/14 were extraordinary – 69 of the winter's 90 days saw measurable rain, while 'trace' amounts were recorded on a further 10 days, leaving just 11 days which remained completely dry.

At the other extreme, the winter of 1991/92 was very dry, the only winter to receive less than 50 mm of precipitation; with little recharge of groundwater over the winter months, there were considerable concerns at the time with regard to future water supplies and the risks of shortages.

Table 17.3 Winter precipitation at the University of Reading, 1901/02-2014/15 (London Road 1901/02 Dec 1967, Whiteknights Jan 1968 onwards).

Winter mean precipitation 164 mm (average 1981-2010)

Wettest winters			Driest winters			Wettest days	
Total fall,	Per cent of		Total fall,	Per cent of		Daily fall,	
mm	normal	Year	mm	normal	Year	mm	Date
374.6	228	2013/14	47.6	29	1991/92	43.2	8 Dec 1954
344.6	210	1989/90	52.9	32	1963/64	35.8	20 Dec 1989
327.9	200	1914/15	56.6	35	1933/34	33.5	1 Dec 1919
283.3	173	1994/95	69.1	42	1975/76	31.3	19 Dec 1995
274.9	168	1911/12	72.2	44	1931/32	29.2	25 Feb 1933

Snowfall and lying snow

An average winter sees 7.6 days with snow falling, although there are wide variations from year to year. Between 1917/18 and 2014/15, there were only three winters without snowfall (1948/49, 1949/50 and 2001/02 – although in the first two cases some snow fell in the following spring). The winter of 1962/63 was the snowiest winter, with snow observed to fall on 38 days – the only other winter to see more than 25 days with falling snow was 2009/10 with 28 days.

The number of days with lying snow is also skewed towards the occasional snowy month: the winter average is 5.4 mornings with snow cover, although around one winter in five does not see a single morning with lying snow.

The greatest snow depths at 0900 GMT have been 28 cm, 27 cm and 31 cm on 1-3 January 1963, and 27 cm on 6 January 2010 (Table 22.9, Chapter 22). Since the actual quantity of snow that falls is difficult to measure (it may fall combined with rain as sleet, may partially melt or sublime before it is measured next morning, or may blow into drifts) one helpful way to visualise both the depth of snow and its persistence over time is to determine the accumulated snow depth, which is simply the accumulation of measured snow depths each morning. Thus a winter with three days of snow cover, each of 2 cm depth, will accumulate 6 cm. The longer the snow remains on the ground and the deeper the snow, the greater will be the accumulation. Since records of snow depth are available (the winter of 1950/51), the winters of 1962/63, 1981/82 and 2009/10 stand out as the snowiest– with 1962/63 by far the snowiest of all (Figure 17.1).

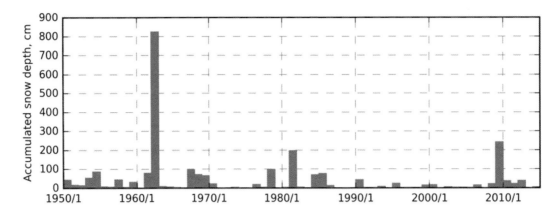

Figure 17.1 *Accumulated snow depth at the 0900 GMT observation for the winters of 1950/51 to 2014/15, indicating the variation and persistence of snow cover from winter to winter.*

SUNSHINE

Winter is the dullest season of the year, with a sunshine quota of just under 2 hours each day – although about one in three days will remain sunless.

Table 17.4 Winter sunshine duration at the University of Reading, 1956/57-2014/15 (London Road 1956/57-1966/67, Whiteknights 1967/68 onwards).

Winter mean sunshine duration 179 hours, 1.98 hours per day (average 1981-2010)

Possible daylength: 787 hours (leap year 797 hours). Mean sunshine duration as percentage of possible: 22.6

Sunniest winters			Dullest winters			Sunniest days	
Duration,	*Per cent of*		*Duration,*	*Per cent of*		*Duration,*	
hours	*possible*	*Year*	*hours*	*possible*	*Year*	*hours*	*Date*
238.6	30.3	2007/08	92.6	11.8	2010/11	9.5	20 Feb 1970
227.7	28.9	1999/2000	111.1	14.1	1971/72	9.5	27 Feb 1973
219.8	27.9	2002/03	124.9	15.9	1956/57	9.5	26 Feb 1977
211.1	26.8	1983/84	132.6	16.8	1992/93	9.4	27 Feb 1959
209.7	26.6	2014/15	135.4	17.2	1965/66	9.3	26 Feb 1995

It is unusual for winter to receive much more than about 210 hours of bright sunshine (a surplus of 30 hours when compared to the average): however, frequent and extensive cloud cover can lead to deficits of 50 hours or more – the winter of 2010/11 was exceptionally dull. With days getting longer as the season evolves, the sunniest days in winter tend to occur towards the end of February.

Fog at 0900 GMT

About one winter in 25 has no fog observed at 0900 GMT; even having less than four mornings with fog is rare. In 1958/59 there were 30 mornings with fog, and 20 in 1933/34 and 1963/64. Since 1991/92, no winter has had more than 16 mornings with fog at 0900 GMT and the statistics would suggest a decline in winter fog since 1970.

TEMPERATURE, PRECIPITATION AND SUNSHINE IN GRAPHS – WINTER

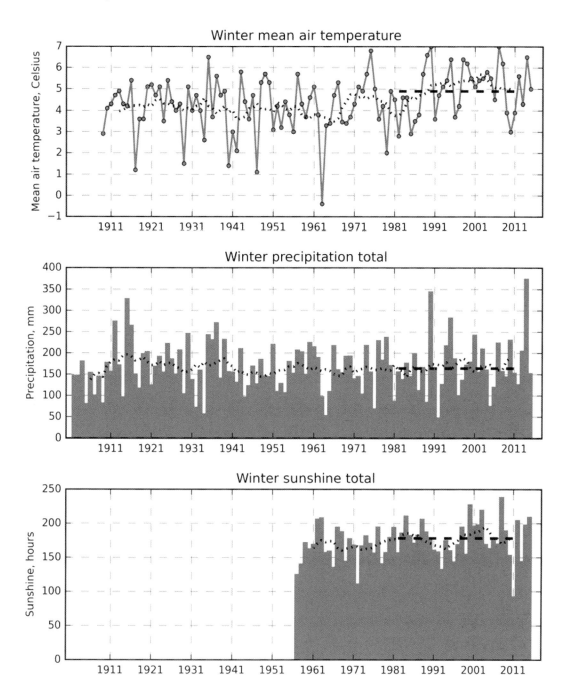

Figure 17.2 *Monthly values of (from top) mean temperature (°C), total precipitation (mm) and sunshine duration (hours) for winter in Reading over the available period of record (plots include London Road rainfall records where available 1901-04, with estimates from other Reading stations to 1907 as necessary)*

The mean temperatures as recorded at London Road 1908-67 have been reduced by 0.4 degC to ensure approximate homogeneity with the records from the Whiteknights site, 1968 onwards. No site adjustments have been made for precipitation or sunshine. For temperature and precipitation, the 10 year running mean centred on the year shown is indicated by a dashed grey line

Spring *(March, April and May)*

Spring marks the transition from the frosts and snows of winter to the warmth of summer, as the days get longer and the temperature rises – rather unsteadily in most springs. Average temperatures rise from around 9 °C during the day (and 2 °C at night) at the start of March to 18-19 °C and 9 °C (respectively) by the end of May.

Despite the association with showers, spring's precipitation average of 139 mm makes it (just) the driest season of the year; measurable precipitation can be expected on 39 days in a typical season. Snowfall can be expected on 2-3 days in spring, most often early in the season, while May sometimes brings the first of the summer thunderstorms.

As daylength increases, monthly sunshine totals increase from an average of 109 hours in March to 188 hours in May.

TEMPERATURE

Over the period 1908-2014, spring temperatures have ranged from -11.3 °C to 31.9 °C. The warmest and coldest spring days and nights are shown in Table 17.5.

Table 17.5 Highest and lowest maximum and minimum temperatures in spring, 1908-2014. Records are from the (slightly milder) London Road site 1908-1967, and from Whiteknights 1968-2014: no corrections for site differences have been applied.

Rank	Hottest days	Coldest days	Warmest nights	Coldest nights
1	31.9°C, 29 May 1944	-0.6 °C, 6 Mar 1942	16.6°C,30 May 1944	-11.3°C, 7 Mar 1947
2	31.3°C, 30 May 1944	-0.1 °C, 1 Mar 1986	16.6°C, 25 May 1922	-7.5 °C, 3 Mar 1909
3	31.2°C, 22 May 1922	0.0 °C, 4 Mar 1965	16.2°C, 9 May 1945	-7.4 °C, 5 Mar 1909
4	30.5°C, 30 May 1947	0.2 °C, 9 Mar 1931	15.4°C, 19 May 1952	-7.2 °C, 3 Mar 1965
5	30.4°C, 23 May 1922	0.4°C, 5 Mar 1947	15.3°C, 23 May 1922 and 25 May 2012	-6.7 °C, 10 Mar 1931

The coldest spring night was 7 March 1947, when the temperature fell to -11.3 °C (almost 4 degC colder than on any other spring night on record), while only two spring days have remained below 0 °C all day, both in the first week of March. Not surprisingly, the warmest spring days tend to occur towards the end of May – temperatures of 30 °C or above have been recorded on seven spring days, although not since 1953: at the slightly cooler Whiteknights site (since 1968) the highest spring temperature to date has been 28.5°C, recorded on 27 May 2005. The period 29-30 May 1944 was exceptionally hot for late spring: two days saw maximum temperatures above 31°C with the temperature falling no lower than 16.6 °C in the intervening night.

Warm and cold springs

The springs of 2007 and 2011 were the warmest in Reading during 1908-2014, being 0.5 degC milder than any other spring in that time, while the springs of 1941, 1962 and 2013 were easily the coldest in the same period – over 2 degC colder than average. In 1962 and 2013 this could be largely attributed to cold March months – in 1917 March was also very cold but temperatures then rose to give a very warm May.

Table 17.6 Spring mean temperatures at the University of Reading, 1908-2014. In spring the London Road site (1908-1967) is about 0.5 degC milder than the Whiteknights site (1968 onwards) due to its location closer to the town centre. The observed mean temperatures at the London Road site (shown in brackets) have been adjusted by this amount to facilitate comparison between the two records.

Spring mean temperature 9.6°C (average 1981-2010)

Mildest springs			Coldest springs		
Mean temperature, °C	*Departure from 1981-2010 normal degC*	*Year*	*Mean temperature, °C*	*Departure from 1981-2010 normal degC*	*Year*
11.1	+1.5	2007	7.2 (7.7)	-2.4	1962
11.1	+1.5	2011	7.4 (7.9)	-2.2	1941
10.6	+1.0	1992, 1999	7.4	-2.2	2013
10.5 (11.0)	+0.9	1945	7.9	-1.7	1979, 1984, 1986
10.4 (10.9)	+0.8	1943, 1952			

Frosts

The consecutive springs of 1959 and 1960 recorded no air frosts at London Road (the last air frost of winter/spring occurring on 20 February and 25 February respectively) – and at Whiteknights spring 1994 had just one air frost. The frostiest springs were in 1917 (26 days with air frost), 1924 (23 days), 1929 (24 days) and 2013 (23 days). Late frosts can damage or even kill tender plants and blossom: based on 80 years record (1925-2014) the median date for the last spring air frost was 13 April (Figure 17.3). Only one in ten springs will have no air frosts after 21 March, while one in ten will see one or more air frosts after 8 May. In 1975 the last air frost occurred on 31 May – easily the latest in the Reading record covering 1925-2014. It should be borne in mind, however, that these statistics relate to the university weather station, and that frost risk is higher in hollows and Reading's rural surroundings.

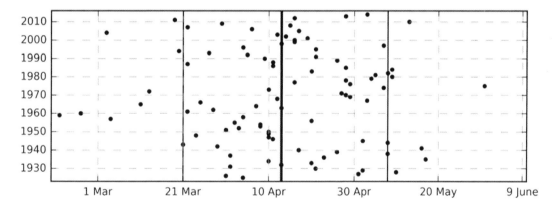

Figure 17.3 The date of the last air frost of winter/spring at the University of Reading during 1925-2014. The three dark vertical lines show (from left to right) the 10th percentile, the median and 90th percentile dates of the last air frost. One tenth of the values lie to the left of the 10th percentile and one tenth to the right of the 90th percentile. The median marks the mid-point; half the values lie to its right and half to its left.

PRECIPITATION

Spring's mean precipitation total in Reading is 139 mm, falling on around 39 days. Some of this can be expected to fall as snow – on 2.5 days in an average spring.

The precipitation total of 278 mm in spring 1979 amounted to exactly twice the normal spring rainfall, and was over 30 mm wetter than any spring during the period 1901-2014. It was also the second of four wet springs in six years (Figure 17.4). Three springs have received less than 50 mm of precipitation – with the sunny spring of 1990 being the driest: rain fell on only 24 days.

About one day every five springs records in excess of 25 mm of precipitation, with heavy falls tending to occur more often in May than in March or April. In 1979 and 1981 rain fell on 59 days during spring (almost two days in every three); it also fell on 59 days in 1972 although that season's total rainfall was just 159 mm, barely above average.

Table 17.7 Spring precipitation at the University of Reading, 1901-2014 (London Road 1901-1967, Whiteknights 1968 onwards).

Spring mean precipitation 139 mm (average 1981-2010)

Wettest springs			Driest springs			Wettest days	
Total fall,	*Per cent of*		*Total fall,*	*Per cent of*		*Daily fall,*	
mm	*normal*	*Year*	*mm*	*normal*	*Year*	*mm*	*Date*
277.9	200	1979	39.2	28	1990	37.3	25 Apr 1908
234.6	169	1981	43.2	31	2011	37.1	21 May 1932
232.0	167	1951	43.8	32	1944	34.5	14 Mar 1964
219.3	158	1937	51.4	37	1976	34.3	11 May 1948
216.5	156	2000	52.4	38	1938	32.5	19 May 1952

Thunderstorms

Thunder is most likely in May than in March or April, and can be expected on around three days in an average spring. Although about one spring in ten misses out on thunder entirely, in spring 1967 there were 12 days with thunder, and in spring 1983, 10.

Snowfall and lying snow

Although snowless springs are not uncommon, seven springs since 1908 have seen 10 or more days with snow or sleet observed to fall: 1917 saw 18 days with snow or sleet and 1970 16 days. The very cold spring of 1917 also had seven mornings with lying snow, and there were five such days in 1965.

Snow has been observed to fall as late as 17 May in 1935, and on 17 and 18 May 1955. Lying snow on the ground (covering at least half the surface) was observed as late as 13 April in 1917, and on both 14 and 15 April 1966, when it lay about 1 cm deep.

SUNSHINE

Spring averages almost five hours of sunshine daily, ranging from about three hours daily in early March to six hours by late May - in fact May in Reading is almost as sunny as each of the three summer months. Around ten days will remain sunless in a typical spring, half of these in March.

Table 17.8 Spring sunshine duration at the University of Reading, 1957-2014 (London Road 1957-1967, Whiteknights 1968 onwards).

Spring mean sunshine duration 457 hours, 4.97 hours per day (average 1981-2010)

Possible daylength: 1268 hours. Mean sunshine duration as percentage of possible: 36.0

Sunniest springs			Dullest springs			Sunniest days	
Duration,	*Per cent of*		*Duration,*	*Per cent of*		*Duration,*	
hours	*possible*	*Year*	*hours*	*possible*	*Year*	*hours*	*Date*
604.6	47.7	1990	321.5	25.3	1981	15.5	30 May 1966
595.7	47.0	1997	345.0	27.2	1991	15.5	30 May 1985
587.7	46.3	2007	355.2	28.0	1983	15.1	27 May 1977
586.0	46.2	2009	371.1	29.3	1975	15.1	29 May 2009
572.3	45.1	1995	375.3	29.6	1996	14.9	23 May 1966,
							22 May 1977,
							26 May 1978

TEMPERATURE, PRECIPITATION AND SUNSHINE IN GRAPHS – SPRING

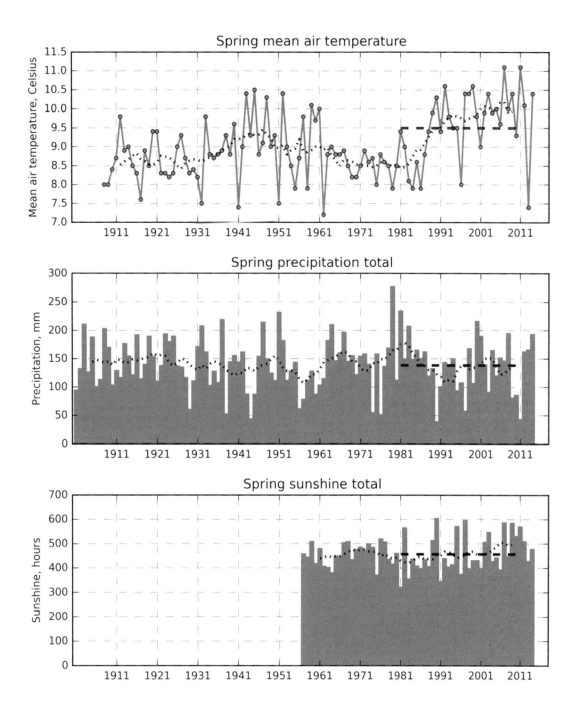

Figure 17.4 *Monthly values of (from top) mean temperature (°C), total precipitation (mm) and sunshine duration (hours) for spring in Reading over the available period of record (plots include London Road rainfall records where available 1901-04, with estimates from other Reading stations to 1907 as necessary).*

The mean temperatures as recorded at London Road 1908-67 have been reduced by 0.5 degC to ensure approximate homogeneity with the records from the Whiteknights site, 1968 onwards. No site adjustments have been made for precipitation or sunshine. For temperature and precipitation, the 10 year running mean centred on the year shown is indicated by a dashed grey line.

Summer *(June, July and August)*

Summer is the warmest season of the year, averaging 16.7 °C. July is the warmest month, and average daily temperatures reach a peak at the end of July - daily maximum temperatures reach around 23 °C in the last week of July and the first week of August, while daily minimum temperatures peak around 13.5 °C at the end of July.

Summer's mean precipitation total is 143 mm, with August being the wettest of all three months - although it is only some 8 mm wetter than the driest, June, on average. Rain falls on about 33 days in an average summer, with about four of those days being thundery.

There is very little difference in the month-to-month sunshine amounts (seasonal average some 578 hours of bright sunshine), although by the end of August the reduction in daylength becomes apparent. August is the least cloudy month of the year in Reading.

TEMPERATURE

During the period 1908-2014, summer temperatures in Reading have ranged from 0.6 °C to 36.4 °C. The hottest and coldest summer days and nights are shown in Table 17.9.

Table 17.9 Highest and lowest maximum and minimum temperatures in summer, 1908-2014. Records are from the (slightly warmer) London Road site 1908-1967, and from Whiteknights 1968-2014: no corrections for site differences have been applied.

Rank	Hottest days	Coldest days	Warmest nights	Coldest nights
1	36.4 °C, 10 Aug 2003	10.6 °C, 3 Jun 1953	20.8 °C, 2 Aug 1995	0.6 °C, 3 Jun 1923
2	36.0 °C, 9 Aug 1911	11.1 °C, 4 Jun 1932	19.9 °C, 29 Jul 1948	1.5 °C, 2 Jun 1991
3	35.5 °C, 3 Aug 1990	11.1 °C, 1 Jun 1964	19.9 °C, 11 Aug 2003	2.0 °C, 9 Jun 2001
4	35.3 °C, 19 Jul 2006	11.3 °C, 4 Jun 1909	19.4 °C, 23 Aug 1997	2.2 °C, 2 Jun 1962
5	34.7 °C, 12 Jul 1923	11.4 °C, 5 Jun 1932	19.4 °C, 9 Aug 2004	2.6 °C, 1 Jun 1962

The coldest nights of summer are most likely in early June – no summer month has ever experienced an air frost although 3 June 1923 came close. The coldest days of summer also tend to occur in June – no July or August day has failed to reach 13 °C in the period 1908-2014.

The very highest temperatures tend to occur in late July or early August – although in any particular summer the highest temperature can occur in any month – sometimes even in May or September. Temperatures in excess of 35 °C have been recorded on four days in the period 1908-2014 (Table 17.9).

Warm and cold summers

Making allowance for the temperature differences between the London Road and Whiteknights sites, in the period 1908-2014 the five warmest summers all occurred between 1976 and 2014, and the five coldest summers all occurred prior to 1955.

The summer of 1909 began with a cool June and July (temperatures remained below 24 °C) although 30 °C was attained in August. After a scorching summer in 1911, in 1912 the temperature reached only 20 °C in August, while in 1920 the hottest day of the year was in May with no day in the three summer months reaching 25 °C. The summer of 1922 was similar to 1920; May reached 30 °C but July and August failed to reach 24 °C. In 1954 a temperature of 25 °C was reached on only one day in summer, although September did manage 28 °C.

The warmth of summer 2006 was largely due to a fine July (the hottest month yet recorded in Reading), while the summer of 1976 will long be remembered for weeks of sunshine and extreme drought, and particularly the very hot fortnight during the last week of June and the first week of July when 30 °C was attained every day. This was by far the longest such hot spell in the Reading record –

the next longest spell of consecutive 30 °C days being the six days 11-16 August 1983. Although July 2003 was hot, it was the warmth of August that helped to complete another very warm summer.

Table 17.10 Summer mean temperatures at the University of Reading, 1908-2014. In summer the London Road site (1908-1967) is about 0.6 degC warmer than the Whiteknights site (1968 onwards) due to its location closer to the town centre. The observed mean temperatures at the London Road site (shown in brackets) have been adjusted by this amount to facilitate comparison between the two records.

Summer mean temperature 16.7°C (average 1981-2010)

Hottest summers			**Coolest summers**		
Mean temperature, °C	*Departure from 1981-2010 normal degC*	*Year*	*Mean temperature, °C*	*Departure from 1981-2010 normal degC*	*Year*
18.6	+1.9	2006	13.7 (14.3)	-3.0	1912
18.5	+1.8	1976	14.1 (14.7)	-2.6	1922
18.4	+1.7	2003	14.2 (14.8)	-2.5	1920
18.2	+1.5	1995	14.6 (15.0)	-2.1	1909
18.0	+1.3	1983	14.6 (15.0)	-2.1	1954

Frosts

No summer has recorded an air frost in Reading during 1908-2014, although ground frosts have occurred in all three summer months.

PRECIPITATION

The mean precipitation total for summer in Reading is 143 mm, falling on around 33 days.

Table 17.11 Summer precipitation at the University of Reading, 1901-2014 (London Road 1901-1967, Whiteknights 1968 onwards).

Summer mean precipitation 143 mm (average 1981-2010)

Wettest summers			**Driest summers**			**Wettest days**	
Total fall, mm	*Per cent of normal*	*Year*	*Total fall, mm*	*Per cent of normal*	*Year*	*Daily fall, mm*	*Date*
314.4	220	1917	33.7	24	1995	60.5	11 Jun 1970 *T*
301.0	210	1903	48.0	34	1921	59.5	18 Aug 2008
270.8	189	1941	55.3	39	1913	55.6	20 Aug 1932 *T*
264.9	185	1927	63.5	44	2006	54.7	10 Jun 1971
260.2	182	1920	69.6	49	1911	52.6	9 Aug 1999

T after the date of the heaviest fall indicates thunder was heard on that date.

The summer of 1917 was outstandingly wet in Reading. Each month was wet - 143 mm fell in July and 105 mm in August. In 1941, both July and August again recorded more than 100 mm of rainfall. Conversely, only two summers during the period 1901-2014 have recorded less than 50 mm of rain; in the remarkably dry year of 1921, June and July combined could only muster 12.3 mm, while in 1995 June and August together managed just 13.0 mm, and the summer just 33.7 mm.

It is perhaps surprising at first glance that the scorching summer of 1976 does not feature in the table of driest summers. The reason for this was a series of thunderstorms overnight 15/16 July of that year, in which 35.1 mm of rain fell in less than 4 hours – almost half of the three-month summer total of 78.5 mm. (Almost 12 mm – 15% of that summer's rainfall – fell in just 6 minutes.) Aside from this, however, the prolonged drought of 1975/76 currently dominates the 'driest period' statistics on the university's records for all durations from 6-18 months (Table 20.2), although the spring and summer of 1990 were drier than similar periods in 1976, and summer 1995 was (by some margin) the driest on Reading's records.

Summers between 1908 and 2014 contained seven days that each received in excess of 50 mm of rain, the wettest summer day being 11 June 1970, which received 60.5 mm, most of that in a short afternoon thunderstorm (see June's chapter). Perhaps surprisingly, only one other of these five days (namely 20 August 1932) reported thunder during the day.

Thunderstorms

Summer is the main season for thunderstorms in Reading. When conditions are favourable moist air from the surrounding seas and warm air from the continent are brought together – with explosive results. Only the summer of 1909 was entirely free of thunder in the period 1908-2014. As with any weather type there can be large variations from season to season: in 11 summers during 1908-2014 there were 10 or more days with thunder, with 1930 (12 days), 1983 (12 days) and 1960 (13 days) being the most thundery. Typically, however, thunder is heard on about four days during the summer.

SUNSHINE

Summer is the sunniest season of the year, with each month having a similar sunshine duration on average (in the range 189 hours to 197 hours): only about four days will remain sunless.

Table 17.12 Summer sunshine duration at the University of Reading, 1956-2014 (London Road 1956-1967, Whiteknights 1968 onwards).

Summer mean sunshine duration 578 hours, 6.28 hours per day (average 1981-2010)

Possible daylength: 1446 hours. Mean sunshine duration as percentage of possible: 40.0

Sunniest summers			Dullest summers			Sunniest days	
Duration, hours	*Per cent of possible*	*Year*	*Duration, hours*	*Per cent of possible*	*Year*	*Duration, hours*	*Date*
842.9	58.3	1976	423.0	29.2	1956	16.0	30 Jun 1976
807.6	55.8	1959	446.3	30.9	1988	15.8	4 Jul 1959
778.4	53.8	1975	457.2	31.6	1965	15.7	24 Jun 1976
733.1	50.7	1989	465.7	32.2	1968	15.7	3 Jul 1968
709.1	49.0	2006	471.5	32.6	1987	15.5	14 Jun 1959, 16 Jun 1959, 29 Jun 1976

The consecutive summers of 1975 and 1976 are noteworthy for their large sunshine totals (see Figures 11.3 and 17.5), while in recent years 1988 stands out as being very dull – and that followed the dull summer of 1987. Summer 1956 was the dullest year since records began at the university in … well, 1956, while the summer of 1959 continued long hours of sunshine well into October. This latter summer was described by *The Berkshire Chronicle* on 7 August of that year as one of the 'most satisfying' for a decade.

When the impact of temperature, sunshine and lack of rain is taken into account, the summers of 1975 and 1976 are arguably the best pair of consecutive summers in the Reading record; however, the summers of 1995 and 2006 were equally as good. However, when considered in terms of temperature and rainfall as well as sunshine, summer 1976 remains without equal on Reading's records (see also Figure 11.3, page 61).

TEMPERATURE, PRECIPITATION AND SUNSHINE IN GRAPHS – SUMMER

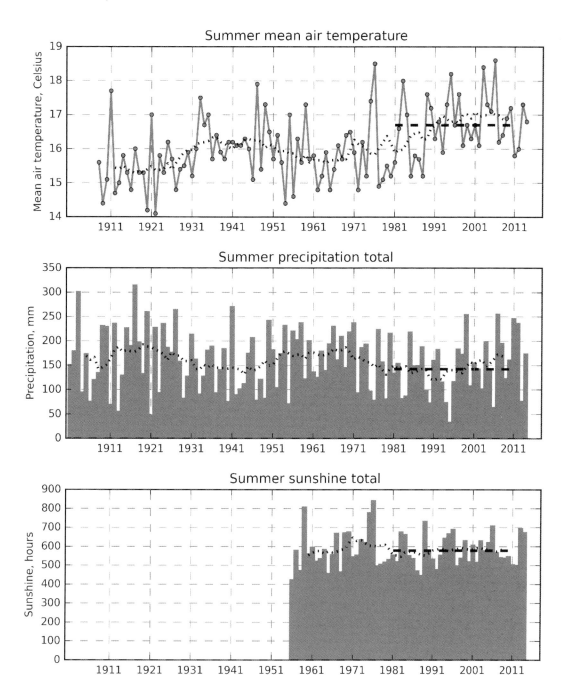

Figure 17.5 *Monthly values of (from top) mean temperature (°C), total precipitation (mm) and sunshine duration (hours) for summer in Reading over the available period of record (plots include London Road rainfall records where available 1901-04, with estimates from other Reading stations to 1907 as necessary)*

The mean temperatures as recorded at London Road 1908-67 have been reduced by 0.6 degC to ensure approximate homogeneity with the records from the Whiteknights site, 1968 onwards. No site adjustments have been made for precipitation or sunshine. For temperature and precipitation, the 10 year running mean centred on the year shown is indicated by a dashed grey line

Autumn *(September, October and November)*

Autumn can be the season of strong winds and storms, anticyclonic fogs, the first air frosts associated with a shortening of the daylight hours and can also produce the first snows of the coming winter. As daylength decreases the temperature falls, from about 20.5 °C (by day) and 11.0 °C (by night) at the start of September, to 9 °C and 3 °C (respectively) at the end of November.

Autumn contains the two wettest months of the year (October and November) and is consequently the wettest season of the year with 189 mm of precipitation expected to fall. Rain falls on about 39 days on average, with snow or sleet falling in one autumn in two on average.

Sunshine can be expected to total 308 hours during autumn, with November receiving about half the sunshine that is registered in September.

TEMPERATURE

Temperatures in autumn have ranged from 31.7 °C to -8.3 °C during the period 1908-2014. The warmest and coldest autumn nights during this period are shown in Table 17.13.

Table 17.13 Highest and lowest maximum and minimum temperatures in autumn, 1908-2014. Records are from the (slightly milder) London Road site 1908-1967, and from Whiteknights 1968-2014: no corrections for site differences have been applied.

Rank	Hottest days	Coldest days	Warmest nights	Coldest nights
1	31.7 °C, 7 Sep 1911	-1.9 °C, 25 Nov 1923	20.3 °C, 5 Sep 1949	-8.3 °C, 23 Nov 1983
2	31.2 °C, 4 Sep 1929	-1.8 °C, 26 Nov 1923	18.0 °C, 5 Sep 2006	-6.7 °C, 26 Nov 1923
3	30.6 °C, 8 Sep 1929	-0.1 °C, 28 Nov 2010	17.6 °C, 5 Sep 2005	-6.7 °C, 27 Nov 1923
4	30.5 °C, 3 Sep 1911	0.1 °C, 23 Nov 1923	17.6 °C, 12 Sep 1945	-6.4 °C, 24 Nov 1983
5	30.3 °C, 11 Sep 1919 and 5 Sep 1929	0.2 °C, 22 Nov 1956	17.5 °C, 3 Sep 1939	-6.4 °C, 26 Nov 1989

With the midday sun gradually sinking lower in the sky as autumn advances, it is not surprising to find that the warmest days and nights tend to occur in early September with the coldest days and nights in late November. Early September can see a continuation of the warmth of late summer while it is possible for ice days to occur in late November. 25-26 November 1923 was remarkable for the fact that the temperature remained below 0 °C for over 48 consecutive hours.

1911 and 1929 both had more than one day reaching 30 °C in September, while the minimum temperature on 5 September 1949 was only the second occasion in any month (the other being in August 1995) when it remained above 20 °C overnight.

Warm and cold autumns

The autumn of 2006 was the outstandingly warmest in the series while 2011 and 2014 were also much warmer than the fourth warmest in the record. In fact the five warmest autumns of 1908-2014 have all occurred after 2004. The autumn of 2016 was 0.7 degC warmer than any other autumn in the record, and followed the warmest summer in the record. The coldest autumns were those of 1919, 1952 and 1922 at London Road with the six coldest autumns all occurring before 1953.

Table 17.14 Autumn mean temperatures at the University of Reading, 1908-2014. In autumn the London Road site (1908-1967) is about 0.4 degC milder than the Whiteknights site (1968 onwards) due to its location closer to the town centre. The observed mean temperatures at the London Road site (shown in brackets) have been adjusted by this amount to facilitate comparison between the two records.

Autumn mean temperature 11.1°C (average 1981-2010)

Mildest autumns			Coldest autumns		
Mean temperature, °C	Departure from 1981-2010 normal degC	Year	Mean temperature, °C	Departure from 1981-2010 normal degC	Year
13.6	+2.5	2006	7.9 (8.3)	-3.2	1919
12.9	+1.8	2011	8.3 (8.7)	-2.8	1912
12.7	+1.6	2014	8.3 (8.7)	-2.8	1952
12.2	+1.1	2005	8.5 (8.9)	-2.6	1922
12.2	+1.1	2009	8.6 (9.0)	-2.5	1915, 1923

Frosts

Only the autumn seasons of 1958, 1986, 1994 and 2009 have been entirely free of air frost. In 1910 and 1919 there were, respectively, 18 and 19 days with air frost while at Whiteknights 1993 had the most autumn air frost (16 days). In 1994 the first air frost of the autumn-winter period did not occur until 15 December, while the earliest air frosts in the record occurred at the (warmer) London Road site on 23 September 1914 and 29 September 1919.

During the period 1925-2014, the median date of the first autumn air frost was 3 November, meaning that half the years can be expected to have their first air frost before, and half after, this date. Only in 10 per cent of the years did the first air frost occur after 24 November, although the 10 per cent of years with the earliest air frost saw this happening before 16 October.

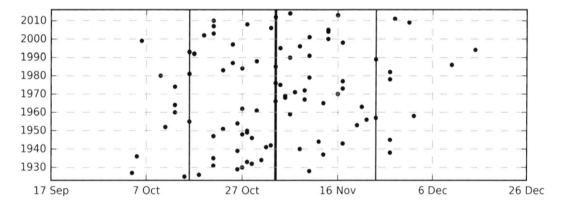

Figure 17.6 *The date of the first air frost of autumn/winter during 1925-2014. The three dark vertical lines show (from left to right) the 10th percentile, the median and 90th percentile dates of the last air frost. One tenth of the values lie to the left of the 10th percentile and one tenth to the right of the 90th percentile. The median marks the mid-point; half the values lie to its right and half to its left*

PRECIPITATION

The average autumn precipitation in Reading is 189 mm, falling on around 43 days.

Table 17.15 Autumn precipitation at the University of Reading, 1901-2014 (London Road 1901-1966, Whiteknights 1968 onwards).

Autumn mean precipitation 189 mm (average 1981-2010)

Wettest autumns			Driest autumns			Wettest days	
Total fall,	Per cent of		Total fall,	Per cent of		Daily fall,	
mm	normal	Year	mm	normal	Year	mm	Date
353.4	187	2000	47.3	25	1978	76.3	22 Sep 1992
352.2	186	1974	62.3	33	1947	50.9	20 Sep 1980 *T*
349.3	185	1960	74.0	39	1964	50.0	11 Sep 1921 *T*
307.0	162	1976	78.3	41	1985	49.8	15 Sep 1968
305.0	161	2006	84.0	44	1922	49.3	29 Oct 2000

T after the date of the heaviest fall indicates thunder was heard on the same date

The three autumns of 1960, 1974 and 2000 stand out as by far the wettest in the record – each with almost twice the normal rainfall. In 2000 all three months were wet with over 150 mm falling in October while in both September and November 1974 over 140 mm fell in each month). However October 1960 was the wettest month of any in the period 1908-2014 although October 1903 was marginally wetter (but the other months that autumn had near-normal rainfall amounts).

Only in the autumn of 1978 did less than 50 mm fall with just 4.1 mm falling in October.

A fall of 76.3 mm on 22 September 1992 made this the wettest of any day during 1908-2014. The rain was thundery but despite the intensity there was little flooding around Reading. However, 20 homes were evacuated in the early hours the following morning from a Lower Earley estate as a nearby tributary burst its banks. Two other days in autumn have also produced falls in excess of 50 mm, namely 11 September 1921 (the pocket register mentions the occurrence of torrential rain throughout the evening and into the following morning, with some thunder) and 20 September 1980 (when most of the fall came from a thunderstorm that commenced in the evening).

Thunderstorms
About one autumn in five escapes any thunder in Reading – and the occurrence of more than five thunder days is rare in this season. In 1974 there were eight autumn days with thunder, and seven in 1976.

Snowfall and lying snow
About 70 per cent of all autumns are snow-free. Snow or sleet fell during 1981-2010 on an average of one day every ten years in October and on four days in every ten Novembers. Four autumns (1919, 1925, 1952 and 1969) have seen at least five days with snowfall (there were six days in 1919) while only 9 November 1921 (depth unknown), 29 October 2008 (1 cm) and 30 November 2010 (2 cm) have had snow lying at 0900 GMT in autumn. The earliest known snowfall in autumn during 1917-2014 was that of 15 October 1934, when sleet fell.

SUNSHINE
Autumn sees a marked decline in daily sunshine totals with an average duration for the season of 308 hours with the sunniest days consequently occurring during the first week of September. In September 2.6 sunless days occur on average – by November this has increased to 8.9 days.

Table 17.16 Autumn sunshine duration at the University of Reading, 1956-2014 (London Road 1956-1967, Whiteknights 1968 onwards).

Autumn mean sunshine duration 308 hours, 3.39 hours per day (average 1981-2010)

Possible daylength: 978 hours. Mean sunshine duration as percentage of possible: 31.5

Sunniest autumns			Dullest autumns			Sunniest days	
Duration, hours	*Per cent of possible*	*Year*	*Duration, hours*	*Per cent of possible*	*Year*	*Duration, hours*	*Date*
435.7	44.5	1971	245.2	25.1	1976	12.6	2 Sep 1982
416.0	42.5	1959	245.8	25.1	1968	12.0	3 Sep 1977
400.3	40.9	2003	247.4	25.3	1984	12.0	2 Sep 1994
396.6	40.5	1964	249.1	25.5	1993	12.0	4 Sep 2003
381.7	39.0	1999	250.2	25.6	1963	11.9	3 Sep 1976, 4 Sep 2004, 7 Sep 2006

The autumns of 1971 and 2003 were the sunniest during 1956-2014 – and the only ones to record over 400 hours of sunshine. After the sunny summer of that year, autumn 1976 was extremely dull – although there was little to choose overall between 1976, 1968, 1984 and 1993 in terms of sunshine totals.

Fog at 0900 GMT

On average one autumn in 15 is fog-free at 0900 GMT with 1920 (20 mornings) and 1908 (22 mornings) being the foggiest autumns. Since 1970 the foggiest autumn was in 1988 (12 mornings) with 10 mornings of fog in three other autumns – suggesting a decrease in incidence since 1970.

TEMPERATURE, PRECIPITATION AND SUNSHINE IN GRAPHS – AUTUMN

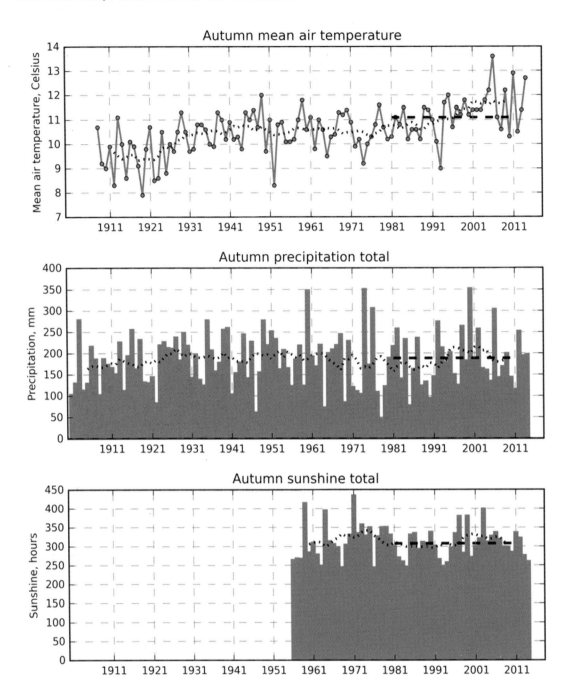

Figure 17.7 *Monthly values of (from top) mean temperature (°C), total precipitation (mm) and sunshine duration (hours) for autumn in Reading over the available period of record (plots include London Road rainfall records where available 1901-04, with estimates from other Reading stations to 1907 as necessary).*

The mean temperatures as recorded at London Road 1908-67 have been reduced by 0.4 degC to ensure approximate homogeneity with the records from the Whiteknights site, 1968 onwards. No site adjustments have been made for precipitation or sunshine. For temperature and precipitation, the 10 year running mean centred on the year shown is indicated by a dashed grey line.

18 Holiday weather

It's a Bank Holiday – does that mean a weekend of bad weather?

When discussing plans for any Bank Holiday weekend, the inevitable question that tends to pop up goes something like 'A Bank Holiday weekend – so it's bound to rain, isn't it?'

Perhaps it's because we're more likely to try to do something special on such weekends, whether that be visiting relatives, taking a short holiday or attending the local village fête, that the weather plays more of a role in our plans than it does on 'normal' weekends. Perhaps cold and wet Bank Holiday weekends persist longer in our memory than ones that go to plan.

So how does Bank Holiday weather compare with that of the preceding and following weeks in Reading? Here we look at weather conditions during the thirty year period 1981 to 2010.

NEW YEAR'S EVE AND NEW YEAR'S DAY

Aside from Christmas, this is the only bank holiday period that is fixed by date. On average the two day period experiences daytime temperatures of 7.7 °C, overnight minima of 2.2 °C, and receives 5.7 mm of rain and 2.7 hours of bright sunshine in all.

However, one holiday period in three is sunless – which is to be expected as the holiday comes only a few days after the winter solstice (the shortest day of the year). Almost half the holiday periods receive less than 1 mm of precipitation, with two-thirds of the 30 New Year's Eves also falling into this precipitation category – a useful statistic for those out and about on this evening.

Interestingly, the holiday period seems to follow a slightly cooler period with the day before New Year's Eve being unusually wet on average. But the New Year does, on average, start on a relatively sunny note after a dull end to the old year.

THE EASTER BANK HOLIDAY

The date of Easter is not fixed, and can occur between 22 March and 25 April, a five-week period. This period corresponds to early to mid-spring and for this reason the weather in any year can be very dependent upon the date. For this reason no analysis of Easter weather has been carried out here. Early Easters are more likely to be cold and to experience snowfall; late Easters can be reasonably warm and sunny, for reasons purely of seasonal advance rather than anything intrinsic to the event itself.

MAY DAY BANK HOLIDAY

An average May Day Bank Holiday weekend (i.e. the three days Saturday to Monday) records daytime temperatures of 15.5 °C, overnight minima of 6.5 °C, receives 3.2 mm of rain and 18.3 hours of bright sunshine.

Only in 1990 and 1995 did the temperature during this weekend rise above 25 °C – both on a Saturday; the warmest Monday was only 21.8 °C, in 1999. The only days during the 30 years to record more than 10 mm of rain were the Monday in 2004 (13.6 mm) and the Sunday in 2006 (12.2 mm). Being early in spring, the holiday weekend often has cold starts to the day – but there was no air frost during 1981-2010.

Statistics from Reading indicate that having the holiday later would make it slightly warmer but not sunnier overall – the former is consistent with the warming of days as spring progresses. In addition, having the holiday earlier might make it slightly wetter.

LATE MAY BANK HOLIDAY

This holiday weekend occurs during late spring at a time when the length of daylight is increasing day by day, and as a result successive days tend to be getting progressively warmer. Analysis of the weather on and around the Bank Holiday confirms that if the weekend were to occur later then it would be slightly sunnier and warmer.

An average Late May Bank Holiday weekend records daytime temperatures of 17.6 °C, overnight minima of 8.8 °C, and receives 7.7 mm of rain and 17.9 hours of bright sunshine.

However, when it comes to rainfall, the Bank Holiday Saturday and Sunday during these thirty years were wetter (on average) than any day in the preceding or following week. Why is this?

During the fortnight period around each of the 30 Bank Holidays, the wettest day occurred on the Sunday of the 2007 holiday (31.6 mm) while the Saturday of the 1987 weekend gave 18.5 mm of rain. In addition the Saturdays of the 1984 and 2000 weekends saw 17.4 mm and 16.6 mm fall, respectively, while the Sundays in the weekends of 1981, 1985 and 2008 were also wet.

Of the 21 wettest days during the week before and after the Bank Holiday, eight occurred during the three-day Bank Holiday period, whereas statistically we would expect just 3.9 days. Thus records do suggest a greater tendency for wet days to occur twice a frequently as might be expected during this weekend holiday period. This is probably just chance – another 30 year period might show the opposite!

LATE AUGUST BANK HOLIDAY

This holiday is, for many of us, the last chance for a small summer holiday before school restarts, and so, maybe, the weather takes on greater importance than during other Bank Holidays.

An average August Bank Holiday weekend records daytime temperatures of 21.1 °C, overnight minima of 11.8 °C, and receives 3.8 mm of rain and 18.0 hours of bright sunshine. The Saturday tends to be about 1.3 degC warmer than the Monday.

Daylength is declining quite quickly at the end of August, and temperatures are beginning to fall away from the levels of high summer, trends confirmed by long-period weather statistics. Thus, if the holiday period was earlier (as it is in Scotland) then it would tend to be warmer. However, they suggest that it would not be any sunnier unless it was made more than a week earlier. In addition, only two days during the 30 three-day Bank Holiday periods received more than 8 mm of rain – in 1992 the Saturday recorded 18.2 mm, while in 1986 27.5 mm fell on the Monday. About two Bank Holidays in five record no measureable rainfall on any of the days.

CHRISTMAS

This three-day period (24th-26th) is a fixed holiday. On average the three day period records daytime temperatures of 7.9 °C, overnight minima of 2.3 °C, and receives 6.5 mm of rain and 3.2 hours of bright sunshine.

Interestingly, the Christmas period seems to coincide with a short-lived mild spell (both Christmas Eve and Christmas Day are milder than any other day in the preceding or following week) although Christmas is also a dull period – Christmas Eve was, on average, the dullest day of the year over the 1981-2010 period, and Christmas Day the third dullest.

CONCLUSIONS

This simple analysis does seem to suggest that moving those Bank Holidays whose dates are not fixed by the calendar date or religious observances would have little noticeable effect upon the holiday weather conditions. Unfortunately, it seems as if one wet day seems to live long in the memory if it leads to a ruined weekend – while after a holiday during which conditions were sunnier or warmer than normal, we tend to expect the same conditions to persist during future holidays.

19 Warmest, driest, sunniest …

The following analysis is based upon daily statistics for the University of Reading over the standard 30 year period 1981-2010, and excludes 29 February. Different analysis periods would probably show slightly different results.

The most reliably warm week of the year in Reading is the final week of July; this also starts out as one of the least rainy periods of the year, although 23 July saw the highest frequency of thunder on any day in those 30 years. Mid-June is the most reliably sunny time of the year, and one of the driest too. Early to mid-February tends to be the coldest time of the year, and the most likely to see snowfall, while late December is the least sunny.

		DAILY VALUES		WEEKLY VALUES	
		Value	*Date*	*Value*	*Week comm.*
WARMEST	Highest mean daily maximum temperature	23.7 °C	29 July	23.2 °C	25 July
	Highest mean daily minimum temperature	13.8 °C	31 July	13.3 °C	25 July
	Highest mean daily temperature	18.6 °C	29 July	18.2 °C	25 July
COLDEST	Lowest mean daily maximum temperature	6.7 °C	30 Jan	7.3 °C 7.4 °C	25 Dec 6 Jan, 14 Feb
	Lowest mean daily minimum temperature	-0.0 °C	14 Feb	0.9 °C	14 Feb
	Lowest mean daily temperature	3.4 °C	14 Feb	4.2 °C	14 Feb
WETTEST	Highest mean daily rainfall	6.5 mm	9 Aug	3.68 mm/day	18 Oct
	Highest frequency of rain days	21 days in 30 years (70%)	4 Jan, 17 May, 8 Nov and 17 Dec	4.2 days/wk	3 Jan
DRIEST	Lowest mean daily rainfall	0.33 mm 0.34 mm	27 July 12 June	1.04 mm/day	2 May
	Lowest frequency of rain days	6 days in 30 years (20%)	16 Feb, 13 Mar, 12 June, 27 July, 15 and 28 Aug	1.9 days/wk	12 June and 28 Aug
SUNNIEST	Highest mean daily sunshine duration	8.30 hours	15 June	6.97 hours/day 6.96 hours/day	15 Aug 13 June
DULLEST	Lowest mean daily sunshine duration	0.67 hours	24 Dec	1.15 hours/day	20 Dec
SNOW COVER	Highest frequency of morning snow cover	6 days in 30 years (20%)	9 Feb	1.0 day/week	7 Feb
THUNDER	Highest frequency of thunder heard	6 days in 30 years (20%)	27 April 23 July	0.57 days/week 0.53 days/week	28 July 10 May

20 Droughts and wet spells

Droughts can take many forms. Meteorologically, two definitions are sometimes used:

- *Absolute drought* - A period of at least 15 consecutive days, during which no day receives as much as 0.2 mm of precipitation.

- *Partial drought* - A period of at least 29 consecutive days, whose mean daily precipitation does not exceed 0.2 mm.

These definitions were introduced in 1887 by G.J. Symons in *British Rainfall* but ceased to be used officially about 50 years ago; however, they remain useful ways of summarising short-term rainfall deficits, particularly in southern England. Table 20.1 shows the longest such droughts recorded during 1908-2015 (April) at the London Road and Whiteknights sites. Such droughts tend to occur in the summer rather than the winter half of the year, but it is interesting to note that the longest partial drought began towards the end of winter.

Drought impacts are more keenly felt in summer when temperatures are higher and the rate of evaporation of water from the soil is higher. In winter the soil can stay quite moist even during a 15 day absolute drought due to minimal evaporation of soil moisture, particularly in cold weather. A major cause of drought in Britain is the persistence of warm anticyclones, and the displacement of mid-latitude depressions northwards.

Table 20.1 Periods of absolute drought lasting at least 25 days, and of partial drought lasting at least 50 days, in order of decreasing drought length. Period January 1908 to April 2015.

Absolute droughts of at least 25 days			**Partial droughts** of at least 50 days		
Start date	*Duration (days)*	*Period total rainfall (mm)*	Start date	*Duration (days)*	*Period total rainfall (mm)*
21 Jul 1976	37	trace	27 Feb 1938	65	12.9
15 Aug 1959	37	trace	17 Jan 1932	65	9.4
20 Feb 1953	34	nil	4 Jul 1955	63	12.5
5 Aug 1947	33	trace	27 Jan 1993	62	10.5
25 Mar 1997	31	0.1	10 Feb 1929	60	11.2
10 Apr 1942	30	nil	4 Jun 1921	59	11.1
11 Jun 1941	30	trace	14 Aug 1959	59	8.5
12 Apr 1984	28	0.1	26 Feb 1997	58	11.0
1 Sep 1929	28	trace	26 Jun 1935	57	11.3
16 Sep 1986	28	trace	17 Jul 1947	57	11.1
14 Nov 1989	27	trace	6 Feb 1948	54	10.1
8 Jun 1949	26	nil	22 Jul 1940	52	9.0
9 Oct 1985	26	0.1	3 Jul 1995	51	9.4
26 Feb 1943	25	trace	4 May 1959	51	9.0
6 Apr 1954	25	trace	18 May 1975	50	8.7
7 May 1961	25	trace			
1 Jun 1925	25	trace			
2 Jul 1911	25	nil			
18 Jul 1916	25	nil			
14 Aug 1972	25	0.1			

Various categories of drought affect water consumers differently, depending upon their water usage requirements. The water supply industry is more likely to be affected by a dry winter, when underground (groundwater) water levels are insufficiently replenished by winter rainfall -

evaporation exceeds rainfall in most summers in southern England. For a farmer the development of a drought occurs more rapidly and might be said to occur when the surface soil layers become too dry. Clearly for these types of consumers a longer-term approach to the statistics is needed.

Table 20.2 shows both the driest and wettest spells of particular durations recorded during 1908-2015 (April). Notable wet spells have included those of late 1929 to January 1930, the very wet winters of 2000/01 (this latter event part of a wet spell lasting over a year and ending in May 2001) and more recently 2013/14, and the prolonged wet conditions during the first world war, from December 1914 to early 1916 (although the spring of 1915 was quite dry at times).

Notable dry periods include early 1975 to September 1976, the dry year of 1990, and particularly dry spells during 1938, 1976 and 1990, along with spring 1929 and the prolonged fine summer of 1959. Note that 1929 is the only year to appear in both tables – the driest 70 day spell from February to April that year received only 15 mm of precipitation, whereas the 70 day spell commencing in November received 353 mm – more than 20 times as much rainfall in the earlier period.

Table 20.2 Precipitation depth-duration extremes (period January 1908 to April 2015) – *continued overleaf*

Wettest spells

Period length	Amount mm	mm/day	(Start and) end dates
1 day	76.3	76.3	22 Sep 1992
2 days	83.3	41.7	22-23 Sep 1992
3 days	88.8	29.6	22-24 Sep 1992
4 days	92.9	23.2	22-25 Sep 1992
	86.1	21.5	29 July - 1 Aug 1917
	77.2	19.3	6-9 June 1910
5 days	93.0	18.6	21-25 Sep 1992
7 days	96.1	13.7	19-25 Sep 1992
	95.8	13.7	8-14 Jun 1971
	95.5	13.6	29 July - 4 Aug 1917
10 days	129.0	12.9	10-19 June 1971
	128.5	12.9	11-20 Dec 1989
14 days (2 weeks)	147.2	10.5	11-24 Dec 1989
	140.2	10.0	7-20 June 1971
15 days	150.7	10.0	11-25 Dec 1989
20 days	171.3	8.6	22 Nov – 11 Dec 1929
	165.0	8.3	8-27 Oct 1949
21 days (3 weeks)	172.8	8.2	22 Nov - 12 Dec 1929
25 days	197.9	7.9	15 Nov - 9 Dec 1929
28 days (4 weeks)	206.8	7.4	15 Nov - 12 Dec 1929
30 days	221.3	7.4	11 Nov - 10 Dec 1929

Where precipitation amounts are identical in adjacent periods, only the first-ending period is given. All are based on 'rainday' (0900-0900 GMT) daily totals. Only one instance is given for each unique (non-overlapping) spell, even though the spell may include other greater extremes than any second-shown occurrence. The period totals are exact day totals, the monthly values shown are an approximation to the number of days shown.

The highest-known sub-daily falls recorded since 1960 are 11.7 mm in 6 minutes on 15 July 1976, 16.9 mm in about 45 minutes on 20 June 1988, 20.3 mm in 48 minutes on 23 July 1967, 34 mm in 27 minutes on 11 June 1970, and 34.5 mm in 2 hours on 22 June 1951.

In November 1894, one raingauge in Portland Place, Reading, recorded 207 mm in the 23 days ending 14 November – only one of which remained dry.

Table 20.2 precipitation depth-duration extremes in Reading, 1901 – April 2015 – *continued*

| Period length | Wettest spells | | | Driest spells | | |
	Amount mm	mm /day	Start and end dates	Amount mm	mm/day	Start and end dates
34 days				nil	0	20 Feb - 25 Mar 1953
35 days (5 weeks)	235.6	6.7	6 Nov - 10 Dec 1929			
37 days				trace	0	15 Aug - 20 Sep 1959
				trace	0	21 July - 26 Aug 1976
40 days	247.0	6.2	5 Nov - 14 Dec 1929			
45 days	268.4	6.0	15 Nov - 29 Dec 1929			
50 days	290.2	5.8	11 Nov - 30 Dec 1929	1.1	0.02	15 Aug - 3 Oct 1959
				1.2	0.02	6 Mar - 24 Apr 1997
55 days	309.2	5.6	11 Nov 1929 - 4 Jan 1930	1.1	0.02	15 Aug - 8 Oct 1959
60 days (2 months)	323.5	5.4	6 Nov 1929 - 4 Jan 1930	8.3	0.14	1 Mar - 29 Apr 1938
65 days	343.2	5.3	15 Dec 2013 - 17 Feb 2014	9.4	0.14	17 Jan - 21 Mar 1932
70 days	353.0	5.0	6 Nov 1929 - 14 Jan 1930	15.3	0.22	16 Feb - 26 Apr 1929
				16.2	0.23	16 May - 24 July 1921
75 days	368.1	4.9	15 Dec 2013 - 27 Feb 2014	17.1	0.23	11 Feb - 26 Apr 1929
80 days	382.0	4.8	14 Dec 2013 - 3 Mar 2014	19.0	0.24	11 Feb - 1 May 1938
85 days	402.6	4.7	19 Sep - 12 Dec 2000	20.6	0.24	1 Mar - 24 May 1938
90 days	419.0	4.7	14 Sep - 12 Dec 2000	22.6	0.25	1 Feb - 1 May 1938
120 days (4 months)	463.4	3.9	8 Sep 2000 - 5 Jan 2001	49.5	0.41	19 Apr - 16 Aug 1990
150 days (5 months)	569.1	3.8	16 Sep 2000 - 12 Feb 2001	70.5	0.47	20 Mar - 16 Aug 1990
180 days (6 months)	621.0	3.5	18 Sep 2000 - 16 Mar 2001	96.8	0.54	2 Dec 1975 - 29 May 1976
240 days (8 months)	759.0	3.2	13 Aug 2000 - 9 Apr 2001	159.2	0.66	1 Jan - 27 Aug 1976
300 days (10 months)	840.4	2.8	3 Jul 2000 - 28 Apr 2001	237.1	0.79	26 Feb - 22 Dec 1990
360 days	995.8	2.8	2 Apr 2000 - 27 Mar 2001	312.3	0.87	28 Sep 1975 - 21 Sep 1976
365 days (1 year)	1002.4	2.7	1 Apr 2000 - 31 Mar 2001	346.4	0.95	21 Sep 1975 - 19 Sep 1976
420 days (14 months)	1101.2	2.6	24 Mar 2000 - 17 May 2001	411.9	0.98	18 May 1975 - 10 July 1976
480 days (16 months)	1251.0	2.6	4 Dec 1914 - 27 Mar 1916	474.4	0.99	18 May 1975 - 8 Sep 1976
540 days (18 months)	1378.5	2.6	6 Oct 1914 - 26 Mar 1916	586.0	1.09	17 Mar 1975 - 6 Sep 1976
630 days (21 months)	1552.1	2.5	31 July 1999 - 17 Apr 2001	759.4	1.21	26 Feb 2010 – 17 Nov 2011
730 days (2 years)	1792.2	2.46	22 Nov 1914 - 20 Nov 1916	829.7	1.14	1 Mar 1990 – 28 Feb 1992

21 Earliest and latest dates

TABLE 21.1 MAXIMUM AIR TEMPERATURES
PERIOD JANUARY 1908 TO APRIL 2015

Maximum temperature	Earliest date	Value, °C	Latest date	Value, °C
< 0 °C	25 Nov 1923	-1.9	6 March 1942	-0.6
> 20 °C	9 March 1948	21.8	5 Nov 1938	20.4
21 °C (70 °F)	9 March 1948	21.8	31 Oct 2014	21.7
25 °C	16 April 1943	25.5	9 Oct 1921	26.0
	16 April 1945	25.8		
	16 April 1949	26.2		
	16 April 2003	25.7		
27 °C (80 °F)	7 May 1976	27.4	6 Oct 1921	27.7
30 °C	22 May 1922	31.2	11 Sept 1919	30.3
32 °C (90 °F)	17 June 1917	33.9	29 August 1930	32.2
35 °C	19 July 2006	35.3	10 August 2003	36.3

TABLE 21.2 MINIMUM AIR TEMPERATURES
PERIOD JANUARY 1908 TO APRIL 2015

Threshold temperature	Earliest date	Value, °C	Latest date	Value, °C
Dates within the winter season, starting 1 July				
5 °C	25 July 1978	4.9	30 June 1972	4.6
0 °C	23 Sept 1914	-0.3	31 May 1975	-0.1
-5 °C	3 Nov 1985	-5.0	23 March 2008	-5.5
-10 °C	13 Dec 1981	-13.4	7 March 1947	-11.3
Dates within the calendar year				
15 °C	9 May 1945	16.2	23 Oct 1998	15.3
20 °C	2 Aug 1995	20.8	5 Sept 1949	20.3

TABLE 21.3 SNOW OR SLEET OBSERVED TO FALL
PERIOD JANUARY 1918 TO APRIL 2015

Earliest dates	Latest dates
15 October 1934, sleet	Snow, 18 May 1955
(at 2-3 pm. Confirmed by local observations	Snow, 17 May 1955
from Ascot and Warfield)	Snow, 17 May 1935
23 October 1921, sleet	Sleet, 14 May 1935
27 October 1933, snow	
28 October 2008, heavy snow	

TABLE 21.4 SNOW LYING AT 0900 GMT
PERIOD SEPTEMBER 1950 TO APRIL 2015

Depth threshold	Earliest date	Latest date
> 50% cover, > 0 cm	29 October 2008, depth 1 cm	15 April 1966, depth 3 cm
≥ 5 cm	8 December 1967, 8 cm	6 April 2008, 6 cm
	8 December 1981, 7 cm	
≥ 10 cm	11 December 1981, 15 cm	30 March 1952, 10 cm
≥ 15 cm	11 December 1981, 15 cm	5 March 1965, 18 cm
≥ 20 cm	30 December 1962, 21 cm	4 March 1965, 20 cm

Note that 2008 had both the latest date for 5 cm snow cover (6 April) and the earliest date for any snow cover (29 October), thus having the shortest snow-free season on the record – less than 7 months

TABLE 21.5 SUNSHINE DURATION THRESHOLDS
PERIOD APRIL 1956 TO APRIL 2015

Daily duration, hours	Earliest date	Duration, hours	Latest date	Duration, hours
≥ 8.0	25 Jan 1986	8.0	14 Nov 1971	8.0
9.0	16 Feb 1985	9.1	29 Oct 1997	9.1
	16 Feb 2002	9.1		
	16 Feb 2008	9.0		
10.0	1 March 2010	10.4	4 Oct 1957	10.2
			4 Oct 1994	10.0
11.0	24 March 1972	11.1	18 Sept 1974	11.4
12.0	8 April 2011	12.5	4 Sept 2003	12.0
13.0	14 April 2014	13.0	27 Aug 2001	13.0
14.0	2 May 1971	14.0	2 Aug 1981	14.5
15.0	27 May 1977	15.1	19 July 1959	15.0

22 'Top ten' extremes

TEMPERATURE

TABLE 22.1 HOTTEST AND COLDEST DAYS – BY MAXIMUM TEMPERATURE
PERIOD JANUARY 1908 TO APRIL 2015

| | Hottest days | | Coldest days | |
| | Maximum temperature, | | Maximum temperature, | |
Rank	*°C*	*Date*	*°C*	*Date*
1	36.4	10 Aug 2003	-6.8	12 Jan 1987
2	36.0	9 Aug 1911	-5.6	24 Jan 1963
3	35.5	3 Aug 1990	-5.0	29 Dec 1908
4	35.3	19 July 2006	-4.5	23 Jan 1963
5	34.7	12 July 1923	-4.5	16 Jan 1985
6	34.6	29 July 1948	-3.9	13 Jan 1987
7	34.3	13 July 1923	-3.8	1 Feb 1956
8	34.2	9 Aug 2003	-3.8	7 Feb 1991
9	34.0	26 June 1976	-3.1	28 Dec 1908
10	33.9	17 June 1917	-3.1	24 Jan 1945

TABLE 22.2 WARMEST AND COLDEST NIGHTS – BY MINIMUM TEMPERATURE
PERIOD JANUARY 1908 TO APRIL 2015; GRASS MINIMUM TEMPERATURES FROM JANUARY 1920

| | Warmest nights | | Coldest nights | | | |
| | Minimum temperature, | | Minimum temperature, | | Grass minimum temperature*, | |
Rank	*°C*	*Date*	*°C*	*Date*	*°C*	*Date*
1	20.8	2 Aug 1995	-14.5	14 Jan 1982	-20.1	14 Jan 1982
2	20.3	5 Sept 1949	-13.4	13 Dec 1981	-17.5	15 Jan 1982
3	19.9	29 July 1948	-13.4	15 Jan 1982	-17.2	13 Jan 1982
4	19.9	11 Aug 2003	-12.9	15 Feb 1929	-16.5	10 Feb 1986
5	19.4	23 Aug 1997	-12.8	30 Dec 1908	-16.1	31 Jan 1972
6	19.4	9 Aug 2004	-12.5	23 Jan 1963	-16.1	3 Jan 1979
7	19.2	23 July 1921,	-12.2	25 Feb 1947	-16.1	11 Feb 1978
8		18 Aug 1947,	-12.1	24 Jan 1963	-16.1	13 Dec 1981
9		5 Aug 1975,	-11.9	31 Dec 1908	-15.9	13 Feb 1985
10		13 Aug 1997 and 24 Aug 2003	-11.7	25 Jan 1963	-15.7	23 Dec 1981

* Note that the lowest 'grass minimum temperature' records are more than likely made above a snow surface

TABLE 22.3 WARMEST AND COLDEST DAYS – BY MEAN DAILY TEMPERATURE
PERIOD JANUARY 1908 TO APRIL 2015

| | Hottest days | | Coldest days | |
| | Mean daily temperature, | | Mean daily temperature, | |
Rank	°C	Date	°C	Date
1	27.3	29 July 1948	-8.9	24 Jan 1963
2	26.8	2 Aug 1995	-8.5	23 Jan 1963
3	26.6	12 July 1923	-8.3	12 Jan 1987
4	26.6	13 July 1923	-7.7	14 Jan 1982
5	26.6	11 Aug 2003	-7.5	15 Feb 1929
6	26.3	10 Aug 2003	-6.7	13 Jan 1987
7	26.3	19 July 2006	-6.5	14 Feb 1929
8	26.2	27 June 1976	-6.1	13 Feb 1929
9	26.1	3 Aug 1990	-6.1	20 Jan 1940
10	26.0	9 Aug 1911	-6.1	29 Jan 1947

The 'mean daily temperature' is the average of the daily maximum and minimum temperatures

TABLE 22.4A HOTTEST MONTHS – BY MEAN TEMPERATURE
PERIOD JANUARY 1908 TO APRIL 2015

Hottest months

Rank	Mean temperature, °C	Departure from 1981-2010 normal degC	Month and year	Mean daily max °C	Mean daily min °C
1	21.1	+3.5	July 2006	27.2	15.0
2	20.6	+3.0	July 1983	26.7	14.5
3	20.1	+2.8	Aug 1995	26.1	14.1
4	20.0 (20.5)	+2.7	Aug 1947	27.0	13.9
5	20.0	+2.7	Aug 2003	25.6	14.3
6	19.8	+2.5	Aug 1997	24.4	15.2
7	19.6	+2.0	July 1989	25.3	13.8
8	19.3 (19.9)	+2.0	Aug 1911	25.9	13.5
9	19.3 (19.9)	+1.7	July 1921	26.9	12.9
10	19.0 (19.6)	+1.4	July 1911	26.5	12.5

The mean daily temperature is the mean of maximum and minimum temperatures; the monthly mean temperature is taken as the average of all available daily mean temperatures within that month.

Records from the London Road site (1908-67) have been adjusted by a monthly correction (Table 2.2) to provide approximate homogeneity with the records from the Whiteknights site, 1968 onwards: the original values are shown in parentheses. No site adjustments have been applied to the monthly mean daily maximum and mean daily minimum temperatures.

TABLE 22.4B COLDEST MONTHS – BY MEAN TEMPERATURE
PERIOD JANUARY 1908 TO APRIL 2015

Coldest months

Rank	Mean temperature, °C	Departure from 1981-2010 normal degC	Month and year	Mean daily max °C	Mean daily min °C
1	-2.5 (-2.0)	-7.3	Jan 1963	0.4	-4.4
2	-1.6 (-1.2)	-6.4	Feb 1947	1.0	-3.4
3	-1.4 (-0.9)	-6.2	Jan 1940	2.4	-4.2
4	-1.0	-5.8	Feb 1986	1.3	-3.4
5	-0.6 (-0.2)	-5.4	Feb 1956	3.1	-3.5
6	-0.3 (0.1)	-5.1	Feb 1963	2.6	-2.4
7	-0.2 (0.2)	-5.0	Feb 1929	3.6	-3.1
8	0.0	-4.8	Jan 1979	3.3	-3.3
9	0.7	-3.7	Jan 1985	3.4	-1.9
10	0.7	-4.3	Dec 2010	3.5	-2.1

The mean daily temperature is the mean of maximum and minimum temperatures; the monthly mean temperature is taken as the average of all available daily mean temperatures within that month.

Records from the London Road site (1908-67) have been adjusted by a monthly correction (Table 2.2) to provide approximate homogeneity with the records from the Whiteknights site, 1968 onwards: the original values are shown in parentheses. No site adjustments have been applied to the monthly mean daily maximum and mean daily minimum temperatures.

TABLE 22.5 WARMEST AND COLDEST MONTHS – BY DEPARTURE FROM THE MONTHLY NORMAL TEMPERATURE
PERIOD JANUARY 1908 TO APRIL 2015, AVERAGE PERIOD 1981-2010

	Warmest months			Coldest months		
Rank	Mean temperature, °C	Departure from 1981-2010 monthly normal degC	Month and year	Mean temperature, °C	Departure from 1981-2010 monthly normal degC	Month and year
1	13.0	+3.9	Apr 2011	-2.5	-7.3	Jan 1963
2	21.1	+3.5	July 2006	-1.6	-6.4	Feb 1947
3	18.0	+3.4	Sep 2006	-1.4	-6.2	Jan 1940
4	8.1	+3.3	Feb 1990	-1.0	-5.8	Feb 1986
5	10.7	+3.2	Nov 1994	-0.6	-5.4	Feb 1956
6	12.3	+3.2	Apr 2007	-0.3	-5.1	Feb 1963
7	8.5	+3.1	Dec 1934	-0.2	-5.0	Feb 1929
8	8.1	+3.1	Dec 1974	0.0	-4.8	Jan 1979
9	20.6	+3.0	July 1983	0.4	-4.4	Feb 1942
10	14.1	+2.9	Oct 2006	0.4	-4.4	Jan 1945

The mean daily temperature is the mean of maximum and minimum temperatures; the monthly mean temperature is taken as the average of all available daily mean temperatures within that month. Records from the London Road site (1908-67) have been adjusted by a monthly correction (Table 2.2) to approximate the current Whiteknights site (1968 to date); the original measured values can be found within the relevant monthly tables.

TABLE 22.6 GREATEST DAILY RANGES IN TEMPERATURE
PERIOD JANUARY 1908 TO APRIL 2015

Greatest daily ranges

Rank	Daily range, degC	Date	Minimum temperature, °C	Maximum temperature, °C
1	22.8	7 Sep 1911	8.9	31.7
2	22.7	28 Mar 2012	-1.3	21.4
3	22.5	9 Apr 1909	0.0	22.5
4	22.5	25 Mar 1953	-2.0	20.5
5	21.9	20 May 1909	2.5	24.4
6	21.8	23 Mar 1923	-0.4	21.4
7	21.8	9 Sep 1921	8.1	29.9
8	21.7	24 Mar 1918	0.6	22.3
9	21.7	8 May 1922	4.7	26.4
10	21.6	29 Aug 1936	6.4	28.0

The daily temperature range is the difference between the maximum and minimum temperatures over the period 0900-0900 GMT.

PRECIPITATION

TABLE 22.7 WETTEST AND DRIEST MONTHS – BY TOTAL PRECIPITATION
PERIOD JANUARY 1901 TO APRIL 2015

Rank	Wettest months Total precipitation, mm	Per cent of 1981-2010 normal	Month and year	Driest months Total precipitation, mm	Per cent of 1981-2010 normal	Month and year
1	179.6	249	Oct 1903	0.5	1	June 1925
2	174.3	241	Oct 1960	0.8	2	April 1912
3	169.0	255	Nov 1951	0.8	2	Sept 1959
4	167.0	252	Nov 1929	0.9	2	April 2007
5	165.4	263	Dec 1934	1.0	2	Aug 1940
6	165.0	229	Oct 1949	1.3	3	Mar 1929
7	163.0	246	Nov 1970	1.7	4	April 2011
8	158.7	239	Nov 1940	1.8	4	April 1954
9	155.3	348	June 1971	2.5	6	Feb 1934
10	154.7	337	July 1920	3.1	7	May 1990

Since November 1970, the latest entry in the above 'wettest months' table at the time of writing, the wettest months have been October 1987 (154.5 mm), October 2000 (153.2 mm) and January 2014 (151.4 mm).

TABLE 22.8 WETTEST DAYS (DAILY RAINFALL TOTALS 0900-0900 GMT)
PERIOD JANUARY 1901 TO APRIL 2015

Wettest days

Rank	Total precipitation, mm	Date	
1	76.3	22 Sept 1992	
2	60.5	11 June 1970	T
3	59.5	18 Aug 2011	
4	55.6	20 Aug 1932	T
5	54.7	10 June 1971	
6	52.6	9 Aug 1999	
7	50.9	20 Sep 1980	T
8	50.8	14 Aug 1980	
9	50.3	25 July 1941	
10	50.0	11 Sep 1921	T

T after the date indicates thunder was heard on that date.

TABLE 22.9 GREATEST SNOW DEPTHS AT 0900 GMT
PERIOD SEPTEMBER 1950 TO APRIL 2015

Cold winters tend to produce a large number of days with similar snow depths, often a slow reduction after one or two major snowfalls. The first table shows the list of absolute ranked snow depths, which is dominated by the winter of 1962/63 and the heavy snowfall of 5-6 January 2010: the second table shows the ranked greatest single snow depth by winter, except for the winter of 1981/82 when the two large snowfalls were almost a month apart and were separated by a mild spell at New Year which melted all the existing snow cover.

Rank	Greatest snow depths		Greatest snow depths by winter	
	Snow depth, cm		Snow depth, cm	Date
1	31	3 Jan 1963	31	3 Jan 1963
2	28	1 Jan 1963	27	6 Jan 2010
3	27	2 Jan 1963	20	4 Mar 1965
4	27	6 Jan 2010	18	14 Jan 1955
5	26	7 Jan 2010	18	12 Dec 1981
6	23	4 Jan 1963	18	6 Feb 1986
7	23	20 Jan 1963	15	13 Jan 1968
8	23	8 Jan 2010	13	26 Feb 1958
9	22	31 Dec 1962, 21 Jan 1963	12	8 Jan 1982
10	21	30 Dec 1962, 5 Jan 1963, 6 Jan 1963, 22 Jan 1963, 9 Jan 2010	11	31 Dec 1961, 13 Feb 1970

TABLE 22.10 GREATEST ACCUMULATED SNOW DEPTHS IN A CALENDAR MONTH
PERIOD SEPTEMBER 1950 TO APRIL 2015

Month	Accumulated snow depth (cm)
January 1963	609
January 2010	182
February 1963	140
December 1981	100
January 1982	96
December 1962	75
January 1962	67
January 1968 and January 1979	66
March 1965	62

This statistic is derived simply by accumulating all of the snow depths at 0900 during the month; thus a month with three mornings with snow cover, each of 2 cm, will accumulate 6 cm. This does not imply that the snow depth reached this level – it is only an integration of the recorded snow depths during the month.

Winter 1962/63 is the only winter in which all three months feature in the table (winter total 824 cm).

Figure 22.1 *Two scenes from the snowy winter of 2009/10.*

Upper photograph: *The Street, Stratfield Mortimer, in heavy snow on the afternoon of 21 December 2009*

Lower photograph: *Deep snow makes Pitfield Lane, Mortimer, almost impassable on the morning of 6 January 2010*

Both photographs © Stephen Burt

SUNSHINE

TABLE 22.11 SUNNIEST AND DULLEST MONTHS – BY TOTAL SUNSHINE DURATION
PERIOD APRIL 1956 TO APRIL 2015

	Sunniest months			Dullest months		
Rank	Total sunshine, hours	Per cent of 1981-2010 normal	Month and year	Total sunshine, hours	Per cent of 1981-2010 normal	Month and year
1	305.6	161	June 1975	7.8	17	Dec 1956
2	298.2	151	July 1959	13.4	29	Dec 2010
3	297.6	151	July 2013	19.2	34	Jan 1996
4	295.1	157	May 1989	21.8	47	Dec 1998
5	291.8	148	July 2006	25.3	55	Dec 1969
6	282.5	143	July 1976	27.2	59	Dec 1958
7	280.9	147	Aug 1976	29.7	53	Jan 2013
8	279.5	148	June 1976	30.7	67	Dec 1989
9	279.4	146	Aug 1995	30.8	55	Jan 1993
10	278.3	147	June 1970	31.5	68	Dec 2002

TABLE 22.12 SUNNIEST AND DULLEST MONTHS – BY PERCENTAGE OF POSSIBLE DURATION
PERIOD APRIL 1956 TO APRIL 2015

	Sunniest months			Dullest months		
Rank	Per cent of possible	Month and year	Sunshine duration, hours	Per cent of possible	Month and year	Sunshine duration, hours
1	62.2	Aug 1976	280.9	3.2	Dec 1956	7.8
2	61.9	Aug 1995	279.4	5.4	Dec 2010	13.4
3	61.6	June 1975	305.6	7.3	Jan 1996	19.2
4	61.0	May 1989	295.1	8.9	Dec 1998	21.8
5	59.8	July 1959	298.2	10.3	Dec 1969	25.3
6	59.7	July 2013	297.6	11.1	Dec 1958	27.2
7	59.2	Sept 1959	224.6	11.4	Jan 2013	29.7
8	58.5	July 2006	291.8	11.7	Feb 1965	32.7
9	56.6	July 1976	282.5	11.7	Feb 1966	32.7
10	56.3	June 1976	279.5	11.8	Jan 1993	30.8

Note that all three summer months of 1976 appear in both of the above 'sunniest months' tables.

23 On this date ...

This chapter lists, by date, newsworthy weather stories or statistics relating to the past 200 years or so in and around Reading. They are mostly based on observations made at the University's weather stations, but include snippets extracted from local news items and other meteorological publications. Statistics refer to the university's weather stations or, occasionally, to other weather sites in the town.

Entries are listed by calendar date. Sometimes, prolonged spells of weather can last for several days, so do look out for reports of conditions in the same year on previous days.

JANUARY

1 January
1949 The lowest 0900 GMT January pressure reading on record, 966.9 hPa. This was associated with a deep depression that moved from western Ireland to north-east Scotland during the day, with a central pressure close to 960 hPa at 9 a.m.

1963 Snow lay 28 cm deep at 0900 GMT, following moderately heavy snowfall overnight that increased the depth of the existing snow cover. There was a cold easterly wind blowing over Reading due to low pressure off south-west England.

2012 One of the mildest January nights on record - minimum air temperature 11.1 °C. Reading lay in a warm sector, and breezy conditions prevented much overnight cooling.

2 January
1976 A severe gale during the evening as a deep area of low pressure moved south-eastwards into the North Sea: a gust of 75 knots (87 mph) was recorded at the university (see January's chapter).

2013 The start of a seven day sunless spell - despite the presence of high pressure close by for some of the time. Such dull winter conditions are sometimes known as 'anticyclonic gloom'.

3 January
1915 One of the wettest four-week spells on record in Reading ended: 168 mm had fallen in the previous 28 days.

Figure 23.1 *Skiing in Prospect Park, Reading, during January 1963. (Courtesy Reading Chronicle collection, Reading Central Library)*

1963 The greatest snow depth in any month - a depth of 31 cm was recorded at 0900 GMT. The weather diary noted: 'Dull conditions continued and overnight snow turned to freezing rain mixed with ice pellets (clear ice) at times. This coated walls and trees with a smooth ice glaze ... the ice covering twigs measured around 3 mm thick and, where dripping occurred, blunt icicles about 25 mm long formed. Trees so covered emitted a cracking sound when blown by the wind.'

1979 The grass minimum temperature of -16.1 °C was one of the lowest on record, the result of cold air, patchy overnight cloud, a snow-covered ground and light winds leading to a rapid cooling at the snow surface.

1981-2010 Over the most recent standard 30 year averaging period, the seven days commencing 3 January was the week when precipitation was most frequent – on average, rain or snow can be expected on four of the next seven days (Chapter 19).

4 January
1948 One of the mildest January nights on record - minimum temperature 11.1 °C. Low pressure close to Iceland and an anticyclone over Spain resulted in a mild flow from the south-west.

1963 22 cm of thawing snow covered the ground this morning. The *Reading and Berkshire Chronicle* reported on 4 January that 'Staggering sums of money and huge quantities of material have had to be used in the fight to clear the snow in Reading and Berkshire: villages on the Downs have been isolated; public transport services and motorists have had difficulty in keeping going; milk, paraffin and vegetables have been in short supply. It is just a small part of the picture presented by this week of Arctic conditions'.

5 January
1867 The temperature in Reading reportedly fell to -13 °C: so cold that a woman froze to death in her bed in Friar's Place, while the railway switchman at Reading's Great Western Railway station was found frozen to death.

1915 After many days of rain (94 mm fell in 11 days at London Road), the water level at Caversham Lock on 5 January 1915 was over 3 m, just 60 cm below that in the great flood of November 1894.

1957 One of the mildest January nights on record - minimum temperature 11.2 °C. A surface flow from the south-west brought mild but moist air to Reading and a dull, drizzly day.

6 January
1971 The maximum temperature was 10.3 degC higher today than yesterday, one of the largest 24 hour rises on record. Over a 48 hour period the wind direction changed from a cold easterly direction to a mild south-westerly one.

1983 One of the mildest January nights on record - minimum temperature 11.0 °C. A very deep low near Iceland ensured a brisk but mild south-westerly to westerly overnight airflow in Reading.

2003 According to the *Reading Evening Post,* Berkshire experienced its worst flooding since 1947. Homes, businesses and roads in Reading and Caversham suffered as water levels reportedly reached record levels. In the town centre, Vastern Road was underwater between the rail bridges and the Kennet swelled to fill the performance area at The Oracle. Across Reading several places experienced hazardous driving conditions, and there were also power cuts.

2010 One of the greatest January snowfalls on record – the snow depth 27 cm at 0900 GMT (Figures 4.5, 22.1 and 23.2). This followed a heavy fall of snow during the previous evening and overnight, associated with a depression passing close to the south coast of England. Enormous transport disruption ensued, and many local villages lost power, some for more than 24 hours.

Figure 23.2 The University of Reading Atmospheric Observatory on the morning of 6 January 2010 – at 27 cm deep, the second-greatest measured snow depth on Reading's records. Photograph Copyright © Rosy Wilson

7 January

1908 One of the wettest January days on record: 27.7 mm fell, associated with a deep depression that crossed the Midlands later in the day.

1920 The maximum temperature was 10.4 degC higher today than yesterday, one of the largest 24 hour rises on record as warm air spread north-eastwards over the area. In winter a change in wind direction can often cause sudden, large temperature changes.

1950 The start of a 22 day drought, the longest on record in January. Under anticyclonic conditions the MSL pressure averaged 1025.5 hPa during this period.

1982 The first of four consecutive ice days - the maximum temperature failed to rise above freezing each day. An easterly wind brought a spell of snow and heralded the start of remarkable cold spell that lasted until 16 January.

1990 In the 28 days ending today 167 mm of rain fell, one of the wettest four-week spells on record in Reading and the wettest such spell for 19 years.

8 January

1901 A man employed in one of the nursery gardens in Reading fell dead from 'stoppage of the heart's action due to the intense cold'.

1982 The snow depth at 0900 GMT today was 12 cm, following one of the worst snowstorms across a wide area of southern and central Britain that led to serious drifting in places. There was major dislocation of road and rail traffic around Reading as a result, and snow lay until the 18th.

2014 In the 28 ending days ending today, 165 mm of rain fell, one of the wettest four-week spells on record in Reading and the wettest such spell since 1990.

9 January

1998 One of the mildest January days on record: maximum temperature reached 14.7 °C. Low pressure to the south of Iceland drew mild south-westerly winds across Reading for several days.

2015 The maximum air temperature today was 15.5 °C, the highest on record for January during 1908-2015 (see January's chapter). The temperature peaked at about 1748 GMT, having risen 3 degC in the previous hour. The weather turned windy in the evening - two houses in a row of terraced houses in Gosbrook Road, Caversham were cordoned off after high winds caused structural damage to gable ends and there were a few local, short-lived, power cuts.

10 January
1989 A 38 day spell without air frost in Reading ended today.

11 January
1962 One of the lowest 0900 GMT January pressure readings - 971.7 hPa, due to a deep low pressure centre west of Scotland in the early hours that moved north-eastwards during the day. At Reading the wind reached gale force during the morning, with a peak gust of 57 knots (66 mph) at 1045 GMT.

1963 The first of three consecutive ice days: high pressure to the north resulted in a feed of cold continental air over England.

1974 A small tornado was reported on the university campus. A note inserted in the observations register states 'small whirlwind 0755 [a.m.] moving from south-west to north-east; Earley Gate TOB2 [one of the single storey buildings close to the entrance of the campus at Earley Gate]; with a roaring sound; no visible damage.'

1987 The first of four consecutive ice days - part of a bitterly cold spell that lasted from 10-20 January over much of England and Wales.

12 January
1987 The coldest day of any month on Reading's long record - the maximum temperature just -6.8 °C (see also January's chapter). The following day was little better, reaching only -3.9 °C.

13 January
1968 The maximum temperature was 10.3 degC higher today than yesterday, one of the largest rises in 24 hours on record. Cold air from over the near continent gave way to milder, Atlantic air.

1982 One of the lowest January grass minimum temperatures on record (-17.2 °C). Reading lay under high pressure today with lying snow, light winds and fog at 0900 GMT.

14 January
1979 A ten day sunless spell started today. High pressure dominated for much of this period.

1982 The coldest night on Reading's records (Figure 23.3): minimum temperature -14.5 °C, grass minimum temperature over snow -20.1 °C at Whiteknights. The snow depth was 9 cm at 0900 GMT.

Figure 23.3 Frost on the inside of a windowpane. This photograph was taken in Bracknell on the morning of 14 January 1982, the coldest morning on Reading's long record, when the temperature fell to -14.5 °C. At Arborfield, the temperature that morning fell to -18.5 °C – the lowest temperature yet known for any site in Berkshire. Photograph Copyright © Stephen Burt.

1987 A fourteen day sunless spell started today, the longest sunless spell in January in Reading between 1968 and 2015, although 23.5 hours of sunshine were recorded in the final four days of the month.

15 January

1918 The wettest January day on record; 29.0 mm of precipitation (including some snow). An additional 25 mm fell in the next three days.

1982 One of the coldest nights on record for any month: minimum temperature -13.4 °C, grass minimum temperature (above snow) -17.5 °C. Fog and rime was observed at 0900 GMT and there was 9 cm of snow lying.

16 January

1926 Deep snow lay in the morning in the area (although the actual depths were not recorded at the time) with some local villages cut off. The observer's notes state 'Snow continued all day'.

1963 A USAF officer was killed in a weather-caused accident on the Twyford-Henley Road and two Tilehurst men died in an accident involving a coach on the Bath Road at Sonning. Both happened in snowy conditions - snow lay 19 cm deep at the university that morning.

1985 One of the coldest January days on record; maximum temperature only -4.5 °C. Snow lay on the ground throughout, and the temperature did not rise above 0 °C until the 18th.

2013 A ten day sunless spell started today: since 1957, only January 1996 was duller than 2013.

17 January

1881 At Stratfield Turgis Rectory, between Reading and Basingstoke, the temperature fell to -14.1 °C. The following day a severe blizzard affected southern England (see 18 January).

1918 Heavy snowfall - 15 cm reportedly fell in five hours in Reading and the surrounding area, causing chaos on the tramlines.

1963 The first of eight consecutive ice days, the temperature remaining below 0 °C throughout this time, the longest unbroken period of sub-freezing weather on Reading's records.

18 January

1881 A tremendous snowstorm and blizzard affected southern England: according to the *Reading Mercury* the county was left 'in a state of utter helplessness'. In Reading, about 22 cm of snow fell, and enormous snowdrifts piled up in the strong north-easterly wind: on the Great Western Railway between Reading and Mortimer drifts averaged 1.2 m deep, and between 90 and 240 cm on the Southern Railway around Basingstoke. Most of the shops in Reading closed due to the snow and hundreds of train passengers were stranded. The line between Wallingford and Moulsford remained blocked for almost a week.

1975 The last day of a 39 day spell free of air frost in Reading.

Figure 23.4 *Snow falling in Forbury Gardens, Reading, on Friday 18 January 2013. Photograph © Craig Selley*

19 January

1930 Until 1998, this was the mildest January day on record, the maximum temperature reaching 14.4 °C. The observer's notes describe a 'bright sunny day'.

1985 The *Reading Evening Post* reported that 'so far in 1985 we've had icy roads, schools shut down, buses freezing up and gas mains fracturing' due to the cold conditions. At least the temperature rose above freezing today – but only to +0.6 °C.

20 January

1966 A seven day sunless spell started today. Freezing rain in the morning rush-hour brought chaos on the roads in the area. Cars and the local trolleybus services were badly affected with a journey time of 90 minutes from Tilehurst to the town centre, for example, as overhead lines became encrusted with ice.

Figure 23.5 Large hailstones remain several hours after a severe winter hailstorm on 20 January 1995. This photograph was taken in Mortimer: the coin is 24.5 mm in diameter. Photograph © Copyright Stephen Burt

1995 A heavy thunderstorm during the early hours of the morning carpeted the villages south and west of Reading with large hail; in Mortimer, some of the hailstones were 15 mm in diameter (Figure 23.5).

2008 The mildest January night on record - minimum temperature was 11.7 °C, in what became one of the mildest Januarys on record.

21 January

1963 One of the greatest January snow depths on record - 22 cm depth at 0900 GMT.

22 January

1963 The snow depth this morning at 0900 GMT had fallen to just 21 cm as no snow fell yesterday or overnight.

23 January

1963 One of the coldest days yet recorded in Reading – minimum temperature -12.5 °C, the lowest in Reading since February 1929, and the maximum temperature just -4.5 °C, giving a mean daily temperature of -8.5 °C. This was also the first of four consecutive mornings with a minimum temperature below -10 °C. The MSL pressure at 0900 GMT was 1043.6 hPa.

2009 One of the lowest 0900 GMT January pressure readings on record - 971.7 hPa.

24 January

1939 42 mm of precipitation fell in 48 hours on 24-25 January 1939: this became one of the wettest Januarys on record, although 1995 and 2014 were slightly wetter.

1945 The first of four consecutive ice days: the observer's notes state that there was fog and some light snow during the day.

1963 The second coldest day of any month; the minimum temperature of -12.1 °C was followed by a maximum temperature of only -5.6 °C (the coldest day on Reading's records to that date: the only colder day came 24 years later, in January 1987 – see January's chapter, and Figure 23.6). The mean daily temperature was -8.9 °C, the lowest for any day on Reading's record. Under an area of high pressure, Reading had fog and rime for much of the day, with a slight fall of ice needles in the fog during the afternoon.

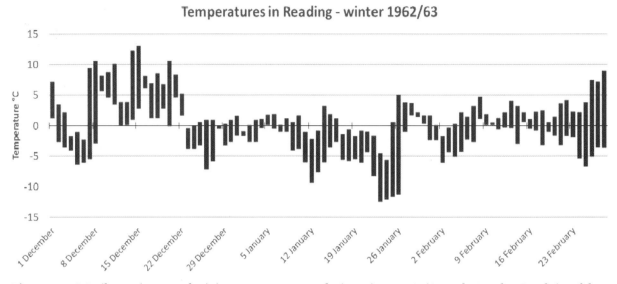

Figure 23.6 *Daily maximum and minimum temperatures during winter 1962/63 at the London Road site of the University of Reading*

25 January

1939 One of the wettest January days with the equivalent of 26.2 mm of rain falling. Much of this fell as wet snow after 3 a.m. on 25th: 7000 subscribers lost their telephone connections in Reading.

1963 One of the coldest January nights on record - minimum temperature -11.7 °C. High pressure continued to bring cold and foggy weather much of the day. By sunset the temperature had reached a maximum of only -6.1 °C, although it later climbed overnight to +0.6 °C.

1986 One of the sunniest January days, 8.0 hours of bright sunshine: after a frosty start there was little cloud during the day under a ridge of high pressure.

1990 A severe gale affected much of north-west Europe including southern England (the 'Burns' Day Storm'); 45 people were killed in England. The strongest wind gust yet recorded at the university occurred around 3 p.m., 76 knots (88 mph) – see January's chapter.

26 January

1932 Barometric pressure reached almost 1050 hPa in eastern England – at Reading, the reading at 0900 GMT was 1049.5 hPa, the highest yet recorded in any month.

1947 The first of five consecutive ice days, below 0 °C each day. High pressure to the north drew a flow of cold air from the east off the continent to Reading. Snow fell at times during this period.

27 January

1940 Described in the observer's notes as a 'dull cold day, rain and sleet showers', temperatures failed to rise above 1.3 °C - this being the reading at 9 a.m. Later in the day there was an ice storm in

Reading with a thick layer of ice building up on trees, roads, roofs and electricity pylons, some of which were brought down under the weight of ice.

1963 The 22nd consecutive day with air frost, one of the longest such spells on record in Reading.

1992 The highest barometric pressure in recent years - 1045.5 hPa at 0900 GMT, as a large anticyclone was centred close to Reading.

2003 One of the mildest January days on record - the temperature rose to 14.3 °C in a mild flow from the south-west and west, partly helped by 6.3 hours of bright sunshine.

28 January

1954 Following two ice days, the temperature fell to -8.1 °C with 8 cm of lying snow. Pipes froze, including those of locomotives at Reading station, while ice build-up meant that the Salvation Army band were unable to play at St Mary Butts Church. High pressure over Norway drew very cold air southwards from the Arctic across the UK.

1978 One of the lowest 0900 GMT January pressure readings - 969.0 hPa - due to an area of low pressure over Ireland that moved across northern England later.

29 January

2002 One of the mildest January days: the temperature reached 14.3 °C in a south-westerly airstream.

30 January

1987 The sunniest January day on record: 8.1 hours recorded, following a frosty start to the day. Reading lay close to the centre of an anticyclone, giving clear settled conditions.

31 January

1947 After five days during which the temperature failed to rise above freezing, the Loddon, Thames and Kennet were frozen over and skaters were seen on Whiteknights Lake.

1954 The first of three consecutive ice days in an easterly flow off a cold northern Europe. Not until 7 February did the temperature reach 5 °C.

1972 One of the coldest January mornings on record – air minimum -10.3 °C, grass minimum -16.1 °C, a result of an area of cold continental air and light winds.

1996 Almost one third of the sunshine recorded during January 1996 was observed on this, the last day of the month, 6.0 hours out of a total of a total of 19.2 hours — the dullest January on record.

FEBRUARY

1 February

1938 The start of the greatest spring drought on Reading's records: in the 90 days commencing 1 February 1938, just 22.6 mm precipitation was recorded.

1956 One of the coldest February days, the maximum temperature only -3.8 °C in an easterly flow off a cold European landmass. The day was bright and frosty.

2008 The last day of a 39 day spell without air frost in Reading.

2014 Extensive flooding on the Thames and Kennet in Reading following the wettest January on record – see Figure 5.4 in February's chapter.

2 February

1956 The second bitterly cold day, although slightly less cold than yesterday – maximum temperature -2.7 °C. After a bright and frosty day, there was slight snowfall in the night.

1963 One of the deepest February snowfalls - 13 cm measured at 0900 GMT. There were slight falls of snow overnight and during the day.

2002 One of the mildest February nights on record, minimum temperature 11.4 °C in a mild south-westerly airflow around a deep low pressure centre located close to Iceland.

3 February

1916 One of the wettest February days: 21.6 mm fell as a deep depression west of Scotland pushed areas of rain across southern England.

1993 The first of 10 consecutive sunless days - the longest sunless spell in February - as Reading lay under a rather gloomy area of high pressure.

4 February

1951 One of the lowest February pressure readings on record - 972.4 hPa at 0900 GMT - as a deep area of low pressure moved into Ireland. The observer's notes show 'gale and rain 6 a.m.'.

2004 The equal-mildest February night on record: minimum temperature 11.5 °C in mild south-westerly winds.

5 February

1895 The commencement of a spell of eight very cold days with the temperature remaining mostly below 0 °C. Ice 22 cm thick formed on the Reading waterworks filters and the water supply failed as a result. Hundreds of pipes burst.

2004 The equal-mildest February night on record: minimum temperature 11.5 °C in mild south-westerly winds.

6 February

1947 The start of a spell of three ice days (maximum temperature below 0 °C each day): maximum temperature just -1.4 °C today.

1959 The first of nine consecutive sunless days - a combination of anticyclonic gloom and southerly winds.

1986 A snow depth of 18 cm was measured this morning after a heavy snowfall in the previous 24 hours, the greatest depth yet observed during any February (Figure 23.7). The snow was to remain on the ground for two weeks, helped in part by further falls over the next three days.

Figure 23.7 A snowy scene in Sandhurst during February 1986, one of the coldest months of the twentieth century: this photograph was taken on 8 February 1986. The snow depth here was 13 cm, down from 21 cm two days previously; 18 cm fell in Reading. Photograph Copyright © Stephen Burt.

1991 Snow fell on 6-7 February and the lying snow was 8 cm deep on 8 February. At Reading station freezing conditions (the maximum temperature was -3.8 °C on 7 February, and the temperature remained below freezing until 10 February) led to the electronic information boards literally freezing up. On the 10th (a Sunday) 40 people were treated for sledging injuries at the Royal Berkshire Hospital at Reading.

7 February

1947 Eighty per cent of the Huntley and Palmer workforce and 3000 employees of Miles Aircraft, based in Woodley, were laid off owing to the severe weather and a lack of coal (see February chapter).

1964 One of the highest barometric pressure readings for any month - 1046.8 hPa at 0900 GMT - as a large anticyclone sat over the British Isles. At the time of writing, this remains the highest post-WWII barometer reading in Reading. The day was cloudless but rather misty.

1990 One of the highest gusts (70 knots, 81 mph) in any month and the second major storm in the space of a month to affect Reading. The event was accompanied by flooding along the Thames, while in Reading one hotel resident escaped death when a chimney crashed through the roof into her bathroom.

1991 The equal-coldest February day on record - maximum temperature just -3.8 °C; the start of a three-day spell below 0 °C.

1981-2010 Over the most recent standard 30 year averaging period, 9 February saw the highest frequency of morning snow cover – six days in 30 years. The week commencing 7 February is the most likely week of the year to see snow cover in Reading, with an average of one morning with snow cover.

8 February

1946 One of the mildest February nights on record - minimum temperature 10.9 °C.

1990 The second day with high wind gusts - 67 knots / 77 mph recorded at Reading. Low pressure over Scotland resulted in a large pressure gradient over southern England - which lessened later in the day.

9 February

1985 A spell of five ice days began today with the temperature remaining below 0 °C. This period was largely sunny by day but about 8 cm of snow lay on the ground. The surface airflow was mainly from the east during this period.

1991 One of the coldest February days on record with the maximum temperature -2.7 °C. There was continuous slight snow at times in Reading with the surface depth remaining about 6 cm. In the cold conditions, the snow was very fine and once cleared drifted easily once more. After a day of travel chaos on the railways, one railway press person uttered the now-famous line '… the wrong sort of snow'.

2009 One of the wettest February days with 26.8 mm falling in 22 hours during the 24 hour period commencing 0900 GMT. A deepening area of low pressure moved eastwards along the south coast of England during the day.

10 February

1953 One of the lowest pressure readings for any month at 0900 GMT - 964.5 hPa - as a deep area of low pressure moved from southern Ireland to East Anglia.

1986 One of the coldest February nights on record (minimum temperature -11.6 °C), together with the lowest February grass minimum temperature on record (-16.5 °C). An area of high pressure was drawing cold air off the continent towards Reading.

11 February

1929 The start of one of the most intense spring droughts on Reading's records: only 17.1 mm precipitation fell in the 75 days commencing 11 February 1929.

1947 The maximum temperature reached only -1.1 °C, the start of a three-day spell remaining below 0 °C. Low pressure to the south meant an easterly wind blowing off the continent in this period. All three days were dull and cold.

1978 One of the lowest February grass minimum temperatures on record, at -16.1 °C. There was little cloud during the day and during the day the air temperature did not rise above -0.2 °C.

12 February
1929 The start of a spell of six days in which the temperature failed to reach 0 °C; the maximum temperature today was -2.2 °C. The observer's notes refer to 'severe frost, bright days' 12-14th while snow fell on the 15th, enough to cover the ground for five days (see also February's chapter).

13 February
1985 One of the lowest February grass minimum temperatures on record, -15.9 °C. The air temperature remained below freezing all day on a sunny day with an easterly wind.

1986 The temperature reached 3.9 °C today - the highest temperature for the month; in every other month of any name at least 5 °C has been reached on at least one occasion.

1998 One of the mildest February days - maximum temperature 16.8 °C. A large anticyclone over France drew mild air northwards towards southern England from a long way to the south.

14 February
1929 One of the coldest February nights on record - minimum temperature -11.5 °C. During the day the maximum temperature was -1.4 °C, part of a spell of six days remaining below 0 °C.

1938 The last day of a 45 day spell without air frost in Reading, the longest such spell on record in the winter season.

1961 One of the mildest February days on record - maximum temperature 16.7 °C, with 6.0 hours of bright sunshine. High pressure over northern Europe brought mild air from a long way south towards southern England.

1981-2010 Over the most recent standard 30 year averaging period, 14 February was the coldest day of the year with a mean minimum temperature just below 0 °C (Chapter 19).

2014 A wind gust of 48 knots (55 mph) was recorded during a windy 24 hours: police reported 165 trees blown down across Berkshire. Firefighters were called to Christchurch Road at around 9.30 p.m. after a 15 metre tall pine tree fell across the road, damaging a passing taxi, but luckily the driver escaped unharmed. Further severe flooding on the Thames, Loddon and Kennet (Figure 23.8).

Figure 23.8 The Kennet close to breaking its banks on 14 February 2014. The London Street bridge is in the centre of the image, and the Queen's Road car park on the left. Photograph © Craig Selley

15 February

1929 The coldest February day on record - minimum temperature -12.9 °C, maximum temperature only -2.1 °C. This was part of a spell of six days when the temperature remained below 0 °C. The Thames was frozen from bank to bank during this cold spell, and many casualties and a number of fatalities resulted from skating activities on the many local streams, rivers and lakes, hypothermia and from falls on icy ground.

1934 The highest MSL barometric pressure reading on record for February, and the second-highest 0900 GMT reading for any month - 1048.8 hPa at 0900 GMT. Early fog and frost was followed by a bright day as the centre of the anticyclone remained over southern England.

16 February

1947 A spell of three ice days began today - the third such spell of three ice days this month, a rare event for February, in what was one of the two coldest February months locally since 1895.

17 February

1934 One of the highest February barometer readings (1046.6 hPa at 0900 GMT) as high pressure persisted over the British Isles but weakened slightly.

18 February

1947 According to the observer's notes, this was the eighth consecutive day to be described as being cold and dull. The maximum temperature was just -1.7 °C in a light to moderate north-easterly wind.

19 February

1947 After three ice days the maximum temperature finally rose above freezing to +0.2 °C; there was some light snow in the evening, though, as a north-easterly wind persisted.

20 February

1861 A violent gale caused much of Reading Abbey Gateway to collapse (Figure 23.9). Before the storm it had been in a dangerous state, and the storm struck within a few hours of sufficient funds being raised to fund a survey towards its repair. (The same storm also brought down the steeple of Chichester Cathedral and one wing of the Crystal Palace in London.) The inner gateway survived the Abbey's dissolution in 1539: between 1785 and 1786 Jane Austen and her sister Cassandra attended the Reading Ladies' Boarding School that was located in the Gateway. The Gateway was eventually restored by architect Sir George Gilbert Scott the following year.

Figure 23.9 Workmen sorting through the rubble after the collapse of Reading Abbey Gateway on The Forbury, February 1861. (Reading Museum collection – image REDMG : 1996.228.25)

1953 The first day of a 34 day drought, the longest such rainless spell to have started outside of high summer.

1970 Equal-sunniest February day on record with 9.5 hours of sunshine recorded. With over 115 hours of bright sunshine, 1970 was one of the sunniest Februarys on record.

21 February
1903 A peculiar dust haze was observed at many places in the south-east of England, and on 22 February a muddy deposit mostly of a sandy or reddish brown colour occurred over a large area of England and Wales including Reading. This was a heavy fall of Saharan dust.

22 February
1914 One of the lowest February pressure readings on record - 969.4 hPa at 0900 GMT, associated with a deep area of low pressure to the west of Scilly. Despite the low pressure, only 2 mm of rain fell in Reading.

23 February
1990 One of the warmest February days on record - maximum temperature 17.0 °C. A south-westerly flow brought mild air to Reading as a large anticyclone lay over the continent.

24 February
1922 One of the mildest February nights on record, minimum temperature 10.8 °C (this was the air temperature at 0900 GMT yesterday, so the night-time minimum temperature was probably higher).

1933 One of the wettest February days on record (28.4 mm fell) and the first of two consecutive days recording over 25 mm of precipitation; heavy snow fell from 9.30 a.m. onwards.

1934 The wettest day of February 1934, with a rainfall total of 1.0 mm. In the entire month just 2.5 mm of precipitation fell, making this the driest February on record.

1947 One of the coldest February nights on record - minimum temperature -11.0 °C, grass minimum temperature -15.4 °C.

25 February
1933 The wettest February day on record (29.2 mm) and the second of two consecutive days recording over 25 mm of precipitation; sleet and rain continued to fall for much of the day.

1947 One of the coldest February nights on record - minimum temperature -12.2 °C. After a bright start it was dull for the rest of the day. February 1947 was the coldest February on the Reading record.

1989 The lowest barometric pressure reading for any month since December 1821. At 0900 GMT, the MSL value was 962.4 hPa: the minimum value reached was 952 hPa around 1700 GMT (see barogram, Figure 16.3). As winds turned northerly at Reading in the evening, rain turned to snow.

26 February
1943 The first day of a 25 day drought, the second-longest February rainless spell on record.

1958 Deep snowfall - 13 cm lying at 0900 GMT. The observer's notes mention a 'snow blizzard from 7 a.m. onwards' the previous day - but 8.5 hours of bright sunshine was measured today.

1977 The equal-sunniest February day on record, with 9.5 hours – ironically following a very cloudy and wet month.

1990 One of the highest gusts in any month – 71 knots (82 mph), and the third major storm in the space of a month to affect Reading; a bus was blown into the path of a lorry in the town. A deep area of low pressure to the north of Scotland and a large pressure gradient to the south of it gave strong winds everywhere in the UK.

27 February
1973 Equal-sunniest February day on record - 9.5 hours of sunshine. Little cloud during the day.

28 February
1959 The warmest February day on record, maximum temperature 17.4 °C. High pressure over Europe helped to draw mild air from a long way south across Reading.

2014 The last day of a 38 day long spell without air frost.

29 February
1948 One of the mildest February days on record – maximum temperature 16.7 °C - as high pressure brought mild air from the south over Reading.

MARCH

1 March
1929 The highest 0900 GMT March pressure reading on record - 1045.3 hPa. Reading lay at the edge of an intense high pressure area: after a sharp frost the day was bright and sunny, although the temperature reached only 3.7 °C.

1986 One of the coldest March days on record - maximum temperature just -0.1 °C. The day was dull and 2 cm of snow lay on the ground.

1990 The final day of a 42 day spell without air frost in Reading.

2 March
1999 One of the mildest March nights on record - minimum temperature 10.8 °C. Reading lay in a cloudy warm sector of a depression overnight.

2000 A heavy fall of Saharan dust mixed in with rain overnight 1-2 March.

3 March
1909 One of the coldest March nights on record, minimum temperature -7.5 °C, rising to just 0.7 °C during the day. Snow fell and also lay on the ground at Reading.

1954 One of the lowest 0900 GMT March pressure readings on record at 973.6 hPa; a deep low pressure area moved from north-west Ireland to north-east England during the day.

1965 One of the coldest March nights on record – minimum temperature -7.2 °C, grass minimum temperature -10.7 °C. Light snow fell later in the day.

4 March
1965 One of the coldest March days on record – maximum temperature only 0.0 °C. There was a 20 cm snow cover at 0900 GMT, the deepest on record for March.

1986 The 28th consecutive day with air frost, one of the longest such spells on record in Reading.

5 March
1909 One of the coldest March nights on record, minimum -7.4 °C. Cold air persisted across the British Isles, as it did for the first eight days of the month.

2001 One of the lowest March grass minimum temperatures on record, -13.0 °C: minimum air temperature -6.4 °C, also very low for early March.

6 March
1937 A wet snowstorm occurred (20 mm water-equivalent of precipitation) as rain in the evening turned to heavy snow at night. Almost 2000 telephone subscribers in the Reading district lost their phone lines due to snow damage. The resulting snow lay for about 48 hours.

1942 The coldest March day on record, maximum temperature just -0.6 °C: a cold, dull day with north-easterly winds.

7 March
1947 The coldest March night on record: minimum air temperature -11.3 °C. There was some light snow later in the day.

8 March

1994 A mild morning, with a high minimum temperature (10.1 °C) as mild air from the south-west blew across Reading.

9 March

1947 The 33rd consecutive day with air frost, the longest such spell on Reading's records.

1948 One of the warmest March days with the maximum temperature reaching 21.8 °C – the earliest date in the year on which 20 °C has been reached. An area of high pressure brought very warm air to southern England on its northern flank.

10 March

1931 One of the coldest March nights on record, minimum temperature -6.8 °C. Cold air from Scandinavia persisted over Reading.

2008 The lowest 0900 GMT March pressure reading on record - 968.2 hPa - due to a very deep depression that moved eastwards from western Ireland during the day. The wind gusted to 41 knots (47 mph) at Reading during the day.

11 March

1997 A large range of air temperature: minimum 1.5 °C and maximum 17.4 °C, range 15.9 degC.

12 March

1969 The longest sunless spell on record in March commenced today and lasted 10 days. With low pressure to the south of Britain, cloudy easterly winds persisted for much of this period.

13 March

1957 A large range of air temperature: minimum 3.8 °C and maximum of 18.3 °C, range of 14.5 degC. March 1957 was the equal mildest March in the Reading record.

1991 A multiple-vehicle collision occurred during foggy conditions on the eastbound carriageway of the M4 motorway near Hungerford, between the Membury service station and junction 14. Ten people were killed in the carnage, which involved 51 vehicles, making it one of the deadliest crashes in the history of Britain's motorway network. Car fuel exploded along with highly combustible material being carried in one of the vehicles affected and the resultant series of explosions closed the carriageway for four days. The crash led to warning signals being introduced on British motorways to warn drivers of fog.

14 March

1947 After a cold and snowy winter, a thaw that had been ongoing for about a week brought devastating floods: the Thames, Loddon and Kennet all burst their banks (see March chapter).

1964 The wettest March day on record, 34.5 mm fell. Rain fell for 22.8 hours out of 24.

15 March

1924 A large range of air temperature, minimum -3.6 °C, maximum 15.2 °C, diurnal range 18.8 degC. Large diurnal temperatures ranges had occurred on preceding days too, due to the presence of high pressure and little cloud, resulting in clear and cool nights followed by sunny days.

16 March

1947 Severe gale in southern England: two fatalities in Reading (see March's chapter).

1961 Reading lay under high pressure and after early thick fog, a sunny day followed with 8.5 hours of bright sunshine – following 10 hours the previous day. There was a large range of air temperature today, minimum temperature 1.9 °C and maximum of 21.7 °C, giving a diurnal range of 19.8 degC.

17 March

1932 Cold dry air was being pulled across Reading from the north by a large anticyclone centred near Iceland. No rain had fallen for a week. This dry air resulted in the lowest 0900 GMT dew point on record for March, -11 °C, with correspondingly low relative humidity – just 32%.

18 March

1985 Reading and eastern England lay under cold, continental air: one of the lowest March grass minimum temperatures on record (-12.8 °C) was followed by almost 9 hours of bright sunshine.

19 March

1919 One of the wettest March days on record: 26.7 mm fell, some of this as snow, especially during the night and into the following day. During 18-20 March 43 mm of precipitation fell – close to the average for the whole of March.

1966 A 57 day spell without an air frost ended today, the longest such spell encompassing the winter season on record, although 19 of the days were in spring.

1990 One of the mildest March nights on record – minimum temperature 11.8 °C, rising only 0.1 degC higher later in the day as a cold front brought cooler air to Reading soon afterwards.

20 March

1985 The lowest March grass minimum temperature on record at -13.2 °C. Light anticyclonic winds led to freezing fog that obscured the sky at 0900 GMT.

21 March

1935 A large range of air temperature - minimum of -0.2 °C, maximum of 18.7 °C, a diurnal range of 18.9 degC. Reading lay under high pressure and, after early fog, it was a bright and warm day.

22 March

1980 One of the lowest March grass minimum temperatures on record, at -13.1 °C.

23 March

1918 One of the largest diurnal temperature ranges for any month: the temperature rose from -0.4 °C to 21.4 °C, a range of 21.8 degC. High pressure and little cloud allowed the temperature to fall sharply at night, but the strengthening mid-March sunshine and light winds allowed the day to warm rapidly.

1984 One of the wettest March days on record; 23.8 mm fell, and rain fell for almost 14 hours. It was also windy at times, with a gust of 36 knots (41 mph) in the evening.

24 March

1840 Henry West (aged 24 years) lost his life in a tornado at the Great Western Railway Station (now Reading railway station). Henry, an unmarried carpenter from Wilton in Wiltshire, was working on the station roof at the time, attending to the station lantern. The squall blew him off the roof and carried him some 60 metres from the station, where his insensible body was discovered in a trench. He had been killed instantly. This incident is commemorated in a brass plaque which remains today on Platform 7 at Reading station (adjacent to the Pumpkin Café), while Henry West's gravesite at nearby St Laurence's churchyard is marked with a commemorative board (see Figure 23.10).

1918 A sunny day with high pressure led to one of the warmest March days on record as the temperature climbed to 22.3 °C.

1986 The highest March wind gust yet recorded at the University, 66 knots (76 mph) at 1152 GMT. A deepening area of low pressure crossed from west Ireland to Denmark during the day, resulting in one of the lowest March 0900 GMT pressure readings on record (972.9 hPa).

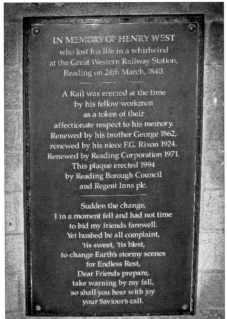

Figure 23.10

Upper photograph: *The commemorative plaque to Henry West which remains adjacent to platform 7 at Reading station.*

Lower photograph: *Henry West's gravesite and marker board at St Laurence's churchyard in Reading.*

Both photographs Copyright © Stephen Burt

25 March
1953 One of the largest diurnal temperature ranges for any month - minimum temperature 2.0 °C to maximum temperature 20.5 °C, a range of 22.5 degC.

1997 After just 0.1 mm of rain today, no further rain fell for the next 30 days.

26 March
2006 Southerly winds and air in the warm sector of a depression led to one of the mildest March nights on record - minimum temperature 10.8 °C.

27 March
1916 One of the wettest March days on record: 27.4 mm fell, accompanied by strong winds.

2006 One of the mildest March nights on record: minimum temperature 11.0 °C. Low pressure west of Ireland meant that air arriving at Reading had a long track from the south and was consequently mild.

28 March

1929 One of the warmest March days on record – maximum temperature 21.9 °C, despite a dawn temperature of only 0.4 °C. It was described in the observer's notes as a bright and warm day - the second of four consecutive such days.

1965 One of the warmest March days on record – maximum temperature 22.1 °C, helped by 10.5 hours of bright sunshine. This was part of a three-day warm spell.

2012 One of the largest diurnal temperature ranges for any month at 22.7 degC - minimum temperature -1.3 °C to the maximum of 21.4 °C). This was the result of ample sunshine - in fact this was the equal-sunniest March day on record with 11.4 hours.

29 March

1929 A large area of high pressure brought good weather to many parts of the British Isles: Reading had one of its warmest March days on record with a maximum temperature of 21.8 °C.

1952 A return to winter took place with a maximum temperature of 1.2 °C; the observer's notes says 'Snow blizzards 6.30 a.m. onwards', and by the next morning 10 cm of snow was lying. The Reading Co-operative Society choir were victims of the snowstorm; after giving a concert to the inmates of Broadmoor they left by coach in the evening and became stuck in snow. Eventually they trudged home to Reading from Wokingham.

1965 The warmest March day on record, as the temperature reached 22.8 °C, part of a three-day warm spell. Plenty of sunshine helped lift the temperature from the day's minimum of 1.7 °C.

30 March

1952 10 cm of lying snow at 0900 GMT, the greatest depth of the 'winter' of 1951/52. This followed yesterday's snow (see 29 March entry), and there was further slight snow today.

1968 Today's maximum air temperature was 12.2 degC lower than the previous day, one of the largest 24 hour falls on record. The previous day was sunny, while today was cloudy with rain at times.

1998 The mildest March night on record - minimum temperature 12.4 °C.

31 March

1997 *and* 2003 The equal-sunniest March day with 11.4 hours of bright sunshine.

2007 The first day of a 23 day drought: only 0.9 mm of rain fell in April, the driest April since 1912.

APRIL

1 April

1994 The highest April gust on record, 52 knots (60 mph).

2 April

1922 The coldest April night on record, minimum temperature -4.2 °C: a fine, bright day ensued.

1968 One of the coldest April days on record: maximum temperature only 2.8 °C as an area of cold air swept towards Reading from the north-west.

1970 One of the coldest April nights on record - minimum air temperature -3.3 °C, grass minimum temperature -10.1 °C.

3 April

1922 One of the coldest April days on record - the temperature reaching only 2.7 °C.

1969 The first of seven consecutive days each having at least 9 hours of sunshine, as an area of high pressure brought settled weather to Reading.

1984 One of the coldest April nights on record, the minimum temperature -3.5 °C and the grass minimum temperature -10.0 °C. A sunny day followed.

2000 One of the wettest April days on record, 22.4 mm fell, some as snow early the next morning. The previous day was also very wet, with 20.3 mm rainfall: 80 per cent of the normal April rainfall occurred in just 48 hours.

2006 Following a long dry spell, Thames Water instituted a hosepipe ban that began today.

2013 Very poor air quality in Reading. A flow from the south-east had brought falls of Saharan dust to the Reading area on 31 March and a continuing surface flow off the near continent under high pressure led to a near-surface temperature inversion. This produced fog for several hours on 1 April and then rather hazy conditions due to atmospheric pollution – from both the UK and further afield – leading to health warnings.

4 April
1996 Little cloud cover led to one of the lowest April grass minimum temperatures on record, -11.5 °C. A clear, sunny day followed.

5 April
1911 One of the coldest April days on record - maximum temperature just 2.3 °C in a cold north-easterly flow.

1946 A sudden change in temperature occurred today - the maximum (11.3 °C) was 13.5 degC lower than yesterday.

1989 Snow lay 1 cm deep at 0900 GMT this morning and fell for much of the morning.

1990 One of the coldest April nights on record - minimum temperature -3.3 °C. This was also the coldest night of 1990 - the only instance of the lowest temperature of the year occurring in April.

2012 A hosepipe ban started today in the Thames Water region - just as a dry spell of several months ended. After an unusually wet April and June the ban was lifted in mid-June.

6 April
1911 One of the coldest April days on record – maximum temperature only 2.9 °C, with a strong and cold easterly wind.

1929 One of the coldest April nights on record – minimum temperature -3.6 °C. A sharp frost was followed by a bright day.

1954 The first day of a 25 day drought, while only 1.8 mm of rain fell all month. April 1954 remains the fourth driest April on Reading's records.

2008 The greatest April snow depth on record; 6 cm was unusually deep for April and, indeed, for any spring day in Reading. Snow, heavy at times, fell from 0500 to 0810 GMT, with local thunder and lightning during the snowfall. This was the latest date with snow cover in Reading since 1966.

7 April
1975 John Simpson of the University's Geophysics Department noted 'I watched the approach of a very dark [squall] line from the north-west at 1530 GMT. This had little "incipient twisters" hanging down from it. A small tornado (no low cloud) must have passed across our road [Stanhope Road, about 1 km south-west of the university], with its centre about three houses away. Four houses next to mine, and two opposite, had patches of roof tile blown out, and a small tree was twisted off just above the ground. A builder's hut disintegrated and the main section landed about 50 metres away.'

2013 One of the coldest April nights on record: minimum temperature -3.4 °C.

8 April
2003 High pressure drew dry air off the continent, leading to a cold, clear might and one of the lowest April grass minimum temperatures on record with a reading of -12.3 °C.

9 April

1909 One of the largest diurnal temperature ranges for any month: minimum temperature 0.0 °C, maximum temperature 22.5 °C during the afternoon - a diurnal temperature range of 22.5 degC.

1993 One of the wettest April days: 22.0 mm fell during a cold, wet day – the maximum temperature reached during the day was only 9.8 °C.

2003 The lowest April grass minimum temperature on record, at -12.5 °C (the minimum air temperature was 9.9 degC higher at -2.6 °C). The grass minimum temperature dropped almost as low on the following three mornings (-10.5 °C, -10.9 °C and -11.1 °C respectively).

10 April

1912 The first day of a 24 day drought. 1912 was the driest April on record at the University with just 0.8 mm of rain in all. Taking all months together, only June 1925 was drier, when just 0.5 mm fell.

1938 One of the highest 0900 GMT April MSL pressure readings on record - 1041.6 hPa.

1942 The first day of a 30 day drought, the longest drought to run across April on record. No rainfall at all was recorded at Reading during this period, not even a 'trace'.

11 April

1938 The highest April 0900 GMT pressure reading on record at 1043.3 hPa. MSL pressure was close to 1045 hPa across north-east England.

1981 One of the mildest April nights on record - minimum temperature was 12.0 °C. A plume of warm air over central Europe could be traced back to North Africa: Reading lay on its western edge.

12 April

1938 A slow-moving area of high pressure persisted across the British Isles today, leading to one of the highest 0900 GMT April pressure readings on record - 1040.5 hPa.

1984 The first day of a 28 day drought. Only 4 mm of rain fell in April 1984, one of the driest Aprils on record.

13 April

1926 The temperature today ranged from 0.4 °C to 19.7 °C - a large diurnal range of 19.3 degC. The observer's notes states that it was a 'bright and cloudy day'.

14 April

1966 The coldest April day on record - maximum temperature only 1.6 °C. Snow fell at times until mid-evening and thawing snow lay 3 cm deep at 0900 GMT.

15 April

1919 A deep area of low pressure over the North Sea led to a blustery day with a hailstorm at 6.50 p.m. The morning also produced one of the lowest 0900 GMT April pressure readings - down to 979.3 hPa.

1945 The mildest April night on record (minimum temperature 12.7 °C) and the first of six warm days, with 25 °C being reached on three of those days. The morning was dull after the mild start, but turned sunny and warm in the afternoon.

1966 Lying snow this morning (3 cm deep) was the latest such occurrence on Reading's records.

16 April

1943 One of the warmest April days - maximum temperature 25.5 °C as an area of warm air spread eastwards across the UK.

1945 One of the warmest April days - maximum temperature rising to 25.8 °C, the second of six warm days.

1949 The warmest April day on record - maximum temperature 26.2 °C on a bright warm day with south-easterly winds.

2003 One of the warmest April days: 25.7 °C was reached in the afternoon as Reading lay on the edge of a large area of high pressure over northern Europe.

2010 The first of ten consecutive days each having at least 9 hours of sunshine; 11.3 hours were measured today. Air pressure remained generally high during this period.

17 April
1929 Following a minimum temperature of -0.6 °C and early mist, the day warmed rapidly to reach 17.6 °C by the afternoon, a large diurnal range of 18.2 degC.

18 April
2004 With a large area of low pressure affecting the British Isles, this morning brought one of the lowest 0900 GMT April pressure readings on record - 979.7 hPa.

2012 The lowest 0900 GMT April pressure reading on record - 978.4 hPa. A deep low pressure area moved across south Wales and the south Midlands during the day.

19 April
1990 The start of the most intense spring and early summer drought on Reading's records – ironically, only a few weeks after the wettest winter then on record: in the 120 days (4 months) commencing 19 April 1990, only 49.5 mm of rain fell, about one month's normal fall at this time of year.

1995 One of the lowest April grass minimum temperatures on record, at -12.1 °C. The next two nights were similarly cold.

2012 One of the lowest 0900 GMT April pressure readings on record - 983.7 hPa. A deep area of low pressure lay just to the north of Reading early in the day.

20 April
1985 The maximum air temperature was 12.4 degC lower today than yesterday, one of the largest 24-hour falls on record.

1995 One of the lowest April grass minimum temperatures on record, at -12.2 °C.

21 April
1995 Another very sharp ground frost - the third consecutive very cold night, the grass minimum temperature falling to -11.6 °C. Each of these days was sunny.

22 April
1969 One of the lowest 0900 GMT April pressure readings on record - 983.0 hPa. A large area of high pressure covered the British Isles but over Reading, and at other places close to the centre, the pressure gradient was slack and so the winds were fairly light.

23 April
1984 The first of eight consecutive days each of which had at least 12 hours of sunshine. April 1984 was the sunniest April on record in Reading, with 234 hours of bright sunshine recorded.

2011 One of the warmest April days on record with the temperature climbing to 26.1 °C.

24 April
1923 A flow from the north brought cool air to Reading although it turned out to be a fairly sunny day. The cool air was dry, resulting in the equal-lowest April dew point at 0900 GMT on record at -6 °C.

25 April

1908 The wettest April day on record. Although snow depth measurements were not made in Reading at the time, heavy snow fell in surrounding areas and counties on 24-26 April with 37.3 mm of precipitation at Reading on 25th when the maximum temperature only reached 5 °C (see April's chapter). Snow melted from 27th onwards and led to severe floods on the Thames and Kennet (Figure 23.11).

1910 Hail fell at London Road and in some parts of Reading the hail inflicted great damage to fruit trees. One observer in Reading noted 'the most prolonged hailstorm for many years, doing considerable damage to fruit trees'.

Figure 23.11 The Thames in flood at Reading, 1 May 1908. Looking upstream from near where Reading Bridge was to be built, with the power station and its tall chimney to the left. Fry's Island (or De Montfort Island) is in the middle of the picture, and the Free Baptist Church in Caversham is prominent on the skyline. This flood followed the thaw of the exceptional late snowstorm of 25-26 April 1908. (Reading Central Library, image 1373 299)

1972 One of the sunniest April days on record: 13.6 hours of bright sunshine. A large anticyclone gave a spell of settled weather to Reading, although the following two days were rather dull.

2007 One of the mildest April nights on record – minimum air temperature 12.6 °C. Reading, along with eastern parts of England, lay in a warm sector with mild southerly winds.

26 April

1940 One of the wettest April days on record - 22.6 mm of rain fell. Heavy rain fell from 2 p.m. to 3.30 p.m. After a mild start, the temperature barely rose during the day.

1948 A large area of high pressure covering the British Isles gave one of the highest 0900 GMT April pressure readings on record at 1040.6 hPa.

1975 One of the mildest April nights on record: minimum temperature 12.5 °C after a warm day was followed by a rather cloudy night.

1981 This (and the previous) day brought an unusual late spring snowfall to the county. Snow fell at Reading but was not reported lying at Whiteknights, although on higher ground in west Berkshire motorists were stranded on the M4 in deep snow. Around Reading some 6000 homes lost power.

27 April

Over 30 year period 1981-2010, 27 April saw the equal-highest frequency of thunder heard (with 23 July) of any day in the year – six days in those 30 years.

1977 The sunniest April day on record with 13.9 hours of bright sunshine - although the temperature reached only 12.6 °C during the day.

1990 The first of 11 consecutive days each having at least 9 hours of sunshine, the result of a large anticyclone that affected southern England during this period.

28 April

1999 One of the sunniest April days on record with 13.7 hours of bright sunshine in anticyclonic conditions.

2004 The first of four consecutive sunless days. A cloudy area of low pressure lay just to the south of Reading and an easterly flow brought cool conditions.

29 April

1991 One of the wettest April days with 30.6 mm falling on a sunless day as a depression crossed southern England. Rain fell for 19.5 hours out of 24, and the temperature reached only 9.2 °C.

30 April

1999 One of the sunniest April days on record with 13.3 hours of bright sunshine resulting in a temperature rise of 16.5 degC by day on a day with light winds.

2005 One of the mildest April nights on record (minimum temperature 12.6 °C); the first of five mild nights with minimum temperatures also above 12 °C on the following two nights.

2007 High pressure gave settled conditions and an easterly flow to Reading. One of the sunniest April days on record with a sunshine duration of 13.6 h.

MAY

1 May

1929 One of the coldest May nights on record; the month began with an air frost and a minimum temperature of -1.6 °C at London Road. Air frosts are uncommon in May in Reading; during the period 1981-2010 air frosts occurred on average once every five years at the slightly cooler Whiteknights site.

1979 The coldest May day on record - maximum temperature reached only 7.2 °C, due to a cold north-westerly airflow blowing around an area of low pressure close to Scandinavia.

2 May

1954 One of the coldest May days on record, the maximum temperature reaching only 7.9 °C as low pressure drew cold air around its western edge.

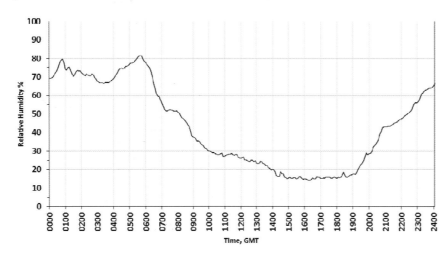

Figure 23.12 The relative humidity plot on 2 May 2013 – the lowest relative humidity on the university's records. Plotted from AWS 5 minute data

2013 At 1610 GMT, the automatic weather station at the university recorded a relative humidity of just 14% (Figure 23.12), the lowest known humidity on the university's record. The reason for the exceptionally low value was descent to near ground level of very dry subsided air within a persistent anticyclone. On the same day, a major forest fire broke out in Bracknell as a result of the dry conditions. Fanned by a stiff north to north-easterly wind, the blaze caused the loss of hundreds of trees and also resulted in some property damage.

3 May

1971 Reading lay under a weak ridge of high pressure and the dry air it brought led to the equal-lowest May dew point at 0900 GMT on record at -3 °C.

4 May

1979 The lowest May grass minimum temperature on record, at -8.4 °C; there was also a slight air frost. The day was cool, with a slight snow shower observed around midday.

2004 A deep and slow-moving area of low pressure over northern Britain led to one of the lowest 0900 GMT May pressure readings on record, at 986.7 hPa.

5 May

2004 Continuing the theme of yesterday, one of the lowest 0900 GMT May pressure readings on record (981.2 hPa) occurred today as a deep area of low pressure continued to be slow-moving over northern Britain.

6 May

2000 An air temperature range of 17.5 degC today, from a minimum of 7.4 °C to a maximum of 24.9 °C later in the day. It was a sunny day, leading to a large temperature rise.

7 May

1944 Late air frosts today and on the following day led to considerable damage to spring blossom. There was also a sharp ground frost, but a bright day followed.

1961 The commencement of a 25 day drought, during which just a trace of rain fell.

1974 One of the lowest May grass minimum temperatures on record, at -8.4 °C, with a slight air frost too. The day was a sunny one although the temperature only rose to 12.5 °C during the afternoon.

2000 A series of evening thunderstorms developed in Berkshire, probably along the line of an earlier sea breeze front. Only 5 mm of rain fell at the university, but 87 mm was recorded at an unofficial raingauge in Bracknell, most of this falling in little more than an hour.

8 May

1938 One of the coldest May nights on record as the air temperature dropped to -1.9 °C around dawn. A bright and sunny day followed but a cool north to north-easterly wind blew for much of the day.

1943 The lowest 0900 GMT May pressure reading on record - 977.4 hPa - as a deep area of low pressure moved from south-west Ireland to north-east England during the day.

9 May

1945 One of the warmest May nights on record - the temperature fell only to 16.2 °C early in the day. High pressure drew warm air northwards across western Europe and a warm day followed (22.2 °C).

1980 Clear skies and light winds led to the coldest May night on record - minimum temperature -2.0 °C, grass minimum temperature -9.1 °C. This was also the first of eight days each having 12 hours or more of sunshine - 108.2 hours of sunshine in all was recorded in this spell.

10 May

1940 One of the lowest May relative humidities at 0900 GMT on record, at 35 %. This occurred as Reading lay under a large area of high pressure giving a bright and warm day later.

11 May

1948 One of the wettest May days with 34.3 mm falling. It was a dull, humid day, conditions that resulted in a thundery deluge.

1983 With low pressure remaining centred close to western Ireland, Reading recorded one of the lowest 0900 GMT May pressure readings - 986.3 hPa.

2005 One of the lowest May grass minimum temperatures on record, at -7.8 °C. With little cloud, this was the first of three sunny days.

12 May

2010 One of the lowest May grass minimum temperatures on record with -8.0 °C recorded; there was also a morning air frost as the air temperature fell to -1.0 °C.

2012 A large area of high pressure lay to the southwest of Ireland early in the day, leading to one of the highest 0900 GMT May pressure readings on record - 1038.3 hPa.

13 May

1915 One of the coldest May days on record – maximum temperature only 8.0 °C during a wet day.

2010 An unusually late air frost – minimum air temperature -0.5 °C, grass minimum temperature -7.6 °C. The average date for the last frost is a month earlier, 14 April.

14 May

1985 One of the wettest May days on record, with 31.8 mm falling. It was also cold day, the maximum temperature being just 11.5 °C.

15 May

1943 One of the highest 0900 GMT May pressure readings on record - 1037.2 hPa - a bright, warm day followed.

16 May

1941 One of the coldest May nights on record and the second-latest air frost on record at London Road: minimum temperature -1.6 °C, grass minimum temperature as low as -5.0 °C. A bright day followed this sharp frost.

1943 A large anticyclone over the British Isles led to the highest 0900 GMT May pressure reading on record - 1042.4 hPa – just eight days after the lowest May value on record (see 8 May 1943).

1992 The first of 12 days each with more than 9 hours of sunshine, 141.0 hours in total being measured over this period.

17 May

1915 One of the wettest May days on record as 32.0 mm fell - a cool day with north-easterly winds.

1935 One of the coldest May nights on record, and the latest air frost on record at the London Road site: minimum air temperature -1.9 °C, grass minimum temperature -4.9 °C. The observer's notes record the occurrence of 'light rain and snow showers, with bright intervals'.

1955 Late spring snow fell on 17 and 18 May 1955, the latest on record: the 17th was a cool and showery day with some snow at night.

18 May

1955 Late spring snow fell on 17 and 18 May 1955, the latest on record: the 18th had heavy showers with thunder and hail. A showery northerly airstream around a low pressure area over the southern North Sea was responsible for the unseasonable conditions.

1960 The first of four consecutive sunless days: winds were north-easterly.

1977 The first of 12 days each with more than 9 hours of sunshine, 154.4 hours in total being recorded during this period.

19 May

1952 One of the warmest May nights on record (minimum temperature 15.4 °C), and also one of the wettest May days on record as 32.5 mm fell.

20 May

1909 One of the largest diurnal temperature ranges for any month: the morning minimum temperature was 2.5 °C while the maximum temperature was 24.4 °C, a range of 21.9 degC.

21 May

1922 For five days starting today maximum temperatures reached at least 26.6 °C each day. High pressure over Europe brought warm air from the western Mediterranean towards the UK.

1932 The wettest May day on record - 37.1 mm fell, a dull day with heavy rain from 4 p.m. onwards.

22 May

1922 One of the warmest May days on record - maximum temperature 31.2 °C. The hot weather triggered slight rain in the evening and lightning during the night. This remains the earliest occurrence of a temperature of 30 °C in any year.

23 May

1918 A sudden change in air temperature - the maximum of 15.7 °C was 14.0 degC lower than yesterday, as an area of very warm air slipped away to the south.

1922 One of the hottest May days (maximum temperature 30.4 °C) after one of the warmest May nights (minimum temperature 15.3 °C). An area of very warm air lay over the nearby continent.

2012 For six days starting today the maximum temperature reached at least 25 °C each day. An area of high pressure and very warm air pushing northwards from south-western Europe was the cause.

24 May

1989 Although there were a number of very severe thunderstorms across southern England today, Reading escaped lightly with only 7.8 mm of rain falling at the university.

25 May

1911 One of the wettest May days as 32.0 mm of rain fell.

1922 The equal-warmest May night on record - minimum temperature 16.6 °C. A south-westerly airflow brought warm air overnight to Reading. After a thunderstorm between 2 a.m. and 6 a.m., a hot day followed.

26 May

1962 A very cool day for late May – the maximum temperature only 8.9 °C.

27 May

1977 One of the sunniest May days with 15.1 hours of bright sunshine under an area of high pressure. The temperature rose to 21.8 °C with little cloud in the sky.

2007 One of the wettest May days - 31.6 mm of rain fell and wind gusted to 28 knots (32 mph) as an area of low pressure tracked eastwards along the English Channel.

28 May

1984 The final day of a four-day long sunless spell - the air temperature reaching only 10.8 °C. Sunless spells of this length occur only about once in 20 years in Reading in May.

29 May

1944 The warmest May day on record – maximum temperature 31.9 °C. Hot air from the south covered much of Europe; in Reading the hot conditions were followed by an evening thunderstorm from 6 p.m. to 8 p.m.

2009 One of the sunniest May days - 15.1 hours of bright sunshine was recorded, with a maximum temperature of 24.5 °C.

30 May

1944 One of the warmest May days (maximum temperature 31.3 °C) after the equal-warmest May night (minimum temperature 16.6 °C).

1947 One of the warmest May days - maximum temperature 30.5 °C. The observer's notes comment that this was the third of seven bright and warm days.

1966 With little cloud during the day, this was the equal-sunniest May day with 15.5 hours of bright sunshine recorded.

1985 The equal-sunniest May day with 15.5 hours of bright sunshine recorded, although the air temperature did not reach 20 °C.

31 May
1975 The latest air frost on record at Whiteknights - minimum temperature -0.1 °C, grass minimum temperature -7.3 °C, in a chilly northerly airflow.

JUNE

1 June
1962 One of the coldest June nights - minimum temperature just 2.6 °C with a touch of ground frost.

1964 One of the coldest June days - maximum temperature only 11.1 °C: a dull day with rain, heavy and thundery at times. The maximum temperature was 12.2 degC lower today than yesterday, one of the largest 24 hour falls on record.

2 June
1962 One of the coldest June nights with the air minimum temperature down to 2.2 °C.

1975 Early morning sleet and snow showers as far south as the south Midlands, with hail in Reading. The temperature at 0900 GMT (10 a.m.) was just 8.8 °C in cold rain.

1991 One of the coldest June nights on record, minimum temperature 1.5 °C, with the lowest June grass minimum temperature on record at -5.7 °C. Air frost occurred in rural surroundings.

3 June
1923 The coldest June night on record – minimum temperature 0.6 °C with a touch of ground frost.

1953 The coldest June day on record - maximum temperature only 10.6 °C: a dull, cold day with very light showers caused by an area of low pressure over The Netherlands; northerly winds in Reading.

4 June
1909 One of the coldest June days on record with the maximum temperature reaching only 11.3 °C.

1932 One of the coldest June days on record - the maximum temperature was just 11.1 °C; a dull day with rain in the evening and into the following morning.

1941 The maximum temperature was 10.4 degC higher today than yesterday, one of the largest rises in 24 hours on record.

1975 The fourth consecutive morning with a June ground frost.

1991 The third morning in four days with a sharp ground frost – in a cold northerly airflow.

5 June
1932 One of the coldest June days - maximum temperature only 11.4 °C; cold winds from the northeast - but marginally warmer than yesterday.

6 June
1975 The first of eight days each of which had at least 12 hours of bright sunshine: June 1975 was the sunniest in the Reading record - the only month to record in excess of 300 hours of sunshine.

7 June
1962 An anticyclone positioned over southwest Norway gave the equal-highest 0900 GMT June pressure reading - 1037.5 hPa.

1969 The first of eight days each of which had at least 12 hours of bright sunshine - June 1969 was a very sunny month with 274 hours of sunshine in Reading.

8 June

1949 The first day of a 26 day drought.

1988 The first of four consecutive sunless days – a rare prolonged sunless spell in June.

2005 The equal-highest June pressure reading - 1037.5 hPa - due to a large anticyclone located over the southern part of the North Sea.

9 June

1910 A tremendous rain- and hailstorm in Reading – see June's chapter for details and photographs.

2001 One of the coldest June nights on record with a minimum temperature of 2.0 °C.

10 June

1971 Heavy rain from the afternoon until early the following morning resulted in one of the wettest June days on record - 54.7 mm fell in the 24 hours from 0900 GMT.

11 June

1941 The first day of a 30 day drought.

1970 The second wettest day of any month on Reading's records; 60.5 mm of rain and hail fell in an afternoon thunderstorm (see June's chapter).

12 June

1981-2010 Over the most recent standard 30 year averaging period, the seven days commencing 12 June was one of two weeks in the year when precipitation was least frequent – on average, rain can be expected on less than two days in the next seven; 12 June is, on average, the second-driest day of the year (Chapter 19).

1996 The first of seven days each of which had over 12 hours of bright sunshine - helping to make the month sunnier than average.

13 June

1977 In nine days starting today, only one day (16 June) had any sunshine.

1981-2010 Over the most recent standard 30 year averaging period, the week commencing 13 June was, on average, the second-sunniest week of the year in Reading (Chapter 19), with just under 7 hours of sunshine expected per day.

1998 One of the wettest June days on record with 42.4 mm falling; a tornado swept through Lower Earley, near Reading – see June's chapter for further details.

14 June

1959 One of the highest 0900 GMT June pressure readings (1036.7 hPa) and one of the sunniest June days on record (15.5 hours); a fine bright day with fresh breezes.

2014 Reading residents were awoken in the early hours by vivid flashes of lightning and loud thunder as thunderstorms affected Reading and nearby towns during the early hours (Figure 23.13). In Reading, 32.6 mm of rain fell at the university in about five hours (beginning just before midnight GMT on the 13th); 56 mm was recorded in Burghfield, south-west of Reading. Lightning struck several homes across Reading and Woodley with several catching fire. Some 400 homes lost power for a time.

Figure 23.13 *Lightning splits the sky above Stratfield Mortimer during the spectacular storms early on 14 June 2014. Photograph © Stephen Burt*

15 June

1959 A bright day with a fresh breeze. However, some cloud meant only 9.0 hours of sunshine, 6.5 hours less than on the 14th and 16th.

1981-2010 Over the most recent standard 30 year averaging period, 15 June was the sunniest day of the year in Reading (Chapter 19), with an average 8.3 hours of sunshine.

16 June

1959 One of the sunniest June days on record - 15.5 hours.

17 June

1917 One of the warmest June days with 33.9 °C reached in Reading.

1977 The first of five consecutive sunless days - a very long dull spell for June as Reading lay to the east of the centre of an area of high pressure.

18 June

1971 One of the wettest June days on record; 35.8 mm fell due mainly to heavy rain in the evening.

19 June

1971 in the 28 days ending today, 168 mm of rain fell, one of the wettest four-week spells on record in Reading. It was the longest such spell to have occurred in summer; such events are usually confined to autumn and winter months. June 1971 was cool and wet – see June's chapter for more details.

20 June

1988 Flash flooding was reported in Reading; 16.9 mm of rain fell in about 45 minutes at the university.

2005 One of the warmest June nights on record (minimum temperature 18.1 °C). This warm night followed a warm day with 30.6 °C recorded on the 19th.

21 June

1997 Low pressure over the British Isles resulted in one of the lowest June 0900 GMT pressure readings - 991.3 hPa.

22 June

1951 An 'urban rainstorm' in the Reading area: 34.5 mm of rain fell at London Road in two hours from 1530 GMT. In the area which suffered the heaviest fall (around the university and, from eye-witness reports, eastwards for 1-2 km), street drains were quite unable to cope with the excessive volume of water until well after the rain ceased. Many streets were under water for two or three hours, and a number of wading and rescue scenes were illustrated by photographs in the Reading newspapers. Most unprotected basements in the area affected were flooded, and many calls were made to the Reading and Berkshire fire brigade.

1976 The first of 18 days each of which reached 25 °C. After a dry start to the year, this prolonged heatwave led to many forest and woodland fires. The 66 day period 22 June-26 August was the climax of the exceptional summer of 1976 - consistently dry (just 47 mm rainfall, 35 mm of which fell in a thunderstorm on 15 July), sunny (679 hours of bright sunshine) and hot (average temperature 19.4 °C). The summer also saw the culmination of a prolonged drought starting in spring 1975.

23 June
1976 The first of 10 days each of which had at least 12 hours of bright sunshine. June 1976 recorded a total of 279.5 hours of bright sunshine.

2004 The lowest 0900 GMT June pressure reading on record - 989.9 hPa - due to a deep area of low pressure over southern Ireland that then moved across northern England.

24 June
1976 One of the sunniest June days with 15.7 hours of bright sunshine; part of a memorable fortnight of weather during June-July 1976.

25 June
1935 One of the warmest June nights - minimum temperature 17.8 °C. A thunderstorm later in the day gave 32.3 mm of rain.

1949 The first of ten days all of which reached 25 °C.

1976 The first of 14 consecutive days, all of which reached 30 °C or more – the most intense heatwave on Reading's records.

26 June
1859 The first Southern Eastern Railway station at Reading (the end of the line to/from south London) was struck by lightning and burned down. Rebuilding was completed the following summer.

1976 The hottest June day on record as 34.0 °C is reached.

27 June
1976 One of the warmest June days (maximum temperature 33.8 °C) and June nights (minimum temperature 18.5 °C) on record. The observation register says simply 'HOT'.

2011 One of the warmest June nights on record with a minimum temperature of 17.7 °C.

28 June
1917 One of the wettest June days as 47.8 mm fell – part of a very large cyclonic storm across southern England: 243 mm of rain was recorded at Bruton in Somerset.

1976 One of the warmest June days - the maximum temperature reached 33.5 °C.

29 June
1949 The warmest June night on record with a minimum temperature of 18.9 °C.

1957 One of the warmest June days on record - maximum temperature 32.3 °C.

30 June
1934 The first of 12 days each reaching at least 25 °C; Reading lay under a warm, high pressure area.

1976 The sunniest day of any month with 16.0 hours of bright sunshine being recorded. The observer's notes records that there was very good visibility all day.

JULY

1 July

1924 One of the coldest July nights on record - minimum temperature just 5.3 °C, with a slight ground frost. Pressure was fairly high and winds were light.

1968 One of the warmest July nights on record with a minimum temperature of 18.9 °C. In warm sunshine the temperature rose to over 31 °C in the afternoon. Earlier a shower around 0600 GMT brought a fall of dust (red, pink, beige and rust coloured according to press reports; fawn-coloured according to the observer's notes). This was of Saharan dust.

1986 One of the sunniest July days on record with 15.3 hours of bright sunshine observed.

2 July

1911 The first day of a 25 day drought. Only 9 mm of rain fell this month, one of the driest Julys on record.

1987 The first day of an eight day spell with each day having at least 9 hours of sunshine.

1999 One of the wettest July days; 42.5 mm of rain fell in 90 minutes, but no thunder was heard at the university.

3 July

1968 One of the sunniest July days on record, with 15.7 hours of bright sunshine. This was more than a tenth of the sunshine total for the month, one of the dullest Julys on record in Reading.

1976 One of the warmest July days on record (maximum temperature 33.5 °C), and part of a fortnight-long hot spell in June-July 1976.

1988 An area of low pressure moved slowly from Ireland to the Midlands giving rain and a cool day in Reading along with one of the lowest July 0900 GMT pressure readings on record (985.6 hPa).

1990 A cool night produced one of the lowest July grass minimum temperatures (-1.8 °C) on record.

2013 The first day of a 21 day long drought, the longest July drought since 1995.

4 July

1959 The sunniest July day on record (15.8 hours of bright sunshine). It was the first of five days each of which had at least 14 hours of sunshine.

1965 One of the coldest July nights as the minimum temperature fell to 5.1 °C.

1976 One of the warmest July nights on record: the minimum temperature was 19.0 °C - climbing to 32 °C later in the day.

5 July

1920 One of the coldest July days on record – maximum temperature only 13.4 °C; a cool day with heavy rain turning showery - over 25 mm of rain fell at the university.

2013 The first of 15 consecutive days each of which saw more than 9 hours of bright sunshine. This was the longest such spell on record in July, due to persistent high pressure over the British Isles. In these 15 days 193 hours of sunshine were recorded, the month as a whole recorded 298 hours.

6 July

1922 A deep area of low pressure over southwest England moved northwards towards Shetland during the day and cloudy conditions meant the temperature only rose to 15.2 °C in Reading. The system also gave one of the lowest July 0900 GMT pressure readings - 983.8 hPa.

1959 One of the sunniest July days with 15.4 hours of sunshine; a bright and hot day.

2013 Temperatures reached 25 °C on 15 days during 6-24 July 2013.

7 July

1910 The equal coldest July day on record – maximum temperature only 13.3 °C as Reading lay on the edge of cold air over northern Europe.

1983 The first of 13 consecutive days, each of which reached 25 °C or above. The month was the warmest month of any name on record to that date – only July 2006 has since been hotter.

2013 12 hours of sunshine were recorded each day from 7-13 July 2013; 95 hours of sunshine occurred in this period and the month as a whole had 298 hours – a very sunny month.

8 July

1917 The equal coldest July day on record with a maximum temperature of only 13.3 °C.

1921 A temperature of 25 °C or more was reached on 18 consecutive days from today. July 1921 remains one of the warmest Julys on Reading's records.

9 July

1921 A temperature of 30 °C or more was reached on five consecutive days starting today.

1959 Nearby Wokingham had a severe thunderstorm, but in Reading only 9 mm of thundery rain fell. Detailed analysis of this storm ('The Wokingham Storm') led to the understanding of airflow in severe convective cells, and introduced the concepts of 'updraughts' and 'downdraughts' (Keith Browning and Frank Ludlam's classic paper *Airflow in convective storms*, which appeared in the *Quarterly Journal of the Royal Meteorological Society* in April 1962).

10 July

1911 Today saw the equal-highest July 0900 GMT pressure reading on record (1035.2 hPa) as Britain lay under a large area of high pressure.

1923 The first of seven consecutive nights, each remaining above 15 °C. Both today and tomorrow turned thundery later in the day - today was described as 'dull and sultry' in the observer's notes.

2006 The maximum temperature of 20.4 °C today was the lowest maximum temperature of the month - one of only five months when 20 °C has been reached every day (see Figure 10.1).

11 July

1911 The equal-highest July 0900 GMT pressure reading (1035.2 hPa) occurred today as a large area of high pressure remained across Britain.

1983 A temperature of 30 °C or more was reached on six consecutive days from today. July 1983 was the warmest month on record to that date – only July 2006 has since been hotter.

1993 One of the coldest July nights on record as the air temperature fell to 5.2 °C with an accompanying ground frost. In Reading a ground frost can occur in any month of the year.

12 July

1923 One of the warmest July days, the temperature reaching 34.7 °C; there were several deaths in the afternoon in Reading attributed to heatwave conditions and glaring sunshine.

1993 A summer ground frost; one of the lowest July grass minimum temperatures, down to -1.5 °C.

13 July

1853 Excessive rain on 13-14 July, producing floods and washing away much hay. In passing Reading it flooded much of the town, and at Swallowfield the meadows were under 1 metre of water.

1923 One of the warmest July days and July nights – minimum temperature 18.9 °C, rising to 34.3 °C in the afternoon. It was also a sunny day.

1941 One of the warmest July nights - the minimum temperature was a high 19.1 °C. After this warm start to the day there was a thunderstorm with heavy rain at 11 a.m. and 1 p.m.

14 July

1983 The first of seven consecutive warm nights, each of which remained above 15 °C. In one of the warmest months on record, the temperature reached 30 °C on some of these days.

2006 The first day of an eight day spell with each day having at least 9 hours of sunshine.

15 July

1976 A series of heavy overnight thunderstorms (15/16 July) gave 35.1 mm of rainfall, almost half of the total fall during summer 1976 – in less than 4 hours.

1989 The first of 12 consecutive days, each of which reached 25 °C or above.

1996 The first day of an eight day spell with each day having at least 9 hours of sunshine. The dry spell ended with a thunderstorm early on 23 July.

2006 The first of 15 consecutive days, each of which reached at least 25 °C. July 2006 was the hottest month yet recorded in Reading.

16 July

2001 A summer ground frost: grass minimum temperature down to -2.0 °C.

17 July

1890 Heavy rain led to flooding in Reading: 71.9 mm of rain fell in Forbury Gardens.

2006 A very large diurnal temperature range of 20.3 degC - minimum 11.3 °C , maximum 31.6 °C.

18 July

1916 The first day of a 25 day drought. No rain fell, not even a 'trace'.

1956 The first day of a four day sunless spell; heavy, thundery rain in the afternoon.

1971 The lowest July grass minimum temperature on record, at -2.2 °C.

1990 The first day of a nine day spell with each day having at least 9 hours of sunshine.

19 July

2006 The hottest July day on record: the temperature reached 35.3 °C. July 2006 was the hottest month yet recorded in Reading (see Figure 10.1).

20 July

2007 One of the wettest July days: 69 mm fell at the university in about 15 hours spanning 0900 GMT, while over 100 mm fell in parts of west Berkshire (see also July's chapter). A small tornado swept through a street in Shinfield at around 11.30 a.m., hurling tiles off roofs and blowing down trees.

21 July

1976 The start of a 37 day drought - the equal-longest in the Reading rainfall record.

1989 The first of six consecutive nights, each of which remained above 15 °C. This was also one of the warmest Julys on record.

22 July

1967 One of the wettest July days; 46.7 mm of thundery rain. Lightning struck an elm tree in Whiteknights Park and 20.3 mm of rain fell in 48 minutes early on the 23rd.

1970 One of the coldest July nights on record - minimum temperature 5.4 °C.

23 July

Over 30 year period 1981-2010, 23 July saw the equal-highest frequency of thunder heard (with 27 April) of any day in the year – six days in those 30 years.

1921 One of the warmest July nights on record – minimum temperature 19.2 °C. A warm day followed that led to a sharp but brief shower early the next morning.

24 July
1934 The maximum temperature of 21.4 °C today was the lowest maximum temperature of the month - one of only five months when 20 °C has been reached every day.

25 July
1941 The wettest July day on record - 50.3 mm fell in heavy thundery rain between 5 a.m. and 9 a.m. on 26th.

1963 The first day of an eight day spell each of which had at least 9 hours of sunshine.

1978 The coldest July night on record - air minimum temperature 4.9 °C, with a ground frost.

26 July
1980 Fog has only been seen on four mornings in July at 0900 GMT since 1908 - on 28 July 1969, 26 July 1980, 4 July 2000 and 20 July 2007.

27 July
1975 A temperature of 25 °C or more was reached on 13 consecutive days from today. Some of these days turned thundery with heavy falls of rain.

1981-2010 Over the most recent standard 30 year averaging period, 27 July was, on average, the driest day of the year in Reading (Chapter 19).

28 July
2004 The first of 12 consecutive days, each of which reached at least 25 °C. Some of this warmth triggered thunderstorms; there was a heavy storm with ice pellets falling on 5 August.

29 July
1948 One of the warmest July days (maximum temperature 34.6 °C) following the warmest July night on record - overnight the temperature did not fall below 19.9 °C.

1956 The lowest July 0900 GMT pressure reading on record - 982.8 hPa - as an area of low pressure moved north-eastwards across England and Wales.

1981-2010 Over the most recent standard 30 year averaging period, 29 July was the warmest day of the year with a mean maximum temperature of 23.7 °C (Chapter 19).

30 July
1917 One of the wettest July days on record - 38.4 mm of rain fell.

1995 A temperature of 30 °C or more was reached on five consecutive days from today.

31 July
1917 The equal coldest July day on record - maximum temperature only 13.3 °C.

AUGUST

1 August
1968 Just 6.7 hours of sunshine occurred in the first nine days of the month, a very dull start to August: only 30 minutes sunshine was recorded today.

1976 In the middle of the scorching summer of 1976, a ground frost: one of the lowest August grass minimum temperatures on record, down to -2.6 °C. With patchy cloud, a sunny day followed.

2 August
1981 The sunniest August day on record with 14.5 hours of bright sunshine. Despite the sunshine, the highest temperature recorded during the day was only 20.9 °C.

1995 The warmest night in any month in the Reading record. The minimum temperature was 20.8 °C, rising to 32.7 °C later in the day – due to a large warm area of high pressure.

2003 The first of ten days to record at least 9 hours of sunshine, with 13.5 hours today. A temperature of 23.3 °C occurred today, but the following 11 days were much warmer - reaching 30 °C at times.

3 August
1944 The first of 14 consecutive days, each of which reached at least 25 °C. After a cloudy start with a north-easterly wind today, it turned brighter in the afternoon.

1986 One of the coldest August days on record, the maximum temperature only 13.9 °C.

1990 One of the warmest August days on record. Following a minimum temperature of 16.6 °C, the temperature rose to 35.5 °C in Reading as an area of very warm air affected much of western Europe.

4 August
1974 One of the coldest August days on record in Reading. Despite only falling to 12.4 °C overnight the air temperature could reach only 13.9 °C during the day; a thunderstorm began at 1335 GMT and 6 mm of rain fell in 15 minutes during the peak of the storm.

1976 One of the sunniest August days on record with 13.7 hours of sunshine recorded; but a north-westerly wind meant the day was not very warm (maximum temperature 22.3 °C).

1998 The first of nine days, each of which recorded at least 9 hours of sunshine. After the 5th, temperatures climbed above 25 °C each day as pressure remained high over Reading.

5 August
1947 The first day of a 33 day drought; only 7.2 mm of rain fell in August 1947.

2003 This morning the minimum temperature was 18.4 °C, the first of nine consecutive nights during which the temperature did not fall below 15 °C.

2007 One of the sunniest August days on record with 13.7 hours helping to lift the temperature to 27.6 °C in the afternoon.

6 August
1968 The first of four consecutive sunless days - an unusually long dull spell for August. This helped to make August 1968 the dullest August on record with just 117 hours of sunshine in all.

7 August
1911 The first of 14 consecutive days, each of which reached at least 25 °C.

8 August
2005 One of the sunniest August days on record, 13.7 hours of bright sunshine being recorded.

9 August
1911 Today's maximum temperature (36.0 °C) remained the hottest day on Reading record's record until beaten 92 years later by 36.4 °C on 10 August 2003; it remains the second-hottest day on record..

1999 One of the wettest August days on record with 52.6 mm of rain falling. It was a dull day with the temperature only climbing to 20.5 °C under an area of low pressure that covered southern Britain.

2003 One of the warmest August days on record, with the air temperature climbing from 16.4 °C to 34.2 °C as an area of hot air pushed northwards over western Europe.

2004 One of the warmest August nights on record - the temperature fell no lower than 19.4 °C - but then only rose to 21.2 °C during the day. It was a wet day (44.2 mm fell, with thunder in the late afternoon) and also a dull one.

1981-2010 Over the most recent standard 30 year averaging period, 9 August was the wettest day of the year with a mean rainfall of 6.5 mm (Chapter 19), owing to three very wet days on this date in those 30 years – 1989, 34.1 mm; 1999, 52.6 mm; 2004, 44.2 mm.

10 August
2003 The hottest day of any month on Reading's records – maximum temperature 36.4 °C (see Figure 11.1). This came at the start of a warm month when 30 °C was measured on six out of eight days commencing 4 August - the eight days had an average maximum temperature of 32.4 °C.

11 August
1947 The first of 26 consecutive days, each of which reached at least 25 °C. This was a remarkably long and late warm spell, August 1947 being one of the warmest months recorded in Reading.

1972 One of the sunniest August days on record, with 13.7 hours of bright sunshine and only patchy cloud cover.

1999 This morning's near-total solar eclipse led to a drop in air temperature of about 2.5 degC as the sunlight was blocked out at around 1030 GMT (Figure 23.14).

Figure 23.14
Air temperatures (°C) at the University of Reading during the near-total solar eclipse on 11 August 1999. Plotted from 5 minute AWS data

2003 One of the warmest August nights on record – minimum temperature 19.9 °C, rising to 33.3 °C during the day.

12 August
1949 The highest August MSL pressure on record – 1034.8 hPa at 0900 GMT.

2008 Three centres of low pressure lay over the British Isles during the day. As a result Reading had one of the lowest 0900 GMT August pressure readings on record - 988.8 hPa.

13 August
2008 A dull, cool day - as low pressure persisted over northern Britain the temperature in Reading could reach only 17.9 °C under rather cloudy skies.

14 August
1959 The first of seven days, each of which recorded at least 9 hours of sunshine.

1972 The first day of a drought lasting 25 days.

1980 One of the wettest August days on record as 50.8 mm fell in a succession of thunderstorms during the evening and early morning.

15 August

1887 An observer in Russell Street, Reading noted a sharp ground frost with the effect that 'Vegetable marrows cut by frost'. At Stratfield Turgis Rectory, between Reading and Basingstoke, the minimum temperature that morning was just 1.5 °C, the grass minimum temperature -1.7 °C.

1947 The first of five consecutive days each of which reached 30 °C, and the first of nine consecutive warm nights during which the temperature remained above 15 °C.

1959 The first day of a 37 day drought – the equal-longest on record (with July-August 1976) - marking the start of an unusually prolonged spell of fine late summer and early autumn weather.

1976 The first of 12 days, each of which recorded at least 9 hours of sunshine, as fine summer weather returned.

1981-2010 Over the most recent standard 30 year averaging period, the week commencing 15 August was, on average, the sunniest week of the year in Reading (Chapter 19), with just under 7 hours sunshine expected per day.

16 August

1966 High pressure persisted over south-east England, leading to one of the highest 0900 GMT August pressure readings - 1033.1 hPa.

17 August

1940 One of the highest 0900 GMT August pressure readings on record - at 1034.0 hPa: a large anticyclone was centred close to southern England during the day.

1997 The first of nine consecutive warm nights, during which the temperature did not fall below 15 °C.

18 August

1970 One of the lowest August grass minimum temperatures, at -2.4 °C.

2011 The wettest August day on record: 59.5 mm of rain fell at the university, and 66.2 mm at Stratfield Mortimer (the wettest day on local records there extending back to 1910). An area of rainfall turned heavy and thundery as it moved from Portland towards Berkshire and then further northwards. The main rain area was quite narrow in extent but led to flooding in and around Reading. Vehicles were abandoned on the M4 and A33, and platform 4 at Reading station was inundated - along with several underpasses.

19 August

1932 One of the hottest August days on record - minimum temperature 16.9 °C was followed by a maximum temperature of 33.8 °C.

1954 One of the coldest August days on record with the maximum temperature being just 13.6 °C. It was described as a 'dull, threatening day'; heavy rain fell in the evening.

1977 The coolest August day on record – maximum temperature only 13.5 °C; a dull day with heavy rain in the afternoon and evening - and lighter rain at other times.

20 August

1932 After a hot, sunny day (the temperature reached 29.3 °C), there was a thunderstorm with heavy rain in the evening: 55.6 mm of rain fell, one of the wettest August days on record.

21 August

1932 After torrential rain in the early hours of the day, it turned much cooler and the maximum temperature was 6.6 degC lower than yesterday.

22 August

1997 The first of three consecutive nights during which the temperature remained above 18 °C. During these days the temperature only rose by about 5-6 degC as skies over Reading remained rather cloudy.

23 August

1918 A sudden change in temperature today - the maximum (17.2 °C) was 13.1 degC lower than yesterday.

1935 The maximum temperature was 12.0 degC lower today than yesterday, one of the largest 24 hour falls on record.

1997 One of the warmest August nights on record – minimum temperature 19.0 °C: the first of four very warm nights.

24 August

1931 One of the coldest August days on record - maximum temperature just 13.8 °C; a dull cold day with light rain in the evening as a pool of cold air moved over Reading.

25 August

1986 The Bank Holiday was washed out as the remnants of hurricane *Charlie* brought 27.5 mm of rain in just over 13 hours to Reading.

2014 A rather damp and sunless day as a nearby low pressure system gave 19 mm of rain in Reading on Bank Holiday Monday. Overall, it was the wettest August Bank Holiday weekend for 22 years - in 1992, 22.6 mm of rain fell compared to this year's total of 20.5 mm over the three days.

26 August

1922 One of the coldest August nights on record – minimum temperature 3.9 °C, although there was no ground frost.

1986 One of the lowest 0900 GMT August pressure readings on record (984.6 hPa), associated with the remnants of former hurricane *Charlie*.

27 August

1920 Dry air this morning led to the lowest August dew point at 0900 GMT on record, 2 °C. High pressure dominated the weather today.

28 August

1917 In late August 1917, the weather turned nasty, as reported on 1 September in the *Reading Mercury* under the headline 'Summer gale - damage to crops and fruits'. It continued: "Phenomenal weather for the time of year has been experienced this week. Rain fell on Sunday [26th], and on Monday afternoon and evening there was a perfect deluge. On Tuesday the conditions were but very little improved, and it was not until Wednesday afternoon that an improvement showed itself. All the same, a strong gale, which at times blew like a hurricane, prevailed. [The 0900 GMT mean wind speed at London Road on the 28th was gale force 8, and the MSL barometer reading just 975.4 hPa – still the lowest on record for August in Reading.] Large branches of trees have been blown down, and in the country districts there has been interference with traffic, whilst the Thames, Kennet, and the Loddon, have risen, with a very strong current running. The heavy rains have had a bad effect on the corn crops in the district, and some of the low-lying fields, in which wheat is standing in sheaves, are pretty much under water; and there are instances where the water having over-run the banks, the corn is floating. A great deal of damage has been done to fruit, thousands of bushels having been brought to the ground. There is such an abundance of fruits that the damage is less serious than would otherwise have been the case."

1961 The first of eight consecutive days, each reaching at least 25 °C.

1979 One of the coldest August nights on record, minimum temperature just 3.4 °C with a slight ground frost.

1981-2010 Over the most recent standard 30 year averaging period, the seven days commencing 28 August was one of two weeks in the year when precipitation was least frequent – on average, rain can be expected on less than two days in the next seven (Chapter 19).

29 August

1993 The fifth consecutive ground frost to Reading, as autumn seemed to arrive a little early. However, screen minimum temperatures remained above 5 °C during this period.

30 August

1940 One of the highest 0900 GMT August pressure readings - 1032.3 hPa - as an anticyclone remained anchored to the south-west or south of England for a few days.

1992 One of the lowest 0900 GMT August pressure readings on record - down to 985.6 hPa. An area of low pressure moved from southern Ireland to northern Scotland during the day.

31 August

1921 One of the coldest August nights (minimum temperature 3.9 °C) with the lowest August grass minimum temperature on record (-5.0 °C). However, during the day the temperature rose to 20.8 °C.

1934 The coldest August night on record – minimum air temperature 2.9 °C.

SEPTEMBER

1 September

1929 The first day of a 28 day drought; September received only 10 mm of rainfall.

2 September

1929 The first of eight consecutive days, each reaching at least 25 °C. September 1929 remains one of the warmest Septembers on the university record.

1982 The sunniest September day on record, with 12.6 hours of bright sunshine.

3 September

1911 One of the warmest September days – maximum temperature 30.5 °C.

1939 One of the warmest September nights – minimum temperature 17.5 °C, grass minimum temperature 16.1 °C. During the day it was bright but cloudy.

1977 One of the sunniest September days on record, with 12.0 hours of bright sunshine. Despite this the temperature only reached 19.1 °C during the day after a cool start; the minimum temperature of 6.6 °C was 8.4 degC cooler than yesterday.

4 September

1929 One of the warmest September days on record – maximum temperature 31.2 °C.

2003 One of the sunniest September days on record with 12.0 hours of bright sunshine.

5 September

1929 One of the warmest September days on record – maximum temperature 30.3 °C, the second day above 30 °C. Temperatures during the first half of this month remained in the very warm to hot range.

1949 The second-hottest night on Reading's records – minimum temperature 20.3 °C, later climbing to 28.1 °C during the day.

2006 One of the warmest September nights on record - minimum temperature 18.0 °C. Although the day was rather cloudy, the temperature still reached 25.5 °C.

6 September

1929 Another warm day in this exceptional September heatwave, although slightly cooler at 25.8 °C.

1959 The first of seven consecutive days each reaching at least 25 °C.

7 September

1911 The warmest September day on record and the largest diurnal temperature range for any month. The temperature rose from 8.9 °C to a maximum of 31.7 °C, a diurnal range of 22.8 degC.

1995 A deep area of low pressure moved eastwards along the English Channel today. Being to the north of the low, winds remained relatively light with a maximum gust of just 20 knots (23 mph) in Reading, but the barometer was very low for September – just 984.1 hPa at 0900 GMT.

8 September
1929 The exceptional heatwave continued – the maximum temperature reaching 30.6 °C.

9 September
1921 One of the largest diurnal temperature ranges for any month - 21.8 degC. Following a minimum temperature of 8.1 °C, the temperature rose to 29.9 °C in the afternoon.

10 September
1921 After a maximum temperature of 29.9 °C yesterday, today was much cooler with the maximum temperature only reaching 19.3 °C as low pressure moved towards the British Isles from the west.

11 September
1919 One of the warmest September days on record, as the temperature rose to 30.3 °C. This remains the latest date in the year to surpass 30 °C.

1921 One of the wettest September days on record as 50.0 mm fell. The observer noted the occurrence of torrential rain throughout the evening and into the following morning, with some thunder. The year 1921 was the driest year on Reading's records, and this single fall contributed 12% of the annual total.

12 September
1945 After one of the warmest September nights in Reading - minimum temperature 17.6 °C - a dull and warm day followed with some light rain, described as 'close' (i.e. humid) by the observer.

1969 The first day of a five day sunless spell, following just 4.7 hours during 7-11 September. This remains one of the dullest Septembers on record.

13 September
1922 A deep low pressure area moving from Northern Ireland towards south-east England during the day gave one of the lowest 0900 GMT September pressure readings on record - 984.1 hPa.

1975 One of the wettest September days on record with 43.0 mm of rainfall. Rain turned heavy in the evening, with some thunder and lightning; winds reached almost gale force for a time in the evening.

14 September
1968 Two days of prolonged heavy rainfall - 20.3 mm of rain on 14 September and 49.8 mm on 15th, a total of 70.1 mm falling in just 26 hours; much flooding resulted in and around Reading.

15 September
1968 One of the wettest September days: a pronounced trough of low pressure brought exceptionally heavy rain and thunderstorms to south-east England. In Reading heavy rain fell on-and-off from late morning until the early hours of the 16th; 49.8 mm fell during the day.

1986 One of the coldest September days on record: northerly winds resulted in a maximum temperature of just 10.4 °C.

1994 One of the coldest September days on record: northerly winds resulted in the temperature reaching just 10.5 °C.

16 September
1986 The first day of a 28 day drought.

17 September
1935 A September gale which affected a large part of England. At 0900 GMT the Reading observer noted a Beaufort Force 6 wind and the weather for the day was noted as 'Gale continued all day,

showery'. Many trees were felled with roads and railway lines becoming blocked, and the roof was blown off a hanger at Woodley Aerodrome and the contents damaged.

18 September
1986 Pressure began rising from the west - and was to remain high over Reading for the remainder of the month, helping to create a dry finish to September.

19 September
1976 The end of the driest 12 month period on Reading's records. Between 21 September 1975 and 19 September 1976 only 346 mm of precipitation fell – just under 55% of the 1981-2010 average annual rainfall. A very wet spell then set in – the 346 mm that had taken 12 months to accumulate had already been surpassed by year-end, less than 15 weeks later.

1986 The highest 0900 GMT September pressure reading on record - 1039.5 hPa - as a large area of high pressure lay over south Britain.

20 September
1980 One of the wettest September days on record as 50.9 mm fell, most of it in an evening thunderstorm accompanied by a spectacular lightning display. Rain fell for just under nine hours.

21 September
1975 The start of the driest 12 month period on Reading's records (see 19 September 1976).

22 September
1992 The wettest day in any month on Reading's rainfall records back to 1901: 76.3 mm fell. The rain was thundery, but despite the intensity there was little flooding around Reading, although 20 homes in Lower Earley had to be evacuated in the early hours of the following morning as a nearby stream burst its banks.

23 September
1914 One of the coldest September nights and the earliest autumn air frost at London Road: minimum air temperature this morning -0.3 °C.

24 September
2003 One of the lowest September grass minimum temperatures on record, at -6.7 °C. There was a sharp frost in rural districts around Reading but there was no air frost at the university site.

2012 An area of low pressure over southern England led to one of the lowest 0900 GMT September pressure readings on record - 984.6 hPa.

25 September
1931 A large anticyclone over the British Isles produced one of the highest 0900 GMT September pressure readings on record - 1037.9 hPa.

26 September
1981 The 0900 GMT pressure was the lowest on record for September - 981.2 hPa, the result of a deep depression near the Scilly Isles. Winds gusted to 31 knots (36 mph) during the day.

27 September
1993 The coldest September day on record - maximum temperature just 9.6 °C.

28 September
2011 The first of six consecutive days each reaching at least 25 °C - an unusually late warm spell.

29 September
1912 One of the wettest September days on record with 42.2 mm of rain measured, as north-westerly winds blew around an area of low pressure to the south-west of Cornwall.

1918 One of the coldest September days with a maximum temperature of 10.0 °C; it was only 0.8 degC warmer just two days previously with 11.4 °C measured on the following day.

1919 One of the coldest September nights on record; an early air frost, minimum temperature -0.8 °C.

30 September

1914 One of the coldest September nights on record; an early air frost, minimum temperature -0.3 °C.

1919 The coldest September night on record in Reading: the minimum temperature fell to -1.1 °C under high pressure. The second of two consecutive air frosts - occurring very early in the autumn.

1952 One of the coldest September days - maximum temperature just 10.6 °C. After early fog and rain, it was a rainy day with strong winds due to an area of low pressure over the English Channel.

OCTOBER

1 October

1973 The sunniest October day on record - 10.3 hours of bright sunshine recorded.

1997 One of the warmest October nights on record, the temperature only falling to 15.6 °C. A very warm October day followed, with a temperature of 24.7 °C being reached in the afternoon.

2011 One of the hottest October days on record, as the afternoon temperature peaked at 27.8 °C, only 0.4 degC below October's highest on record. At other sites in the Reading area, this was the hottest day of 2011. Winds were light and warm air covered much of western Europe and eastern England.

2 October

1997 One of the sunniest October days on record with 10.2 hours of sunshine recorded today, as high pressure continued to prevail.

2011 Another warm day and again one of the warmest October days on record - the temperature reached 27.0 °C during the day - only slightly cooler than yesterday.

3 October

1959 One of the warmest October days on record, the temperature reaching 26.5 °C during the day.

1985 One of the warmest October nights on record, the minimum temperature no lower than 15.6 °C.

4 October

1921 One of the warmest October nights (minimum temperature 16.4 °C). This month the maximum temperatures reached 25.7 °C, 28.2 °C and 27.7 °C on 4th, 5th and 6th, remarkably late 'summer temperatures' in what was becoming the driest year in the Reading record.

1957 One of the sunniest October days on record, with 10.2 hours of bright sunshine. High pressure brought north-westerly winds to Reading – and the afternoon was rather cool despite the sunshine.

1994 One of the sunniest October days on record, 10.0 hours of bright sunshine were recorded.

2013 The minimum air temperature today was 16.5 °C - the warmest October night since 2005 and one of the mildest October nights on record, the result of a southerly wind in a warm sector.

5 October

1921 The warmest October day on record - the temperature reaching a hot 28.2 °C. After a heavy dew and hazy start, it was a fine bright day.

6 October

1921 One of the warmest October days on record, maximum temperature 27.7 °C - just 0.5 degC cooler than yesterday.

1999 The earliest winter air frost on the Whiteknights record from 1968 - minimum temperature -0.3 °C, following a clear night with light winds.

7 October
1971 A very large variation in air temperature, rising from a minimum of 0.7 °C (grass minimum temperature -7.2 °C) to a maximum of 19.4 °C, a range of 18.7 degC.

8 October
1914 The diurnal temperature range today was a large 16.3 °C, as the air temperature rose from -0.1 °C to 16.2 °C. Clear skies and light winds led to a frosty start, sunshine lifted the temperature by day.

9 October
1967 One of the warmest October nights on record with the air temperature not falling below 15.6 °C.

1972 The first of four sunless days as Reading lay on the boundary between low and high pressure.

1985 The first day of a 26 day drought, resulting from rather persistent high pressure.

1987 One of the wettest October days: 31.7 mm of rain fell in Reading. This was part of a very unsettled spell of weather 4-22 October 1987, which included 'The Great Storm' (see 16 October).

10 October
1994 A large range of air temperature - minimum of 2.4 °C, maximum 18.2 °C in the afternoon, a rise of 15.8 degC.

11 October
2000 The 0900 GMT pressure of 973.6 hPa was one of the lowest in the October record - due to a deep and complex area of low pressure affecting much of the UK.

12 October
2005 The warmest October night on record – minimum temperature 16.6 °C: but it was a cloudy day and the afternoon temperature could only rise to 18.5 °C.

13 October
1985 One of the highest 0900 GMT October pressure readings on record - 1039.4 hPa – as high pressure remained centred over eastern parts of England for much of the day.

2002 The first of four sunless days as low pressure systems remained over or close to southern England throughout this period.

14 October
1999 A large range of air temperature, from a minimum of 1.5 °C in the morning to a maximum of 16.1 °C, a range of 14.6 degC. Clear skies under high pressure led to an early ground frost followed by 8.9 hours of bright sunshine.

15 October
1931 One of the highest 0900 GMT October pressure readings on record - 1039.6 hPa - as high pressure lay centred across northern England.

1934 Light snow fell today at London Road, the earliest autumn snowfall on record.

1987 One of the wettest October days on record; 31.3 mm of rain fell during the evening and overnight as part of 'The Great Storm' which caused widespread wind damage early the following day.

16 October
1967 One of the wettest October days on record with 35.6 mm of rain falling; at one stage 7.6 mm of rain fell in just 15 minutes during the evening.

1987 The so-called 'Great Storm', which caused severe and widespread damage across a large area of south-east England: see October's chapter for more details and photographs. The barometric pressure fell to 959 hPa in the early hours of the morning, and the wind gusted to 67 knots (77 mph).

17 October
1921 A large daily temperature range of 17.1 degC – the minimum temperature of 2.8 °C being followed by a maximum temperature of 19.9 °C. As is often the case when large diurnal ranges occur, this was the result of dry soil conditions and the presence of largely clear skies overnight followed by a sunny day.

18 October
1981-2010 Over the most recent standard 30 year averaging period, the seven days commencing 18 October was the wettest week of the year with a mean daily rainfall of 3.7 mm (Chapter 19).

19 October
1926 One of the coldest October nights on record – minimum temperature -4.6 °C, grass minimum temperature -7.8 °C, resulting from a clear, still night under high pressure.

1960 Much of October 1960's rainfall (111 mm of 174 mm in all, the wettest month since October 1903) fell during the final 13 days of the month; five of these received in excess of 10 mm.

20 October
1929 One of the lowest October relative humidities at 0900 GMT on record, down to 45 % with the dew point being -3 °C at the same time.

21 October
1982 One of the wettest October days on record; 33.0 mm fell. Rainfall was almost continuous throughout the day.

2003 One of the lowest October grass minimum temperatures on record, at -9.5 °C. However, the minimum air temperature of -0.1 °C meant that there was only a very slight air frost.

2012 The first of five sunless days with just 0.3 hours of sunshine in the previous two days.

22 October
1983 The equal-highest 0900 GMT October pressure reading on record - 1040.1 hPa - as a large area of high pressure lay centred almost over Reading.

23 October
1925 One of the lowest 0900 GMT October pressure readings on record - 975.1 hPa - as a large area of low pressure led to a windy day in south-east England with heavy showers.

1937 One of the lowest 0900 GMT October pressure readings on record - 977.5 hPa - as an area of low pressure moved eastwards across England during the day.

1958 The equal-highest 0900 GMT October pressure readings on record - 1040.1 hPa: a dull but mild and settled day's weather in Reading.

24 October
1999 This morning produced one of the lowest 0900 GMT October pressure readings on record - 974.6 hPa as a deep depression moved from south-west Ireland to the south Midlands.

25 October
2003 One of the lowest October grass minimum temperatures on record, -9.8 °C; a sharp ground frost formed, although the air temperature fell only to -0.8 °C.

26 October
1954 One of the lowest October dew points at 0900 GMT as -6 °C was observed. Winds were light and after a sharp frost it was a dull day with heavy rain from 3 p.m. onwards.

27 October
1931 One of the coldest October nights on record as the air temperature fell to -3.9 °C. As well as frost, there was dense fog early in the day as Reading lay under an area of high pressure.

1959 The lowest 0900 GMT barometric pressure on record for October – 971.8 hPa.

28 October

1926 One of the coldest October days on record with the temperature reaching only 6.2 °C on a day described in the observer's notes as 'overcast with rain all day': 15.7 mm of rain fell during the day.

1931 The coldest October night on record, with a very sharp frost - minimum air temperature -4.7 °C.

2003 One of the lowest October grass minimum temperatures with a reading of -9.6 °C. There were clear skies and a slightly misty start to the day.

2008 Rain turned to sleet and eventually to moderate to heavy snow late in the evening, ceasing about 0200 GMT. This was the earliest autumn snowfall since 1934.

29 October

1922 One of the coldest October days on record as the air temperature rose to only 5.3 °C; the day was cold and windy with rain and sleet at times.

1997 One of the coldest October nights on record (minimum air temperature -4.4 °C) with the lowest October grass minimum temperature on record (-12.1 °C).

2000 The wettest October day on record; 49.3 mm of rain fell at the university in prolonged heavy rainfall during the night. It was also very windy, with a gust of 43 knots (50 mph) recorded. Roads around Reading were blocked with fallen trees and floodwater.

2008 Snow lay 1 cm deep at 0900 GMT. Lying snow, of any depth, in very rare in Reading in October; this was the earliest on local records since 19-20 October 1880, almost 130 years. (The year 2008 had both the latest date for 5 cm snow cover (on 6 April) and the earliest date for any snow cover (on 29 October), thus having the shortest snow-free season on the record – less than 7 months.)

30 October

1909 One of the coldest October days - maximum temperature just 5.6 °C in a northerly airflow.

1927 A very warm late October day – maximum 18.9 °C at London Road: a warm southerly wind drew air from a long way south towards Reading.

1974 One of the coldest October days on record, maximum temperature just 5.7 °C as an area of low pressure over Europe drew a northerly flow across south-east England.

1983 One of the lowest October grass minimum temperatures on record, at -9.6 °C (the air minimum temperature was -2.8 °C).

1997 One of the coldest October nights; minimum temperature -3.9 °C. The grass minimum temperature -11.5 °C was also one of the lowest on record in October.

2000 Following the wettest October day in the Reading record (since 1901) flooding occurred around the Reading area, notably in Burghfield, Mortimer and Pangbourne. The following morning one of the busiest roads into Reading was closed - the Loddon Bridge roundabout in Winnersh was impassable after the River Loddon burst its banks in the early hours of 31 October. (See also October's chapter.)

31 October

1915 One of the wettest October days on record; 32.0 mm of rain fell as a deep area of low pressure moved south-eastwards from Ireland towards the south-west Approaches.

1934 The coldest October day on record; maximum temperature just 4.4 °C. Not until the following January was there a colder day.

1997 A sharp frost - minimum temperature -3.5 °C, grass minimum temperature -10.1 °C. Under prevailing high pressure there was little cloud overnight, with 8.0 hours of sunshine during the day.

2003 One of the lowest 0900 GMT October pressure readings on record - 977.4 hPa - as a deep area of low pressure moved eastwards across southern England.

2014 A very warm southerly airstream led to an exceptionally warm Halloween with the temperature rising to 21.7 °C. Previously the highest temperature recorded on this date was 17.3 °C in 1968.

NOVEMBER

1 November

1960 In the 28 days ending today, 167 mm of rain fell, one of the wettest four week spells on record.

1969 One of the sunniest November days: anticyclonic conditions led to 8.3 hours of bright sunshine.

1984 One of the warmest November days on record, with the maximum temperature reaching 17.9 °C in a south-westerly airflow.

2010 During the first five days of November 2010 the maximum temperature was never lower than 14 °C while three nights had minimum temperatures of 12 °C or above.

2 November

1894 The River Thames was so high today that the Reading-Sonning road became impassable.

2001 One of the highest 0900 GMT November pressure readings on record - 1042.4 hPa - as a large area of high pressure lay centred just to the south of Reading.

3 November

1940 One of the wettest November days on record; 29.5 mm of rain 'continued all day'.

1971 During the period 3-14 November 1971, a duration of 8.0 hours of sunshine was measured on four days (including today) - thereby helping to make that month the sunniest November on record.

1996 The mildest November night on record – minimum temperature 14.2 °C. A cloudy day followed, with 17 mm of rain: the air temperature then rose to 16.5 °C.

4 November

1946 One of the warmest November days on record with a maximum temperature of 18.2 °C. High pressure over Europe drew warm air northwards from Spain across southern England.

2010 One of the warmest November days - 18.1 °C by day in a mild south-westerly airflow.

5 November

1938 The warmest November day, following one of the mildest November nights: maximum 20.4 °C reached at the London Road site, part of a four-day spell (4th-7th) when the temperature did not drop below 10 °C.

1946 One of the warmest November days on record - the temperature rose to 18.7 °C, the second '18' in succession.

1951 Rain continued to fall all day. The wettest November day on record - 38.4 mm fell.

1970 The sunniest November day on record - 8.5 hours of bright sunshine.

2000 One of the wettest November days on record, 28.3 mm of rain fell in about 12.5 hours during the day. In the 28 days ending today, 175 mm of rain fell, one of the wettest four week spells on record in Reading. Much of this fell in the ten days commencing 28 October. Flooding along the Thames was relatively minor compared to some past events – but further heavy rain on several days in December caused more inundation by mid-December.

2010 One of the mildest November nights on record – minimum temperature 14.0 °C.

6 November

1973 One of the sunniest November days with 8.3 hours of bright sunshine recorded.

2000 One of the lowest 0900 GMT November pressure readings on record - 973.7 hPa. A deep area of low pressure moved eastwards along the western end of the English Channel.

7 November

1921 Dry air today led to the lowest November 0900 GMT dew point at on record, down to -10 °C.

8 November

2010 One of the lowest 0900 GMT November pressure readings on record - 972.3 hPa. Pressure remained low all day as a low centre pushed south-eastwards towards Cornwall.

9 November

1921 Lying snow at 0900 GMT is rare in November in Reading; this was the first of only two such occurrences, the next not for almost 90 years. This was the earliest occurrence of lying snow on Reading's records until 2008, when snow lay on 29 October (see October's chapter).

2010 One of the lowest 0900 GMT November pressure readings on record, 973.2 hPa, as a low pressure system moved along the English Channel.

10 November

1979 After a frosty start, this was one of the sunniest November days on record with 8.4 hours recorded.

1988 One of the mildest November nights on record – minimum temperature 13.1 °C. A breezy day followed with the temperature rising no higher than 15.1 °C.

11 November

1973 One of the sunniest November days - 8.2 hours of bright sunshine were recorded today: Reading lay on the north-eastern edge of an area of high pressure.

12 November

1930 One of the highest 0900 GMT November pressure readings - 1042.4 hPa recorded. A large anticyclone drifted eastwards along the English Channel during the day.

1947 One of the mildest November nights on record; minimum temperature just 13.4 °C this morning. At 0900 GMT, the wind was westerly, Beaufort Force 6.

1949 In the 28 days ending today, 169 mm of rain fell, one of the wettest four-week spells on record.

13 November

1894 The first of a four-day long spell of rain that led to widespread flooding.

1940 One of the wettest November days on record as 30.2 mm of rain fell - the second day with over 29 mm of rain falling in the space of 10 days. Rain fell from 11 a.m. onwards with a gale later at night.

14 November

1989 The first day of a 27 day drought - the average MSL pressure at 0900 GMT was 1023.3 hPa during this period.

15 November

2001 One of the highest 0900 GMT November pressure readings on record - 1041.8 hPa. High pressure was centred close to Reading.

16 November

1922 The highest 0900 GMT November pressure reading, 1043.9 hPa. With light winds, the day began cool and foggy; the previous two days had been foggy throughout.

17 November

1894 One of the greatest floods on the Thames in the last two centuries. At Caversham Bridge the ordinary summer level is 36.73 m above Ordnance Datum; on 16 November 1894 it reached 38.42 m. By 17 November the River Thames had flooded Caversham Road and Great Knollys Street. Blake's Cottages bedside the River Kennet were also submerged, and the inhabitants had to leave their lower rooms. Hundreds of families were forced to abandon their homes, while more had to reach theirs by boat and cart. Huntley and Palmer's biscuit factory was swamped, extinguishing the furnaces and putting 4000 people out of work: in Bridge Street, the horses at Simonds Brewery almost drowned in their stables. King's Meadow, Caversham Meadows and Sonning Meadows were completely submerged, presenting the appearance of an inland lake stretching completely across to Lower Caversham. One raingauge in Portland Place, Reading, recorded 207 mm in the 23 days ending 14 November – only one of which remained dry.

1930 One of the coldest November nights on record, minimum temperature -6.2 °C. Early fog gave way to a dull, cold day, the day's maximum temperature only 2.4 °C.

1958 The first day of a 13 day sunless period: November 1958 had 15 sunless days.

1974 One of the wettest November days on record, exactly 30 mm of rain fell.

18 November
1852 The so-called 'Duke of Wellington's flood'. A report from Reading stated 'No parallel flood has occurred since 1841, and none exceeding it except that in 1809, which was produced by the sudden melting of deep snow. The Thames was highest on 17 November, but the Kennet was higher on 28 November. Caversham lock was much damaged.'

1969 A severe ground frost this morning - the equal-lowest November grass minimum temperature on record, at -12.7 °C (the air minimum temperature was a relatively high -3.9 °C). Ice on local ponds.

2005 Another severe ground frost, one of the lowest November grass minimum temperatures at -11.8 °C (minimum air temperature -5.0 °C). Reading lay on the cold side of a ridge of high pressure that drew northerly winds across the area.

19 November
1912 At Lynmouth Road, Reading there was a report of a 'slight earthquake shock accompanied by a noise like thunder.'

1916 The lowest 0900 GMT barometer reading for November – 969.6 hPa.

1929 The maximum temperature rose to 13.2 °C, quite a rise after a minimum temperature of -1.0 °C. The observer noted 'rain continued all day, strong winds'.

20 November
1994 One of the mildest November nights on record, minimum temperature only 13.7 °C. A south-westerly flow brought mild air to Reading, but the maximum temperature was only 14.4 °C.

21 November
1988 One of the lowest November dew points at 0900 GMT on record, -7 °C: a large anticyclone resulted in cold and dry air being pulled towards southern England from the continent.

22 November
1940 In the 28 days ending today, 175 mm of rain fell, the third-wettest four-week spell on record in Reading. November 1940 was very wet, although the final week was dry.

1956 One of the coldest November days on record - maximum temperature only 0.2 °C. The day was described as being bright and frosty.

2003 One of the wettest November days as 28.7 mm fell. This was the second day in a very wet five-day spell (respective daily rainfall totals were 12.3, 28.7, 22.3, nil and 20.5 mm).

23 November
1983 The coldest November night on record – minimum temperature -8.3 °C.

1993 One of the coldest November days on record, the maximum temperature just 0.1 °C. Reading lay under an area of light winds and generally high pressure and the observer noted the presence of a 'rather heavy rime frost' under foggy conditions at 0900 GMT.

24 November

1948 The eight days from today to 1 December was a very foggy period that, at times, slowed traffic to walking pace. The register notes 'Fog all day, thick at night' (28th); 'Cold foggy day' (29th and 30th); 'Fog all day' (1st). Buses became lost in country lanes and trains were cancelled.

1951 In the 28 days ending today, 179 mm of rain fell, one of the wettest four-week spells on record and culminating in the wettest November on record in Reading.

1983 Today's maximum temperature of 13.0 °C was 10.9 degC warmer than yesterday, as a mild flow from the south-west replaced cold, stagnant air (yesterday's minimum was -8.3 °C).

25 November

1852 Heavy rains which had continued for more than two months produced widespread destruction and loss of life. Reading and other local towns and villages were inundated; traffic on the Great Western Railway and its branches was interrupted in many places. (See also 18 November.)

1923 The coldest November day on record, the maximum temperature remaining well below freezing at -1.9 °C in persistent freezing fog. Winds were light and pressure high.

26 November

1923 A foggy start today after one of the coldest November nights (minimum temperature -6.7 °C). The second day below 0 °C - maximum temperature just -1.8 °C.

1989 One of the coldest November nights on record - minimum temperature -6.4 °C, along with one of the lowest November grass minimum temperatures at -11.5 °C.

27 November

1923 The day dawned with one of the coldest November nights on record with the temperature falling to -6.7 °C this morning - this was the same reading as yesterday.

1950 A much milder day today; the maximum temperature (13.1 °C) was 11.3 degC higher than yesterday.

1978 A severe ground frost - the equal-lowest November grass minimum temperature on record, at -12.7 °C. The grass minimum temperature dropped below -10 °C on four out of five mornings commencing today.

28 November

1963 The first of nine consecutive sunless days.

2010 One of the coldest November days on record - maximum temperature just -0.1 °C. Despite the presence of low pressure, an area of very cold air lay over the British Isles.

29 November

1965 One of the lowest 0900 GMT November pressure readings occurred this morning, 979.0 hPa. A deep area of low pressure moved rapidly from south-west Ireland to north-east England during the day; windy conditions led to a maximum gust of 50 mph at Reading.

1978 A severe ground frost was marked by one of the lowest November grass minimum temperatures on record, down to -11.5 °C. The third day of a five-night long very frosty spell.

30 November

2010 There was 2 cm of lying snow at 0900 GMT this morning, following overnight snowfall – only the second time lying snow has been recorded in Reading in November, the last occasion being almost 90 years previously, on 9 November 1921.

DECEMBER

1 December

1919 One of the wettest December days on record as 33.5 mm of rain fell. The day was rather a cyclonic one with low pressure centres close by.

2 December

1966 One of the lowest 0900 GMT December pressure readings on record, 973.1 hPa, as an exceptionally deep area of low pressure crossed northern Britain, giving gales to Reading for a while in the morning.

1975 The six months commencing 2 December 1975 was the driest such period on Reading's records – only 97 mm had fallen by the end of May 1976 (see Table 20.2).

1985 The mildest December day; 15.8 °C was reached late in the evening, well after dark.

3 December

1968 The first of 13 consecutive sunless days, the longest sunless spell on record for December.

1976 The equal-sunniest December day on record with 7.1 hours of bright sunshine.

1985 The mildest December night on record, minimum temperature 12.4 °C: not until 6 December did the air temperature fall below 10 °C.

4 December

1909 One of the lowest 0900 GMT December pressure readings on record, 972.8 hPa. A deep area of low pressure lay over northern Britain with strong winds and gales in Reading yesterday.

1931 One of the mildest December days on record as the air temperature rose to 15.4 °C. It was a mainly dull day with gale force winds and showers.

1962 The first of three consecutive ice days when the air temperature failed to reach 0 °C. Morning fog led to a coating of rime on all exposed surfaces.

1976 The equal-sunniest December day on record with 7.1 hours of bright sunshine. The same duration was recorded on the previous day with 7.0 hours on the 5th.

5 December

1962 Dense fog around Reading 4th to 8th - at the 0900 GMT observation on these days a visibility of 50 metres was reported. The Reading weather diary notes that later on 3 December visibility was reduced to just 15 metres, with ice needles being observed on the 4th.

1976 One of the sunniest December days on record with 7.0 hours of sunshine, the third day of a three-day long sunny spell.

1979 One of the mildest December days on record as the air temperature rose to 14.6 °C. Winds gusted to 43 knots (50 mph) as a result of a deep depression to the north of Scotland.

1986 One of the mildest December nights, minimum temperature 12.0 °C. Winds gusted to 42 knots (49 mph) during the day.

6 December

1962 With a maximum temperature of just -2.3 °C, this was the coldest December day in Reading since 20 December 1938 (-2.8 °C), and the third consecutive ice day.

2007 One of the mildest December days - maximum temperature 14.6 °C on a mild and windy day.

7 December

1962 A much milder day today; the maximum temperature (9.4 °C) was 11.7 degC warmer than yesterday, the largest 24 hour rise in maximum temperatures on record (Table 16.4).

1996 The first of seven consecutive sunless days.

1998 The first of nine consecutive sunless days.

8 December
1954 One of the lowest 0900 GMT December pressure readings at 973.6 hPa; the area of low pressure that caused this gave Reading its wettest December day on record with 43.2 mm of rainfall.

1981 December 1981 and January 1982 had spells of heavy, disruptive snow and low temperatures. Today snow began in Reading at about 0700 GMT and was 7 cm deep at Whiteknights at 0900 GMT.

9 December
1954 The lowest 0900 GMT pressure reading on record for December, and one of the lowest for any month, 966.0 hPa.

1967 One of the lowest December grass minimum temperatures on record at -15.2 °C. Snow lay 9 cm deep on the ground and further snow fell in the afternoon.

1970 An intense anticyclone moved from south Ireland to Cumbria during the day: Reading recorded one of the highest 0900 GMT December pressure readings, at 1043.9 hPa.

1973 One of the sunniest December days on record with 6.9 hours of bright sunshine being recorded.

1990 An early snowfall; 2 cm depth at Whiteknights from snow flurries the previous afternoon added to be a succession of heavy pre-dawn snow showers.

10 December
1981 The first of three consecutive days when the temperature remained below 0 °C. With snow lying on the ground and further snowfalls to come, very cold nights occurred during this spell.

1994 One of the mildest December days on record - maximum temperature 14.8 °C. Reading lay in a mild south-westerly airstream: each day 10-12 December reached 14 °C.

11 December
1930 The air temperature today varied from a minimum value of -2.3 °C to a maximum of 9.2 °C, a range of 11.5 degC. Such a range is quite unusual for December.

12 December
1929 In the 28 days ending today, 207 mm of rain fell, the wettest four-week spell on the university's records, one which included the second-wettest November on record. By the end of the November the Thames was approaching a state of flood and it duly burst its banks in several places. Not until mid-December did it turn dry in Reading for a few days.

1956 The first of 10 consecutive sunless days. The 1st to 5th of the month were also sunless, and only three days had over one hour of sunshine during the month. This was the dullest month in the Reading record, with just 7.8 hours sunshine.

1994 One of the mildest December days on record with the temperature rising to 14.6 °C. A mild south-westerly airflow blew across Reading.

2011 One of the wettest December days on record with 28.7 mm falling. A vigorous depression to the south of Iceland pushed several fronts across Reading, and winds gusted to 32 knots (37 mph).

13 December
1981 The coldest night on the university's records to that date – minimum temperature -13.4 °C, grass minimum temperature -16.1 °C. Although temperatures were to fall even lower just a month later, both remain the lowest on record for December at the time of writing. A vigorous Atlantic depression gave blizzard conditions during the afternoon before snow turned to rain during the late evening; the barometer fell to 969 hPa around 2230 GMT.

14 December
1918 One of the mildest December nights on record - minimum temperature 11.8 °C, followed by a mild day with drizzle throughout.

1981 One of the coldest December nights on record - the temperature fell to -9.8 °C over snow-covered ground. The wind gusted to 43 knots (50 mph) during the late morning.

1991 One of the coldest December days on record with the air temperature reaching only -2.0 °C in a dry but rather foggy day.

15 December
1996 The first of seven consecutive sunless days, the second sunless spell of this length this month.

1998 One of the mildest December nights - the minimum temperature was 11.9 °C, later climbing to 14.4 °C on a cloudy day with relatively light winds and a little rainfall.

16 December
1997 The first of seven consecutive sunless days. Despite the lack of sunshine it was not particularly cold - in winter it is often the wind direction and the source of the air that tends to govern temperatures rather than sunshine duration.

2000 The first of nine consecutive sunless days.

17 December
1989 This morning produced one of the lowest 0900 GMT pressure readings for any month, 966.1 hPa, as a very deep area of low pressure dominated the weather across the British Isles. In Reading the wind gusted to 59 knots (68 mph).

2008 The start of a 21 day drought, the result of persistent high pressure; at Reading the average 0900 GMT MSL pressure during this period was 1030.5 hPa.

2009 Snowfall today led to 8 cm of lying snow by 0900 GMT next morning and caused gridlock on some major roads in Reading. Vehicles were abandoned on the hilly roads in Caversham and there were early afternoon closures for schools.

18 December
1938 The first of three consecutive days when the temperature failed to rise above 0 °C: not until Boxing Day did the temperature rise above 3 °C again.

2006 The first of nine consecutive sunless days. With high pressure for much of this time, this might be classified as a period of 'anticyclonic gloom'.

Figure 23.15 A lunchtime snowball fight in Forbury Gardens on 18 December 2009. Photograph © Craig Selley

19 December
1938 One of the coldest December days - maximum temperature -2.3 °C in a cold flow off the nearby continent.

1995 One of the wettest December days on record: 31.3 mm of rain fell for a total of 18 hours in 24 up to 0900 GMT on the 20th.

20 December

1938 One of the coldest December days on record, the temperature only reaching -2.8 °C in a cold flow off the nearby continent.

1989 One of the wettest December days on record with 35.8 mm of rain falling. Thunder, lightning and a wind gust of 43 knots (50 mph) also occurred during the day, with local flooding (Figure 15.1).

2010 One of the coldest December nights on record - the minimum temperature was -9.4 °C, and the maximum temperature just above freezing at 0.6 °C.

21 December

1927 A noteworthy ice storm (rainfall in temperatures below 0 °C) occurred today; The Royal Berkshire Hospital was overwhelmed with broken limbs.

2009 Heavy snowfall brought roads across Berkshire to a grinding halt this afternoon (Figure 22.1). Beech Lane in Earley and Sonning Bridge were closed due to the extreme conditions, while traffic in other areas of the town came to a standstill as motorists slowed down or abandoned their cars.

22 December

2006 The highest 0900 GMT December pressure reading on record, 1045.2 hPa, as a large anticyclone lay over the British Isles. Persistent thick fog affected much of the Thames Valley, resulting in the cancellation of hundreds of flights from Heathrow and resulting in road and rail travel disruption for several days (Figure 23.16).

Figure 23.16 Persistent thick fog on 22 December 2006, photographed from Stratfield Mortimer. Photograph © Stephen Burt

23 December

1962 During the 36 mornings starting today, only one failed to record an air frost.

1981 One of the lowest December grass minimum temperatures on record, -15.7 °C above 5 cm of lying snow.

2013 A deep area of low pressure to the west of the British Isles led to stormy conditions over an 18 hour period, into the early hours of Christmas Eve: pre-Christmas travel was severely disrupted. In Reading, winds gusted to 49 knots (56 mph) during the evening, although the strongest winds were within an hour either side of midnight with the peak gust of 58 knots (67 mph) early on the 24th, the strongest gust recorded in Reading since February 1990. A total of 29 mm of rain fell, making it the wettest December day since 1995.

24 December

1841 The Sonning Cutting railway accident occurred during the early hours in the Sonning Cutting through Sonning Hill. A Great Western Railway luggage train consisting of passenger carriages between the tender and the goods wagons entered Sonning Cutting, travelling from London Paddington to Bristol Temple Meads. Recent heavy rain had saturated the soil in the cutting causing it to slip, covering the line on which the train was travelling. On running into the landslip, the engine was derailed, causing it to slow rapidly, and the passenger coaches became crushed between the goods wagons and the tender. Eight passengers died at the scene and seventeen were injured seriously, one of whom died later in hospital. One outcome of a subsequent inquiry was the ruling that all passenger carriages should be built with stronger roofs in order to provide better protection to passengers.

1934 Christmas Eve was the only dry day in December 1934 – the only month since 1903 when it rained on 30 days out of 31. It remains the equal-mildest December on record.

1981-2010 Over the most recent standard 30 year averaging period, 24 December was, on average, the dullest day of the year in Reading, with only an average of 40 minutes sunshine expected (Chapter 19).

25 December

1925 A White Christmas. The 0900 GMT air temperature in Reading in a north-easterly wind was 0.8 °C (following a slight air frost) and this subsequently rose to 8.3 °C in the next 24 hours. Some light snow fell during the day but it then turned dull, with light rain.

1956 A White Christmas. After a dull, cold start to the day, a south-easterly flow brought some snowfall during the day, with the temperature rising from -1.4 °C to 1.8 °C. Some 5.3 mm of water-equivalent precipitation fell leading to about 5 cm of lying snow at 0900 GMT on the 26th. The snow was initially light and turned heavier later. Locally snow lay up to 10 cm deep around Reading.

1968 A White Christmas. One of the few Christmas Days when the Reading weather observer had to contend with falling sleet and snow at the observation time. At 0900 GMT conditions were: air temperature 0.6 °C (following a minimum of 0.1 °C), sky obscured by falling light rain and snow (there had been a spell of continuous snowfall early in the morning), with a north-east wind of 2 knots (2 mph), visibility about 400 m and 8 cm of lying (but thawing) snow. The temperature rose to 2.8 °C later in the day as the clouds thinned out and just 0.3 mm of precipitation fell in the next 24 hours.

1970 A White Christmas. Christmas Day began with a minimum temperature of -3.9 °C and 1 cm of lying snow. The temperature rose later to 0.9 °C and snow fell during the day to give a depth of 5 cm next morning. On the 25th itself the snow was in the form of a shower before noon - more persistent snow was to fall next morning. Despite the morning snow, 3.5 hours of bright sunshine was recorded.

1991 A large anticyclone covered the British Isles today, leading to one of the highest 0900 GMT December pressure readings on record - 1044.8 hPa.

1996 A White Christmas. In Reading, after a slight air frost, some snow fell - but not enough to give a 50 percent ground cover at 0900 GMT. With 3.5 hours of sunshine during the day, traces of lying snow melted by Boxing Day morning.

1999 A White Christmas. Snow fell in Reading but not enough to lie on a ground surface that was wet after 43 mm of rain in the preceding 72 hours. In Reading rain turned to snow around 11 a.m., only to turn back to rain after about ten minutes. It was a cloudy day with another 7.2 mm of precipitation being credited to the 25th. It was also windy, with a gust of 43 knots (50 mph) at the university.

26 December

1911 One of the mildest December days on record - maximum temperature 15.1 °C. Mild air blew across southern England from the west and south-west during the day.

1927 The Boxing Day snowstorm of 1927 was widespread and perhaps the most severe snowstorm since 1891. Heavy snow fell in the evening and the following night (Figure 23.17). However, in Reading the precipitation total was just 6.1 mm, although snow lay as a result until at least the end of the year.

Figure 23.17 Two photographs from King's Road, Reading, shortly after the Boxing Day snowstorm of December 1927. The upper photograph is of Cemetery Junction looking westwards, with The Marquis of Granby public house and London Road to the left and King's Road to the right. The horse-trough and public toilets are in the centre. The lower picture is a few hundred metres to the east along King's Road looking back towards Cemetery Junction: an electric tramcar can be seen in the distance. Snow lay on the ground until New Year. (Reading Central Library: top, image 1395 342, bottom, image 1395 341)

27 December

1962 Snow lay on the ground continuously at Reading from 27 December to 14 February 1963. Altogether, snow fell on 38 days during the three winter months (the average for the period 1981-2010 was just 7.9 days). Despite the snowy conditions, it was reported that there were no delays to Reading's trolley buses by 28 December.

28 December

1908 Maximum temperature just -3.1 °C, one of the coldest December days on record. Snow fell in Reading, as it did in other parts of southern England.

1914 One of the wettest December days on record: 26.4 mm fell, some of this as snow from 9 p.m. onwards - part of a heavy snow event that affected southern England.

1961 One of the lowest December grass minimum temperatures on record, -14.3 °C.

1994 One of the mildest December nights - minimum temperature 12.0 °C in a mild south-westerly airflow.

29 December

1821 The Kennet and the Thames overflowed to their greatest extent since the snowmelt floods in January 1809. The road from Reading to Caversham was impassable, one bridge being carried away, and all communication with Oxford was stopped. At Pangbourne some houses had 2-3 metres of water in their ground-floor rooms.

1908 The coldest December day on record - the temperature climbed to only -5.0 °C after a minimum temperature of -5.6 °C. High pressure over Scandinavia advected an area of cold air across England.

1961 December 1961 ended with temperatures down to -7.8 °C on the 28th and 29th with the Thames frozen over at Reading. This was the result of cold air spreading from Scandinavia due to the westward extension of a large anticyclone from Russia.

1976 One of the lowest December grass minimum temperatures on record at -13.8 °C: freezing fog at 0900 GMT, with 2 cm of lying snow on the ground.

1979 The River Thames was flooded in stretches around Reading; early December had been wet and then a further 22 mm of rain fell in Reading on 27 December.

30 December

1908 One of the coldest December nights on record as the temperature fell to -12.8 °C. Snow lay 15 cm deep at 0900 GMT, with a northerly wind blowing.

1962 Snow depth at 0900 GMT was 21 cm: the Reading observer noted snowdrifts of 75 to 90 cm in the strong easterly wind.

2006 A small tornado caused damage around the A329(M)/M4 junction near Sindlesham during the late afternoon.

31 December

1908 One of the coldest December nights on record with the air temperature falling to -11.9 °C. This was only 0.9 degC higher than yesterday.

1962 The greatest December snow depth on record at 0900 GMT, with 22 cm lying. Much of this had fallen between the 26th and 30th with about half the total falling early on the 30th as moderate to heavy snow fell for a while before dawn.

1973 One of the sunniest December days on record with 6.9 hours of bright sunshine due to an anticyclone that lay close to southern England all day. There was also some shallow freezing fog at times.

1978 One of the coldest December days on record with a maximum temperature of -2.2 °C. High pressure over Scandinavia had been drawing cold air from the north-east towards England for several days: with a depression over the English Channel this cold air was steered across central and southern England. Snow had fallen too - 10 cm of snow lay on the ground.

1996 The first of four consecutive days when the air temperature remained below freezing point. High pressure to the north and low pressure to the south brought a cold easterly surface flow from the continent to Reading: not until 11 January 1997 did the temperature rise above 3 °C.

APPENDIX 1

Climatological averages for 1981-2010

University of Reading

Berkshire

Current site details					As at April 2015
Record began	*Lat*	*Long*	*NGR*		*Altitude AMSL*
1901	51.441N	0.938W	SU(41) 739 719		66 m

Averages and extremes for period

1981-2010   *Vs = more than one date*

	Ob time	*Temperature*	09-09GMT
	0900GMT	*Rainfall*	09-09GMT

TEMPERATURE °C	Jan	Feb	Mar	Apr	May	June	July	Aug	Sept	Oct	Nov	Dec	Annual
Mean daily maximum	7.7	8.0	10.8	13.5	17.0	20.0	22.4	22.1	19.0	14.9	10.7	7.9	14.5
Mean daily minimum	1.9	1.7	3.5	4.7	7.7	10.6	12.7	12.5	10.3	7.6	4.4	2.2	6.7
Mean temperature	4.8	4.8	7.1	9.1	12.4	15.3	17.6	17.3	14.6	11.2	7.5	5.0	10.6
Average highest maximum	12.6	13.0	16.2	20.0	24.3	27.2	28.9	28.5	24.4	20.1	15.9	13.2	30.3
Average lowest minimum	-4.9	-4.5	-2.8	-1.2	1.7	5.4	8.0	7.3	4.4	0.3	-2.5	-4.8	-7.1
Highest maximum	14.7	17.0	20.4	25.7	28.5	31.4	35.3	36.4	29.6	25.5	18.1	15.8	36.4
Year	1998	1990	1990	2003	2005	1995	2006	2003	2006	1985	2010	1985	10 Aug 2003
Lowest minimum	-14.5	-11.6	-6.4	-3.5	-1.0	1.5	5.2	5.1	1.2	-4.4	-8.3	-13.4	-14.5
Year	1982	1986	2001	1984	2010	1991	1993	1983	1987	1997	1983	1981	14 Jan 1982
Lowest grass minimum	-20.1	-16.5	-13.2	-12.5	-8.0	-5.7	-2.0	-2.2	-6.7	-12.1	-12.5	-16.1	-20.1
Year	1982	1986	1985	2003	2010	1991	2001	1993	2003	1997	1983	1981	14 Jan 1982
Highest minimum	11.7	11.5	12.4	12.6	15.1	18.1	18.7	20.8	18.0	16.6	14.2	12.4	20.8
Year	2008	2004	1998	Vs	1989	2005	2006	1995	2006	2005	1996	1985	2 Aug 1995
Lowest maximum	-6.8	-3.8	-0.1	3.3	8.5	11.5	14.8	13.9	9.6	6.6	-0.1	-2.0	-6.8
Year	1987	1991	1986	1989	Vs	1989	1987	1986	1993	1981	2010	1991	12 Jan 1987
Air frosts	9.1	9.3	4.8	2.2	0.2	0	0	0	0	1.1	4.4	9.8	40.9
Ground frost	19.8	18.0	16.6	14.7	7.2	2.1	0.3	0.5	3.5	8.4	14.2	18.2	123.5

PRECIPITATION *mm*	Jan	Feb	Mar	Apr	May	June	July	Aug	Sept	Oct	Nov	Dec	Annual
Monthly mean	60.5	40.9	44.4	48.0	46.5	44.6	45.8	52.3	50.3	72.0	66.1	63.0	634.4
Days =>0.2 mm	15.8	12.2	13.6	12.9	12.4	10.8	11.3	11.2	10.8	13.6	14.6	14.6	153.8
Days =>1.0 mm	11.3	9.0	9.7	9.3	8.8	7.7	7.7	7.9	8.0	10.5	10.7	10.6	111.2
Wettest day	21.6	26.8	23.8	30.6	31.8	42.4	42.5	52.6	76.3	49.3	28.7	35.8	76.3
Year	1999	2009	1984	1991	1985	1998	Vs	1999	1992	2000	2003	1989	22 Sep 1992
Wettest month	128.7	108.5	111.4	132.6	100.8	120.2	115.6	136.3	113.5	154.5	141.9	150.7	851.9
Year	1995	1990	1981	2000	2007	1998	2007	2004	1992	1987	2009	1989	2000
Driest month	8.7	3.2	10.7	0.9	3.1	8.9	9.5	3.3	5.0	26.6	18.7	9.9	463.0
Year	1987	1993	1990	2007	1990	1996	1990	1995	2003	1985	1988	1988	1990

SUNSHINE *hours*	Jan	Feb	Mar	Apr	May	June	July	Aug	Sept	Oct	Nov	Dec	Annual
Monthly mean	56.5	76.0	108.9	160.3	188.1	189.4	197.5	191.3	138.2	106.6	63.1	46.1	1522.0
Daily mean	*1.82*	*2.71*	*3.52*	*5.34*	*6.07*	*6.31*	*6.37*	*6.17*	*4.61*	*3.44*	*2.11*	*1.49*	*4.17*
Possible hours daylight	*261.7*	*279.5*	*368.4*	*416.1*	*483.8*	*496.1*	*498.8*	*451.4*	*379.6*	*331.2*	*267.3*	*246.1*	*4480.0*
% possible	*21.6*	*27.2*	*29.6*	*38.5*	*38.9*	*38.2*	*39.6*	*42.4*	*36.4*	*32.2*	*23.6*	*18.7*	*34.0*
Days nil sunshine	11.4	7.9	5.6	2.7	2.3	1.7	1.3	1.3	2.6	5.4	9.2	13.3	64.7
Sunniest day	8.1	9.3	11.4	13.7	15.5	15.3	15.3	14.5	12.6	10.2	8.2	6.9	15.5
Year	1987	1995	Vs	1999	1985	Vs	1986	1981	1982	1997	1986	1986	30 May 1985
Sunniest month	91.2	126.7	178.7	234.0	295.1	266.4	291.8	279.4	178.3	162.0	95.6	74.6	1810.1
Year	1984	2008	2007	1984	1989	1996	2006	1995	2004	1999	1989	2001	2003
Dullest month	19.2	46.6	57.5	100.0	118.7	109.4	135.1	117.9	85.8	65.2	34.6	13.4	1337.8
Year	1996	1982	1992	1998	1991	1990	1988	2008	1993	1982	1994	2010	1992

CLOUD COVER at 0900 GMT	Jan	Feb	Mar	Apr	May	June	July	Aug	Sept	Oct	Nov	Dec	Annual
Monthly mean - oktas	6.0	5.9	5.9	5.7	5.7	5.8	5.6	5.4	5.7	5.6	5.9	6.1	5.8
Monthly mean - %	75	74	74	71	71	72	70	68	71	70	74	76	72

MSL PRESSURE *hPa*	Jan	Feb	Mar	Apr	May	June	July	Aug	Sept	Oct	Nov	Dec	Annual
Monthly mean at 0900 GMT	1016.6	1017.3	1015.8	1014.9	1015.9	1017.0	1016.4	1016.1	1016.4	1014.2	1014.4	1015.6	1015.9

DAYS WITH ...	Jan	Feb	Mar	Apr	May	June	July	Aug	Sept	Oct	Nov	Dec	Annual
Snow/sleet falling	2.7	3.5	1.6	0.9	0	0	0	0	0	0.1	0.4	1.7	10.9
Snow lying at 0900 GMT	1.5	2.0	0.4	0.1	0	0	0	0	0	0	0	1.8	5.8
Thunder heard	0.3	0.1	0.4	0.9	1.4	1.2	1.5	1.6	0.8	0.4	0.3	0.1	9.0
Fog at 0900 GMT	2.2	2.4	1.1	0.3	0.2	0.1	0.1	0.2	0.7	1.9	2.3	2.4	13.9
Gale	0.1	0	0.1	0	0	0	0	0	0	0	0	0	0.2

Site and instrument metadata

A well-exposed meteorological enclosure on a campus university, using standard instruments. Some small site changes have occurred during the 30 years; these are most likely to have affected recent sunshine records both early and late in the day.

APPENDIX 2
Unit conversions (°C/°F, mm and inches)

Temperature conversions

°C	°F		°F	°C
-40	-40		-40	-40.0
-35	-31		-30	-34.4
-30	-22		-20	-28.9
-25	-13		-10	-23.3
-20	-4		0	-17.8
-15	5		5	-15.0
-10	14		10	-12.2
-5	23		15	-9.4
0	32		20	-6.7
5	41		25	-3.9
10	50		30	-1.1
15	59		35	1.7
20	68		40	4.4
25	77		45	7.2
30	86		50	10.0
35	95		55	12.8
40	104		60	15.6
45	113		65	18.3
50	122		70	21.1
55	131		75	23.9
			80	26.7
			85	29.4
			90	32.2
			95	35.0
			100	37.8
			105	40.6
			110	43.3
			115	46.1
			120	48.9
			130	54.4

Rainfall conversions

mm	inches		inches	mm
0.10	0.004		0.01	0.25
0.20	0.01		0.02	0.5
0.50	0.02		0.03	0.8
1	0.04		0.04	1.0
2	0.08		0.05	1.3
3	0.12		0.1	2.5
4	0.16		0.2	5.1
5	0.20		0.5	12.7
10	0.39		1	25.4
20	0.79		2	50.8
30	1.18		5	127
40	1.57		10	254
50	1.97		20	508
100	3.94		50	1 270
200	7.87		100	2 540
500	19.69		200	5 080
1 000	39.37		500	12 700
2 000	78.74			
5 000	196.85			
10 000	393.70			

APPENDIX 3

Abbreviations and definitions

Abbreviations and **definitions** are defined within the text when first used; they are listed below only where used more than once.

Footnotes (indicated by superscripted symbols *† and so on) are given at the foot of the page to which they refer.

Air frost	Minimum air temperature over the 24 hours ending at 0900 GMT of -0.1 °C or below
Air temperature	The temperature as measured in a Stevenson screen, a standard enclosure which provides shelter from solar (short-wave) and terrestrial (long-wave) radiation and precipitation for the thermometers or sensors located therein. By convention, in the United Kingdom the air temperature measurement is made at 1.25 m above ground level, normally on a grassed site
Averages	All averages quoted are for the international standard 30 year period 1981-2010 unless otherwise stated
AWS	Automatic weather station – usually a computer-controlled system which both samples and logs electronic sensors of various descriptions, usually providing 'spot', 'averages' and 'extremes' output as digital files at user-definable intervals
Ice day	Maximum temperature over the 24 hours commencing 0900 GMT below 0 °C
GMT	Greenwich Mean Time (also known as UTC). GMT is the same as 'clock time' during the winter months, but during the operation of British Summer Time (BST), BST is GMT + 1 hour. By convention, all meteorological observations are referenced in GMT/UTC. GMT is used throughout this book, except where specifically indicated to the contrary
Grass minimum	The 'grass minimum' is a thermometer conventionally exposed just above the tips of short-bladed grass. On clear nights, it may read several degrees lower than the 'air temperature' measured at 1.25 m above ground level. When snow lies on the ground, the 'grass minimum temperature' normally refers to the 'snow surface temperature'. Grass minimum temperatures have been measured at Reading since January 1920
Ground frost	Grass minimum temperature over the 24 hours ending at 0900 GMT of -0.1 °C or below. This definition has been used throughout this book (earlier published statistics from the university weather station may have used slightly different definitions prior to about 1961)
Maximum temperature	The 'maximum temperature' refers to the highest air temperature attained in the 24 hours commencing 0900 GMT on the date stated
Minimum temperature	The 'minimum temperature' refers to the lowest air temperature attained in the 24 hours ending 0900 GMT on the date stated
MSL	Mean sea level
Precipitation	The 'daily precipitation' refers to the total precipitation in the in the 24 hours commencing 0900 GMT. 'Precipitation' includes rain, drizzle, snow, sleet, hail, dewfall and fogdrip, and is measured in a standard 'five-inch' (127 mm) diameter raingauge with its rim located 30 cm above short grass
Rain day	A day in which 0.2 mm or more of precipitation is measured using the standard raingauge. A 'trace' is less than 0.1 mm precipitation
Sunshine	The duration of bright sunshine, measured in hours, from the records of a Campbell-Stokes sunshine recorder
Snow cover	Lying snow covering at least 50 per cent of the area representative of the site

APPENDIX 4

Publications on various aspects of Reading's weather

WEATHER EVENTS IN THE READING AREA

The Thames in flood: a pictorial record. County Borough of Reading, 1947

An 'urban rainstorm' in the Reading area [22 June 1951] by M. Parry. *Weather*, **11** (1956), p 41

Earth temperature changes in winter 1962-63 by G. W. Hurst and Y. Lenz. *Weather*, **19** (1964), pp 124-128

Winter 1978/79 - New Year period in Reading by T. J. Harrington. *Weather*, **34** (1979), pp 204-205

The severe gale of 16 October 1987 in Berkshire and Hampshire by Stephen Burt. *International Journal of Meteorology*, **12**, pp 332-8

The Great Storm of 15-16 October 1987 by Stephen Burt and Doug Mansfield. *Weather*, **43**, pp 90-114, 229

Winter cold spells in Reading by J. I. L. Morison. *Weather*, **42** (1987), pp 152-154

The exceptional hot spell of early August 1990 in the United Kingdom by Stephen Burt. *International Journal of Climatology*, **12** (1992), pp 547-567

A violent January hailstorm [20 January 1995] by Stephen Burt. *Weather*, **50** (1995), pp 325-327

A cluster of intense rainfall events in west Berkshire, summer 1999 by Stephen Burt. *Weather*, **55** (2000), pp 356-363

High-resolution observations of the Bracknell storm, 7 May 2000 by Tim Allott, Will Hand and Malcolm Lee. *Weather*, **57** (2001), pp 73-77; also *The Bracknell storm, 7 May 2000* by Stephen Burt, *Weather*, **57** (2001), pp 422-4

The August 2003 heatwave in the United Kingdom by Stephen Burt. Part 1 – Maximum temperatures and historical precedents: *Weather*, **59** (2004), pp 199-208. Part 2 (with Philip Eden) – The hottest sites *Weather*, **59** (2004), pp 239-246. Part 3 – Minimum temperatures. *Weather*, **59** (2004), pp 272-273

Factors contributing to the summer 2003 European heatwave by Emily Black, Mike Blackburn, R. Giles Harrison, Brian Hoskins and John Methven. *Weather*, **59** (2004), pp 217-223

Prolonged day darkness and extreme rainfall in Berkshire, 20 July 2007 by Stephen Burt. *Weather*, **63** (2008), pp 24-26

READING'S URBAN HEAT ISLAND

Local temperature variations in the Reading area by M. Parry. *Quarterly Journal of the Royal Meteorological Society*, **42** (1956), pp 45-57

Observing an urban heat island by bicycle by Edward Melhuish and Mike Pedder. *Weather*, **53** (1998), pp 121-128

SEA BREEZES

Sea Breeze and Local Wind by John Simpson. Cambridge University Press, 1994: includes detailed observations of south coast sea breezes arriving in Reading

READING AND BERKSHIRE WEATHER

The Berkshire weather book by Ian Currie, Mark Davison and Bob Ogley. Froglets Publications, Westerham, Kent, 1994

Index

Events or occurrences are listed only when they are referenced in more than one section of the book. For example, events listed in the July chapter are not individually indexed (refer to the appropriate monthly, annual and seasonal chapters for detail), whereas there are index entries for July 1976 detail under 'Summer 1976' and July 2006 under 'Hottest month'